avid Kent
oy Woodward
eith Pledger
hn Hackney
raham Newnam

HEINEMANN MATHEMATICS A

Upper Course

ese are the different types of pages and symbols used in

Simple flow diagrams	**24**

These pages develop mathematical skills, concepts and facts in a wide variety of realistic contexts.

Problem solving	**53**

These pages develop mathematical problem-solving skills.

Do Worksheet 1

This shows you when you need to use a Worksheet.

Remember

This is a reminder of the key information essential for the work of the pages.

Investigation

Investigations enhance the work of the page by providing additional opportunities to develop problem-solving skills.

Heinemann

Contents

PART 2

PART 4

It's all in the mind

Charles has been asked to work out 60×0.2 mentally (in his head).

He rearranges the problem to make it easier.

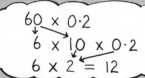

$$60 \times 0.2$$
$$6 \times 10 \times 0.2$$
$$6 \times 2 = 12$$

So 60×0.2 gives the same answer as $6 \times 2 = 12$.

1 Work out mentally:

(a)	25×0.2	**(b)**	34×0.1
(c)	50×0.4	**(d)**	22×0.3
(e)	35×0.5	**(f)**	224×0.2
(g)	800×0.3	**(h)**	450×0.4
(i)	600×0.12	**(j)**	400×0.11
(k)	300×0.02	**(l)**	800×0.04
(m)	200×0.13	**(n)**	450×0.06

Karen has been asked to work out $50 \div 0.2$ in her head.

She also rearranges the problem to make it easier.

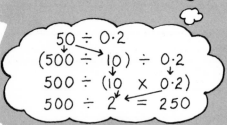

$$50 \div 0.2$$
$$(500 \div 10) \div 0.2$$
$$500 \div (10 \times 0.2)$$
$$500 \div 2 = 250$$

So $50 \div 0.2$ gives the same answer as $500 \div 2 = 250$.

2 Work out mentally:

(a)	$40 \div 0.2$	**(b)**	$600 \div 0.4$
(c)	$200 \div 0.5$	**(d)**	$300 \div 0.1$
(e)	$120 \div 0.3$	**(f)**	$150 \div 0.5$
(g)	$26 \div 0.13$	**(h)**	$480 \div 0.12$
(i)	$6.0 \div 0.15$	**(j)**	$2.4 \div 0.2$
(k)	$8.8 \div 0.22$	**(l)**	$36 \div 0.09$
(m)	$0.56 \div 0.007$	**(n)**	$0.64 \div 0.16$

3 Work out mentally:

(a)	$(30 \times 0.8) \div 2$	**(b)**	$(40 \times 0.5) \div 4$
(c)	$(80 \times 0.2) \div 10$	**(d)**	$(50 \times 0.4) \div 0.2$
(e)	$60 \times 0.6 \div 0.3$	**(f)**	$400 \times 0.6 \div 0.8$
(g)	$200 \times 0.01 \div 0.5$	**(h)**	$600 \times 0.15 \div 2.5$
(i)	$(50 \times 0.4) \div 0.2$	**(j)**	$50 \times (0.4 \div 0.2)$
(k)	$(400 \times 0.6) \div 0.8$	**(l)**	$400 \times (0.6 \div 0.8)$
(m)	$24 \times 0.8 \div 0.4$	**(n)**	$24 \div 0.8 \times 0.4$

4 Kuldip has been told that the area of a certain rectangle is 20 cm². He has to work out possible dimensions of the rectangle. Without using a calculator, copy and complete this table:

Area	Length	Width
20	20	
20		2
20		4
20	0.5	
20		50
20	0.2	
20	0.02	

5 John is working on a similar problem. This time the perimeters of the rectangles must all be the same. The perimeter is 20 metres. Without using a calculator, copy and complete:

Perimeter	Length	Width	Area
20	8		
20	5		
20	2		
20	1		
20	0.2		
20	0.1		

6 Copy and complete these number patterns:

$40 \times 80 = 3200$	$40 \div 80 = 0.5$
$40 \times 8 = 320$	$40 \div 8 = \boxed{}$
$40 \times 0.8 = \boxed{}$	$40 \div 0.8 = \boxed{}$
$40 \times 0.08 = \boxed{}$	$40 \div 0.08 = \boxed{}$
$40 \times 0.008 = \boxed{}$	$40 \div 0.008 = \boxed{}$

7 Write down the effect of multiplying a number by a second number which is less than 1.

Many investigative and problem-solving exercises lead to a sequence of numbers.

To find a general result for each sequence:

One sequence might be

Result	1	2	3	4	5	6
Sequence	3	7	13	21	31	43

The general result can be found by differencing.

To do this:

• subtract the first number in the sequence from the second

• subtract the second number in the sequence from the third

• subtract the third number in the sequence from the fourth and so on.

The **second** differences can be found by taking the differences of the differences. The third differences can then be found and so on again.

In the example this gives:

No. in						
sequence	3	7	13	21	31	43
1st difference		4	6	8	10	12
2nd difference			2	2	2	2
3rd difference				0	0	0

This helps to develop the pattern.

Find the first, second and third differences for each of the following sequences.

(a) 5, 8, 11, 14, 17, 20

(b) 1, 3, 6, 10, 15, 21

(c) 2, 6, 12, 20, 30, 42

(d) 1, 9, 25, 49, 81, 121

(e) 1, 8, 27, 64, 125, 216

(f) 1, 2, 4, 8, 16, 32, 64

2 Substitute whole number values of n from 1 to 6 into each of the following general expressions.

(a) $3n + 2$

(b) $5n - 3$

(c) n^2

(d) $n^2 + 3n$

(e) $2n^2 + n + 1$

(f) $n^3 + 2$

(g) $n^3 + n^2 + 1$

(h) 2^n

(i) 3^n

In each case find the first, second and third differences. Comment on your results.

3 The Fibonacci sequence of numbers is

   1, 1, 2, 3, 5, 8, 13, 21, 34, 55, 89

Show that the sequence of first differences for the Fibonacci sequence is also the Fibonacci sequence.

Differencing can be used to develop a sequence of numbers further.

To extend the sequence 7, 15, 25, 37, 51, 67

No. in								
sequence	7	15	25	37	51	67	**85**	**105**
1st difference		8	10	12	14	16	**18**	**20**
2nd difference			2	2	2	2	**2**	**2**

4 Find the next two numbers in each of these sequences.

(a) 4, 10, 18, 28, 40, 54, 70

(b) 0, 14, 78, 252, 620, 1290, 2394

(c) 2, 4, 6, 10, 16, 26, 42

(d) 4, 5, 7, 11, 18, 29, 47

Whatever next?

George has been given this problem to solve:
The London Marathon is run over a distance of approximately 26 miles. What is the distance in kilometres?

| I mile = 1·609 km |

George realises this is a multiplication or division problem but is not sure which. He decides to make the problem easier:

Suppose I mile were equal to 2 km, then 26 miles would equal 52 km.

To get this you **multiply**
26 × 2

So if I mile is actually 1·609 km you **multiply**
26 × 1·609

26 × 1·609 = 41·834 km
        = 42 km to 2 significant figures

1 A ream of paper contains 500 sheets. If each sheet of paper is 0·124 mm thick, what is the total thickness of:
   (a) I ream of paper
   (b) 4 reams of the same paper?

2 A petrol tank in a car holds 45·5 litres of petrol. What is this capacity in gallons if
   I gallon = 4·55 litres?

3 If I kilometre is approximately equal to 0·621 miles, find:
   (a) how many miles are approximately equal to 38 kilometres
   (b) how many kilometres are approximately equal to 38 miles.

4 750 sheets of copying paper are placed in a pile which is 9·3 cm high.
   (a) How high will 3400 sheets of paper be?
   (b) A second pile is 7·2 cm high, how many sheets does it contain?

5 A ball always rises to 0·625 of the height from which it was dropped, or the height of its last bounce.
   (a) Find the height this ball reached on:
      • the first bounce
      • the fourth bounce.
   (b) How many times will the ball bounce before it rises to a height of less than 2 metres?

30 m

6 A milkman delivers 12 438 pints of milk in one day. He delivers the same amount each day. Find out:
   (a) how much he delivers in a week
   (b) how much he delivers in a year
   (c) the capacity he delivers in a year in litres (I litre = 1·76 pints).

7 A new by-pass is to be built around Ashburn. The by-pass is 14·5 km long. It takes 32 tonnes of tar to surface I kilometre of road. Find out:
   (a) how many tonnes are needed to surface the new road
   (b) how many tonnes will be needed for a second by-pass 21·25 km long
   (c) the mass, in kilograms, needed to surface a small road 126 metres long.

8 In a yacht race a boat reaches a maximum speed of 25 knots. I knot is approximately equal to 1·143 mph, and I kilometre = 0·621 miles. Find:
   (a) the maximum speed in mph
   (b) the maximum speed in km/h.

9 A tank fires a test shot at a target 5·452 km away. This first shell only travels a distance of 3·488 km. Raising the gun I degree will make a shell travel 0·109 km further.
   How many degrees must the gun be raised before a shell will hit the target?

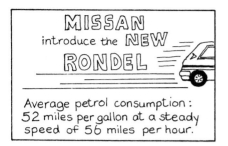

MISSAN
introduce the NEW
RONDEL

Average petrol consumption:
52 miles per gallon at a steady
speed of 56 miles per hour.

10 Find the metric equivalent of the petrol
consumption of this car in km per litre.
(1 mile = 1·609 km)   (1 litre = 0·22 gallons)

11 During a charity walk Jill
walked at a rate of 84
paces per minute. She
measured the length
of one of her paces.
The charity walk was 12 km. Find:

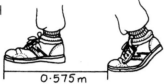

0·575 m

(a) how many paces she took

(b) how long it took her to complete the walk.

12 The basic cost to produce and deliver cement is
£64·48 per tonne. The producer sells it at £80·60
per tonne. Find:

(a) the cost to a builder who needs 32·5 tonnes

(b) the cost to a builder who needs 82·25 tonnes

(c) the number of tonnes sold to a builder whose
bill came to £3675·36

(d) the profit the producer made from a builder
whose bill came to £1612.

13 Simpson & Co. pays its employees to use their own
transport at the rate of:

33p for each of the first 75 miles
20p for each of the next 200 miles
10p for each additional mile.

Andy, one of its employees, travels from Derby to
London, a distance of 127 miles.

(a) How much should Andy claim for the return
journey?

(b) A second company, Abbeydale, pays its
employees a single rate of 25p per mile. How
much should an employee claim for a return
trip to London?

(c) Calculate the amount claimed from both
systems for a journey of 320 miles.

(d) For a certain distance both systems would pay
the same amount of money. Find the distance.

14 To make an alarm system one of each of these
parts is needed:

case   £12·50
LEDs   £ 5·65
switches   £ 8·49
resistors   £ 4·52
chips   £16·85
wiring   £ 7·42
alarms   £ 4·30

(a) What is the total cost to make one alarm
system?

(b) What is the cost to make 25 alarm systems?

(c) An investor puts £1000 into the company. How
many alarm systems can be made for £1000?

15 At a school fair orange squash is made in a
25 gallon barrel. The squash is sold in 250 ml
glasses, each costing 12p.

(a) 1 gallon = 4·545 litres. Calculate how many
full glasses of squash could be sold.

(b) All the orange squash was sold. How much
money was taken?

16 Mr Dhear went on holiday to Germany. He
changed £1000 into Deutschmarks at a rate of
2·45 marks to £1. His hotel and other expenses
came to 125 marks per day for 10 days. On
returning home he changed his remaining marks
back into pounds. Find:

(a) how many marks he received for £1000

(b) his hotel and other expenses per day in pounds

(c) the amount in pounds that he brought home.

17 The new Rondel car does
52 miles per gallon when
travelling at 56 mph and
41·2 miles per gallon at
70 mph.

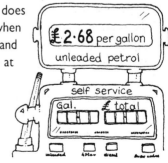

£2·68 per gallon
unleaded petrol
self service
Gal.   £ total

Calculate:

(a) the cost of a 150 mile journey, travelling at
56 mph

(b) the extra cost of travelling the same distance
at 70 mph

(c) how much time is saved.

Down Memory Lane

Johnny has been given these fractions to add

$\frac{1}{2} + \frac{2}{3} + \frac{3}{5}$

I wish it wasn't fractions. —I'm just no good at them.

He decides to change the fractions into decimals and use the 'memory' features on his calculator.

Min	stores numbers in the memory
MR	recalls the number in the memory

- Enter **1** Press **÷** Enter **2** Press **=** to give **0.5**
- Store this answer in the memory by pressing **Min**
- Press **Clear**
- Enter **2** Press **÷** Enter **3** Press **=** to give **0.6666667**
- Add this result to the 0·5 stored in the memory.

  Press **+** Press **MR** Press **=** to give **1.1666667**
- Store this total in the memory by pressing **Min**
- Press **Clear**
- Enter **3** Press **÷** Enter **5** Press **=** to give **0.6**
- Obtain the final answer by adding 0·6 to the total stored in the memory.

  Press **+** Press **MR** Press **=** to give **1.7666667**

1 Change these fractions into decimals using the memory features on your calculator. Write the full calculator display.

(a) $\frac{1}{4} + \frac{3}{5}$ (b) $\frac{3}{7} + \frac{5}{8}$

(c) $\frac{2}{3} + \frac{3}{4} + \frac{4}{5}$ (d) $\frac{4}{9} + \frac{3}{7} + \frac{4}{11}$

2 A ball is dropped from a tower 18·5 m high. The ball always bounces to 0·554 of the height from which it was dropped, or the height of its last bounce.

Find the height the ball bounces on:

(a) the first bounce
(b) the second bounce
(c) the sixth bounce.

The ball bounces to a height of 0·554 from the height from which it was dropped and the height of its last bounce. Enter this into the memory of the calculator

Enter **0.554** Press **Min** Press **Clear**

To find the height reached on the first bounce:

Enter **18.5** Press **×** Press **MR** Press **=**

Write down this answer and then solve the rest of the problem.

---

3 Kirsten invests £100 in the Woodley Building Society. The building society pays an interest rate of 10% per annum.

(a) What number must the £100 be multiplied by to work out how much money she will have at the end of the first year?
(b) How much money will she have in her account at the end of the first year?
(c) How much money will she have at the end of the second year?
(d) How much will she have at the end of the fifth year?
(e) How many years will it take for her investment to at least double in value?

4 Avtar invests £100 in the same building society at an interest rate of 10%. She invests a further £100 at the beginning of each year.

(a) Find how much she has in her account at:
- the end of the first year
- the beginning of the second year
- the end of the second year
- the end of the fifth year
(b) How many years will it take for Avtar to have more than £1000 in her account?

Find the total cost of these items:

12 hammers at £6·45 each
5 hack saws at £12·42 each
8 screwdrivers at £2·50 each
25 bolts at 96p each
14 sheets of plasterboard at £8·32 each
36 clips at 55p each.

On average the value of a new car depreciates by:

23% during its first year
19% during the second year
16% for the next three years
13·75% for each year thereafter.

Each figure is a percentage of the value of the car at the start of each year.
A new car costs £13 500. Find its value at the end of these years:

(a) first   **(b)** second   **(c)** sixth   **(d)** tenth.

This flow diagram can be used to solve equations.

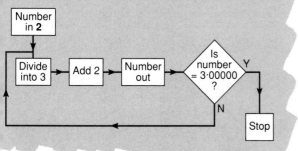

(a) Use the flow diagram and the memory features on your calculator to help you copy and complete this table of results.

Calculation	Number in	Number out
1st	2·0	3·5
2nd	3·5	
3rd		
4th		
5th		
6th		
7th		
8th		

(b) How many calculations do you need to do before you get an answer of 3·00000 correct to 6 sig fig?

This flow diagram can also be used to solve equations.

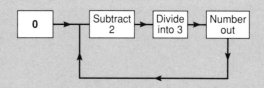

8 (a) Copy and complete this table of results:

Calculation	Number in	Number out
1st	0	⁻1·5
2nd	⁻1·5	
3rd		
4th		
5th		
6th		
7th		
8th		

(b) Towards which number does the sequence appear to be heading?

9 Helen puts £1000 in her bank account on the 1st January. Floyd's Bank pays an interest rate of 0·257% per month. The interest is paid on the last day of each month. On the first day of each month after January Helen has £50 transferred from her account to pay for an insurance policy that she has taken out.

(a) Copy and complete her balance sheet for that year:

(b) Helen puts a further £1000 into her account on the 1st January the following year. What should her balance statement read?

Prime time

Any number can be expressed as a product of prime numbers.

To express the number 36 as product of its prime numbers, first divide by the smallest prime number that will divide equally into it

the smallest prime number 2	) 2	36
the smallest prime 2 again	) 2	18
the smallest prime 3	) 3	9
the smallest prime 3	) 3	3

So 36 expressed as a product of primes is

$2 \times 2 \times 3 \times 3$ or $\mathbf{2^2 \times 3^2}$

1 Copy and complete this table. Continue up to $n = 24$.

Number	Product of primes	
2	2	or 2^1
3	3	or 3^1
4	2×2	or 2^2
5	5	or 5^1
6	2×3	or $2^1 \times 3^1$
7	7	or 7^1
8	$2 \times 2 \times 2$	or 2^3
9		

2 Express each of these numbers as a product of primes:

(a) 48   (b) 63   (c) 84
(d) 108   (e) 256   (f) 385
(g) 875   (h) 1232   (i) 2520

Giles is marking off a field measuring 504 metres by 540 metres into square plots, all of which must be the same size. If Giles is going to use all the land, what is the length of side of the largest possible squares?

504 expressed as a product of primes = $2^3 \times 3^2 \times 7$
540 expressed as a product of primes = $2^2 \times 3^3 \times 5$

The largest number that will divide equally into both 504 and 540 can be obtained by multiplying together all the common prime factors.

Since $2^2 \times 3^2$ is common to both, the length of side of the largest square will be 36 metres.

36 is the highest common factor of 504 and 540.

3 The entrance hall of the Grand Hotel which measures 1764 centimetres by 1050 centimetres needs retiling. Jasper, the designer, wants all the tiles to be the same size and as large as possible.
(a) Express 1764 as product of its primes.
(b) Express 1050 as a product of its primes.
(c) What is the highest common factor of 1764 and 1050?
(d) What is the area of one of the tiles?
(e) How many tiles does Jasper need?

4 A gear wheel which has 168 teeth drives a second gear wheel which has 140 teeth. Each gear wheel has a spot marked on one tooth and the operation starts with the spots 'in line'.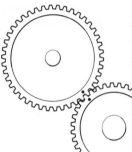
(a) Express 168 as a product of primes.
(b) Express 140 as a product of primes.
(c) How many times must each wheel turn before the spots are back in line?

5 Four students belong to the bell ringing club.

During one practice they follow this sequence:
Peter rings his bell every 8 seconds
Jane rings her bell every 9 seconds
Kelly rings her bell every 12 seconds and
Jeff rings his bell every 15 seconds.
If they all start at the same time how long will it be before they all ring their bells simultaneously?

6 George makes model planes and cars. He has four lengths of wood which he wants to cut into pieces, all of which must be the same length and be as long as possible. The lengths of the four pieces of wood are 140 cm, 238 cm, 168 cm and 210 cm.
(a) Express each of the four lengths as a product of primes.
(b) Find: • what length each piece should be
• how many pieces he will have.

The number 7 can be made by adding combinations of 4s and Is in a variety of different ways. Two ways are:

= 4 + I + I + I
= I + I + 4 + I

and a third way is:

= I + I + I + I + I + I + I

Show that the number 7 can be made in five different ways by adding 4s and Is.

How many different ways are there of making these numbers by adding 4s and Is:
(a) 8   **(b)** 10   **(c)** 15?

Investigate the number of different ways **any positive whole number** can be made by adding combinations of 4s and Is.

You are advised to:
- **record your observations and comments**
- **record and analyse any data, information and results**
- **explain your strategies and working**
- **make and test any conjectures**
- **form any generalisations, with appropriate explanations, justifications or proofs.**

Compounding the problem 1

The 0805 train from Derby to London takes 1·44 hours to complete the journey of 127 miles.

The train does not travel at a constant speed throughout the journey. However, the average speed can be found by dividing the total distance by the time taken to complete the journey.

Average speed $= \frac{127}{1·44} = 88·2$ mph

1 The *Flying Scotsman* took 7·15 hours to travel from Edinburgh to London, a distance of 393 miles. What was its average speed?

2 Kirk travelled by bus from Newcastle to Harwich, a distance of 308 miles. The journey took 7·2 hours. Calculate the average speed of the bus.

If the time is given in hours and minutes and the average speed is in miles per hour it is helpful to change the minutes into a decimal of an hour.

To change minutes into a decimal of an hour divide the minutes by 60.

45 minutes $= 45 ÷ 60 = 0·75$ hour

3 Change these minutes into hours, giving your answer correct to 2 decimal places where appropriate.
(a) 15 minutes (b) 24 minutes (c) 40 minutes
(d) 42 minutes (e) 35 minutes (f) 8 minutes

4 It took Carole 1 hour 18 minutes to complete the maths examination paper. It took Charles 1·5 hours to complete the same paper. What was the average (mean) time taken by the two students?

To change a decimal of an hour into minutes multiply by 60

0·7 hours $= 0·7 × 60 = 42$ minutes

5 Change these hours into hours and minutes.
(a) 0·4 hours (b) 5·6 hours (c) 2·25 hours
(d) 6·18 hours (e) 3·56 hours (f) 9·42 hours

6 Joe takes 24 minutes to walk to school, a distance of 1·2 km. Find his average walking speed in:
(a) metres per minute (b) kilometres per hour.

7 Kuldip leaves his home at 0930 and cycles to Alan's house, a distance of 18 kilometres. He arrives at his friend's house at 1145. What was his average speed for the journey in:
(a) kilometres per hour (b) metres per minute?

8 The distance from Liverpool to Perth is 256 miles. Travelling by car, it takes Brian 6 hours 23 minutes. Calculate the average speed for the journey.

9 Leanne and Becky set out at 0900 for a 25 km walk. They walk for 2 hours and then have a 30 minute rest before completing their walk in a further 2·3 hours. Calculate their average speed for the walk.

10 A train travels at 60 km per hour for 2 hours and then at 50 km per hour for 3 hours.
(a) How far does it travel altogether?
(b) How long does the whole journey take?
(c) What was the average speed for the journey?

11 If this bath is filled from the cold tap it takes 3 minutes to fill. If it is filled from the hot tap it takes 5 mins. How long does it take to fill when both taps are turned on?

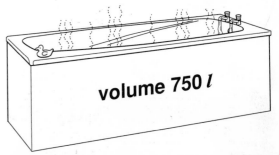

volume 750 *l*

The average fuel consumption of a car is measured in kilometres per litre. A car uses 15 litres of petrol in travelling 165 km.

Average fuel consumption $= \dfrac{165}{15}$

$= 11$ km per litre

1 What is the average fuel consumption of a car which travels 364 km on 34 litres of petrol?

2 When full, the petrol tank on Gary's van holds 36 litres of petrol. He sets out on a journey of 180 km. When he arrives, his petrol gauge indicates $\frac{1}{4}$ full. Calculate the average fuel consumption for his journey.

3 At 56 km per hour the fuel consumption of the Rondel car is 42 kilometres per litre.
 (a) How far will the car travel on 30 litres of petrol?
 (b) How much petrol will the Rondel need to travel a distance of 100 kilometres?
 (c) How long will it take to use 1 litre of petrol?

4 A car travelling at 60 km per hour uses petrol at an average consumption of 8·0 km per litre. What is:
 (a) the consumption in litres per kilometre
 (b) the consumption in litres per hour?

5 The *standard* 4·5v battery costs £1·40 and lasts for 240 hours. The *super gold* battery costs £2·68 and lasts for 500 hours.
 (a) Find: • the cost per hour for each battery
   • the time per £ for each battery.
 (b) Which is the best buy?

6 Last year £1 was worth 1·56 U.S. dollars. At the same time it was worth 2·45 German marks. Calculate the exchange rate between the U.S. and Germany in:
 (a) dollars per mark **(b)** marks per dollar.

7 Solve Martin's problem.

I wonder which paint is the best buy?

The density of a substance is its mass per unit volume

density $= \dfrac{\text{mass}}{\text{volume}}$

This block of lead has a volume of 540 cm^3 and a mass of 6·156 kg.

density $= \dfrac{\text{mass}}{\text{volume}} = \dfrac{6156 \text{ g}}{540 \text{ cm}} = 11·4 \text{ g/cm}^3$

8 A cast-iron pipe has a mass of 210 kg and a total volume of 28 000 cm^3. Find the density of cast iron in g/cm^3.

9 A lead sheet is 2·5 m by 0·75 m by 6 mm thick. Find:
 (a) the volume in cm^3
 (b) the mass if the density of lead is 11·4 kg/cm^3.

10 Tony is watering his garden with a hose pipe which has a cross-sectional area of 1·5 cm^2. Water flows out of the pipe at a speed of 4 cm per second. Find the amount of water flowing out of the pipe in:
 (a) cm^3 per second **(b)** litres per minute.

11 Water is leaking from a tank at a speed of 0·5 litres per minute. How long would it take for a full tank of water to leak away?

2·5m^3

12 Water flows through a plastic pipe at a speed of 240 cm per second. If the cross-sectional area of the pipe is 0·065 m^2, find:
 (a) the amount of water discharged in:
   • cubic metres per second
   • litres per minute
 (b) the time it takes to discharge one cubic metre of water
 (c) the time it would take to fill a bath holding 760 litres of water.

To the *n*th degree I

Peter has this number sequence to explore using matchsticks: 4, 7, 10, 13.
His instructions were to start with one matchstick and then build matchstick squares.

start
with

1 Copy and complete this table:

Term	Value	Difference
1st	4	
2nd	7	3
3rd	10	
4th	13	
5th		

Taking the difference away from the first term gives the starting number/instructions 4 − 3 = 1

Start / then ☐ then ☐─ then ☐──
with | add 3 add 3 add 3

    1 + (1 × 3)
    1 +   (2 × 3)
    1 +   (3 × 3)

From this number
the *n*th term is 1 + (*n* × 3) or 3*n* + 1
where 3 is the extra required each time
and 1 is the starting number/condition

2 Sally has been investigating matchstick triangles. The instructions were to start with one matchstick and build matchstick triangles.

(a) Copy and complete:

Number of triangles	Number of matchsticks	Difference column
1	3	
2	5	2
3	7	
4	9	
5		

(b) Write the next two numbers in the sequence of matchsticks.
(c) Write the 10th term of the sequence.
(d) Copy and complete this diagram.

Start / then △ then ? then ?
with / add 2 add add

(e) Find the general rule for the *n*th term of the sequence.

3 The first six terms of a sequence are:

1st	2nd	3rd	4th	5th	6th
3	10	17	24	31	38

Write:

(a) the next three terms
(b) the difference between two consecutive terms
(c) the starting number/instruction
(d) the rule for finding the *n*th term
(e) the 100th term.

4 Janet has been given this number sequence to explore 5, 7, 9, 11, 13 . . . Write:

(a) the next three numbers in the sequence
(b) the difference between two consecutive terms
(c) the starting number
(d) the *n*th term (the general rule)
(e) the 25th term.

5 For each of these sequences write the *n*th term and the 50th term:

(a) 6, 11, 16, 21, . . .
(b) 4, 7, 10, 13, . . .
(c) 3, 7, 11, 15, . . .
(d) 10, 7, 4, 1, ⁻2, . . .
(e) 4·5, 6, 7·5, 9, . . .
(f) ⁻12, ⁻7, ⁻2, 3, 8, . . .
(g) ⁻2, ⁻5, ⁻8, ⁻11, . . .
(h) 2·7, 3·9, 5·1, 6·3, . . .

6 This pattern of long and short fence poles is used to surround a large field. Work out the rule for the *n*th long pole.

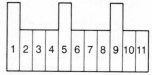

1 Copy and complete:

Term	Value	Difference
1st	3	4
2nd	7	6
3rd	13	8
4th	21	
5th		
6th		

If the first difference is another linear sequence then the *n*th term is going to be a quadratic (n^2) type. The best approach is to look for a squared number pattern.

Term	Value	Squared pattern
1st	3	$1^2 + 2$
2nd	7	$2^2 + 3$
3rd	13	$3^2 + 4$
4th	21	$4^2 + 5$

From the number pattern the *n*th term will be

$$n^2 + (n + 1)$$

2 (a) Copy and complete:

Term	Value	Difference	Squared pattern
1st	6	5	$1^2 + 5$
2nd	11	7	$2^2 + 7$
3rd	18	9	$3^2 + 9$
4th	27		
5th			

(b) Write the squared pattern for the 10th term.

(c) Write the general rule for the *n*th term.

3 For part of their coursework students at Wood Green High School carried out an investigation. One student obtained this sequence of numbers 4, 7, 12, 19, . . .

(a) Write the next two numbers in the sequence.

(b) Draw a table to show this sequence and include a differences column and a squared number pattern column.

(c) Write a general rule for the *n*th term.

(d) Write the value of the 50th term.

4 (a) Draw a table to show the area of these shapes. Continue up to the 6th shape.

(b) Write the rule for finding the *n*th shape.

(c) What is the area of the 100th shape?

5 For each of these sequences, write the next two terms, *n*th term and the 50th term.

(a) 0, 2, 6, 12 . . .   **(b)** 3, 8, 15, 24 . . .

(c) 0, 1, 4, 9 . . .   **(d)** 0, 5, 12, 21 . . .

(e) 8, 14, 22, 32 . . .   **(f)** 1·5, 5, 10·5, 18 . . .

6 (a) Write the first 6 terms of your sequence from question **4**.

(b) Use this sequence to help you find a rule for working out the *n*th triangular number.

(c) What is the 100th triangular number?

7 When completing his maths coursework, Clive obtained this table of results.

Position	1	2	3	4	5
Number	1	3	6	11	18

Unfortunately one of Clive's results is wrong.

(a) Work out which of the results you think is wrong, giving a reason for your answer.

(b) Rewrite the table to include the correct value.

(c) Find the general rule for the *n*th term of the corrected sequence.

8 Two sequences are:

3, 8, 15, 24, 35 . . . and

8, 15, 24, 35, 48 . . .

(a) Find the general rule for the *n*th term for both sequences.

(b) Show that the rule for the first sequence can be expressed in the form $(n + 1)^2 - 1$ and the second rule can be expressed in the form $(n + 2)^2 - 1$.

9 Express the general rule for the sequence 2, 6, 12, 20, 30 . . . in two different ways.

Indices

Janice was asked to complete this sequence on her calculator.

Input **2** Press **inv** **x^y** **6** **=**

The calculator gave a reading of 64.

1 What would the answer be if Janice had input 3 and completed the same sequence on her calculator?

2 Write down the answer if each of these numbers is entered into the calculator and the sequence followed.

(a) Input **2** Press **inv** **x^y** **4** **=**
(b) Input **4** Press **inv** **x^y** **4** **=**
(c) Input **1** Press **inv** **x^y** **1** **0** **0** **=**
(d) Input **5** Press **inv** **x^y** **8** **=**
(e) Input **0** **.** **5** Press **inv** **x^y** **4** **=**

The x^y button is the index or power button so

Input **2** Press **inv** **x^y** **5** **=** means 2^5

2^5 means $2 \times 2 \times 2 \times 2 \times 2 = 32$

3 Evaluate:

(a) 6^3 **(b)** 3^5 **(c)** 12^4
(d) 8^4 **(e)** 2^7 **(f)** $2^3 \times 2^4$
(g) 3^7 **(h)** $3^4 \times 3^3$ **(i)** $3^5 \times 3^2$

$3^4 \times 3^3$ means $(3 \times 3 \times 3 \times 3) \times (3 \times 3 \times 3)$
$= 3 \times 3 \times 3 \times 3 \times 3 \times 3 \times 3$
$= 3^7$

$y^4 \times y^2$ means $(y \times y \times y \times y) \times (y \times y)$
$= y \times y \times y \times y \times y \times y$
$= y^6$

In general $y^m \times y^n = y^{m+n}$

4 Simplify each of the following:

(a) $y^5 \times y^6$ **(b)** $a^4 \times a^9$
(c) $y^3 \times y^4 \times y^5$ **(d)** $b^2 \times b^5 \times b^8$
(e) $y^3 \times y^3 \times y^3$ **(f)** $c^4 \times c^5 \times c^6$
(g) $d^5 \times d^{-3}$ **(h)** $h^5 \times h^2 \times h^{-4}$

$3a^2b^5 \times 4a^3b^3 = (3 \times a^2 \times b^5) \times (4 \times a^3 \times b^3)$
$= (3 \times 4) \times (a^2 \times a^3) \times (b^5 \times b^3)$
$= 12 \times a^5 \times b^8$
$= 12a^5b^8$

5 Simplify:

(a) $2a^2 \times 4a^3$ **(b)** $4c^4 \times 5c^7$
(c) $3a^4b^2 \times 2a^4b^5$ **(d)** $6c^5d^3 \times 2c^5d^8$
(e) $4b^4c^5 \times 3b^5c^4$ **(f)** $2a^2bc^5 \times 2a^2b^3c^2$
(g) $4abc \times 4abc$ **(h)** $4a^2b^5 \times 4a^2b^5$
(i) $2a^2b^2c^2 \times 5a^2b^5$ **(j)** $2x^4y^5 \times 7y^5z^6$

The length of the square is a^4. In terms of a its area must be

$(a^4)^2$

$(a^4)^2$ means $a^4 \times a^4 = a^8$

$(a^m)^2$ means $a^m \times a^m = a^{2m}$

In general $(a^m)^n = a^{m \times n}$

6 Simplify:

(a) $(a^3)^2$ **(b)** $(b^4)^2$ **(c)** $(5a^4b^3)^2$
(d) $(2a^3b^5)^3$ **(e)** $(2a^5b^4)^4$ **(f)** $(3b^7c)^4$

$a^5 \div a^3$ means $\dfrac{a^5}{a^3} = \dfrac{a \times a \times a \times a \times a}{a \times a \times a} = a^2$

In general $a^m \div a^n = \dfrac{a^m}{a^n} = a^{m-n}$

7 Simplify:

(a) $b^5 \div b^2$ **(b)** $a^7 \div a^1$ **(c)** $b^7 \div b^8$
(d) $m^3 \div m^3$ **(e)** $b^5 \div b^4$ **(f)** $c^2 \times c^3 \div c^4$
(g) $\dfrac{9c^4}{3c^2}$ **(h)** $\dfrac{6d^4e^5}{3d^2e^2}$ **(i)** $\dfrac{4b^2c^3}{2bc^2}$
(j) $\dfrac{2a^3b^3}{a^2b}$ **(k)** $\dfrac{12k^4m^8}{3k^3m^7}$ **(l)** $\dfrac{2^5}{2^5}$
(m) $\dfrac{(a^3)^2}{a^6}$ **(n)** $\dfrac{6(a^3b^2)^2}{a^6b^4}$ **(o)** $\dfrac{(3b^4c^5)^2}{9b^6c^7}$
(p) $\dfrac{35a^3b^6c^2}{45a^2b^4c^3}$ **(q)** $\dfrac{64b^4c^5}{(2b^2c^2)^7}$ **(r)** $\dfrac{(4a^4b^5c^6)^2}{(3a^2b^4c^8)^3}$

An inequality is a statement that one number or quantity is 'greater than' or 'less than' another.

This rectangle has a height h and a width w. The h is greater than w. In symbols this is written

$h > w$

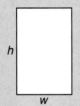

In this rectangle h is less than w. In symbols this is written

$h < w$

The symbol $\geq$ means is greater than or equal to.
The symbol $\leq$ means is less than or equal to.

1 Which of these statements is true and which is false?

(a) $4 < 5$ **(b)** $3 \geq 5$
(c) $^-4 \leq 2$ **(d)** $^-2 < ^-5$
(e) $(^-2 \times ^-3) > 5$ **(f)** $(3 \times 4) \leq (2 \times 6)$

A statement of $n < 4$ can be shown on a number line.

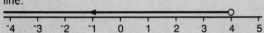

The open circle shows that $x = 4$ is not part of the solution.

To check if a number is part of the solution replace n by the number you want to check and see if the statement is true.

$^-2 < 4$

$^-2$ **is part of the solution**

2 Draw number lines to show these inequalities. Use an open circle to show if the end value is not included in the solution and a full circle to show if it is.

(a) $n < 7$ **(b)** $n \geq 2$ **(c)** $^-2 > n$
(d) $7 \leq n$ **(e)** $n > ^-4$ **(f)** $n \leq ^-4$

3 (a) On the same number line show the solution to the inequalities $3 < n$ and $n < 6$.
(b) On your number line shade the region where $3 < n$ and $n < 6$.
(c) List all the whole numbers which belong to the statement $3 < n$ and $n < 6$.

Statements like $3 < n$ and $n < 6$ can be combined to make a single statement.

$3 < n < 6$ 3 is less than n and n is less than 6

4 If n is a whole number list all its values when:

(a) $9 < n < 12$ **(b)** $^-2 < n < 6$
(c) $0 \leq n < 6$ **(d)** $^-3 < n < ^-2$
(e) $4 > n > ^-4$ **(f)** $5 \geq n \geq 0$

To solve the inequality $2n + 3 \geq 11$

$2n + 3 \geq 11$ subtract 3 from each side
$2n \geq 8$ divide each side by 2
$n \geq 4$

The solution on a number line looks like this

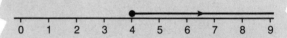

| 0 | 1 | 2 | 3 | 4 | 5 | 6 | 7 | 8 | 9 |

5 Solve these inequalities. Sketch a number line to show each solution.

(a) $3n < 15$ **(b)** $4n + 1 \geq 21$
(c) $3n - 2 > 4$ **(d)** $5n - 4 < 11$
(e) $6n + 5 < 29$ **(f)** $4 + 3n > 10$
(g) $5n + 4 \geq ^-6$ **(h)** $2n - 4 > ^-10$
(i) $^-6 \geq 4 + 2n$ **(j)** $15 \leq 6 + 3n$
(k) $10 < 5 - n$ **(l)** $23 > 3 - 4n$
(m) $^-7 \geq 3 + 2n$ **(n)** $^-4 < 2n - 12$

6 Solve these inequalities.

(a) $7n + 4 \geq 3n + 12$ **(b)** $5n - 10 < 3n + 6$
(c) $8n + 12 < 26 + n$ **(d)** $3n - 22 < 8n + 18$
(e) $6 + 5n > 20 - 2n$ **(f)** $12 - 3n \geq 3 - 6n$
(g) $5(n - 2) \leq ^-20$ **(h)** $3n > 5(8 - n)$

7 Solve the inequality $(x + 3)(x - 2) \leq 0$ by:

(a) solving • $x + 3 \leq 0$
           • $x - 2 \leq 0$
(b) showing both solutions on the same number line
(c) shading the solution interval
(d) writing your answer in the form $a \leq x \leq b$ where a and b are the two limits.

8 Now solve $(x - 5)(2x + 3) < 0$.

Tip it up

The reciprocal of a number is $\dfrac{1}{\text{the number}}$

The reciprocal of 4 is $\frac{1}{4} = 0.25$

1 Write down the reciprocal of:

(a) 5   (b) 2   (c) 8   (d) 10
(e) 20   (f) 100   (g) a (h) b

A number multiplied by its reciprocal always equals 1

$$4 \times \frac{1}{4} = 1 \qquad 8 \times \frac{1}{8} = 1 \qquad a \times \frac{1}{a} = 1$$

This is used to find the reciprocal of a fraction.
For example, to find the reciprocal of $\frac{1}{6}$

$$\frac{1}{6} \times ? = 1 \qquad \text{means} \quad \frac{1}{6} \times 6 = 1$$

The reciprocal of $\frac{1}{6}$ is 6

2 Find the reciprocal of:

(a) $\frac{1}{2}$ (b) $\frac{1}{5}$ (c) $\frac{1}{12}$ (d) $\frac{1}{a}$

(e) 0.5   (f) 0.25   (g) 0.1   (h) 0.05

The reciprocal of $\frac{3}{4}$

$$\frac{3}{4} \times \frac{?}{?} = 1 \qquad \text{gives} \quad \frac{3}{4} \times \frac{4}{3} = 1$$

The reciprocal of $\frac{3}{4}$ is $\frac{4}{3}$

3 What is the reciprocal of:

(a) $\frac{2}{3}$ (b) $\frac{2}{5}$ (c) $\frac{4}{9}$ (d) $\frac{7}{2}$

(e) $\frac{8}{3}$ (f) $\frac{2}{a}$ (g) $\frac{b}{5}$ (h) $\frac{a}{b}$?

Your calculator has a reciprocal button $\dfrac{1}{x}$

Enter **6**   Press **inv** $\frac{1}{x}$ gives $\boxed{0.166666666}$

4 Use your calculator to find the reciprocal of:

(a) 0.22   (b) 2.4   (c) 0.45
(d) 3.6   (e) 0.052   (f) 52.5

5 A formula is given as $y = \dfrac{1}{x}$ find:

(a) y when $x = 16$ (b) y when $x = 20$
(c) x when $y = 4$ (d) x when $y = 32.2$
(e) y when $x = 0.04$ (f) x when $y = 0.04$
(g) y when $x = a$ (h) x when $y = \dfrac{1}{a}$

6 Given that $A = \dfrac{1}{a} + \dfrac{1}{b}$ find A when:

(a) $a = 2$ and $b = 5$
(b) $a = 0.25$ and $b = 0.12$
(c) $a = 15$ and $b = \frac{2}{3}$

7 The formula $\dfrac{1}{R} = \dfrac{1}{R_1} + \dfrac{1}{R_2}$

is used by electrical engineers. Calculate:
(a) $\dfrac{1}{R}$ when $R_1 = 0.5$ and $R_2 = 0.2$
(b) R when $R_1 = 0.5$ and $R_2 = 0.2$
(c) R_1 when $R = 12$ and $R_2 = 6$

8 Given that $y = \dfrac{1}{x}$

(a) Copy and complete:

x	1	2	4	5	10
y	1	0.5			

(b) Plot the points from your table on graph paper like this. Extend the y-axis to 1.0. Extend the x-axis to 10.

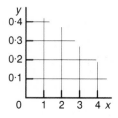

(c) Use your graph to find:
- y when $x = 6$
- x when $y = 0.8$

9 A formula used in physics is $\dfrac{1}{f} = \dfrac{1}{u} + \dfrac{1}{v}$
(a) Find f when $u = 0.275$ and $v = 0.4$.
(b) Find f when $u = 25$ and $v = 16$.
(c) Find u when $f = 0.64$ and $v = 0.2$.
(d) If $\dfrac{1}{f} = \dfrac{u + v}{uv}$
write a formula for f.

These three grey and three black counters are in their starting positions on a rectangular grid of seven spaces.

The aim of the game is to move the counters so that they finish up like this in the minimum number of moves.

The rules governing the movement of the counters are:

- grey counters can only move to the left and black counters can only move to the right

- a counter can slide into an empty adjacent space like this:

- a counter can jump over exactly one counter of the other colour to land in an empty space like this:

- at the start and finish the grey and black counters must be separated by the empty space.

1 Show that the minimum number of moves to get from the start to the finishing position is 15.

2 Examine the game strategies and investigate the relationship between the minimum number of moves and the numbers of grey and black counters.

You are advised to:
- **record your observations and comments**
- **analyse any data and results**
- **explain your game strategies**
- **form and test any conjectures**
- **give any generalisations with appropriate explanations, justifications and proofs.**

You are also advised to follow some of these lines of enquiry:
- **the number of moves it takes if you start with 100 grey and 100 black counters**
- **the number of moves it takes if you start with 100 grey and 50 black counters**
- **the relationship between the cases when the numbers of grey and black counters are equal and when they differ**
- **the relationship between the game strategies and:**
  - **the number of moves made by each counter**
  - **the different colours**
  - **the geometry of the moves**
- **the number of grey and black counters, assumed to be equal, when the number of moves is 120**
- **that the only cases when the number of moves is $p - 1$, where p is a prime number, occur when there are either zero grey or zero black counters. (If you can make a formal proof of this it shows evidence of a very high level of attainment.)**

This is a graph of $y = x$.

The line has a slope or gradient of 1.

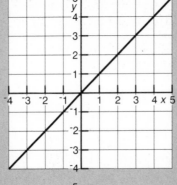

By rotating the line anti-clockwise, the line becomes steeper.

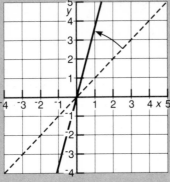

By rotating the line clockwise the line becomes less steep.

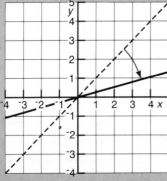

The steepness or gradient of a line is expressed in the form $y = mx$ where m is the gradient.

The gradient, m, of this line can be found by:

- working out the distance from A up to B
- working out the distance from A across to B
- finding the ratio.

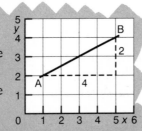

$$\frac{\text{distance from A up to B}}{\text{distance from A across to B}}$$

The gradient, m, of the line $\frac{2}{4} = \frac{1}{2}$

1 Write the gradient of these lines, stating if they are steeper or less steep than the line $y = x$.

(a) $y = 4x$ (b) $y = 1.5x$

(c) $y = \frac{1x}{2}$ (d) $y = 0.6x$

(e) $y = \frac{4x}{3}$ (f) $y = \frac{3x}{4}$

2 Write the gradient of these lines.

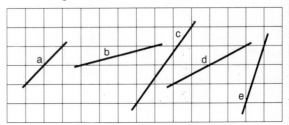

3 (a) Write the coordinates of points A and B.

   (b) What is the gradient of the line?

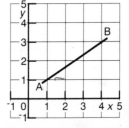

4 Write the gradient of the line joining these coordinate points:

(a) (0, 0) and (7, 3)   (b) (0, 0) and (6, 3)
(c) (2, 2) and (6, 4)   (d) (1, 2) and (7, 10)
(e) ($^-$1, 1) and (9, 5)   (f) (5, 4) and (9, 16)

5 The line $y = x$ is rotated clockwise until it lies along the x-axis.

(a) What is the gradient of the line?

(b) What is the equation of the line?

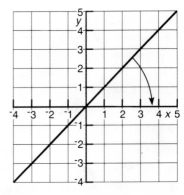

Which of these lines is the steepest?

 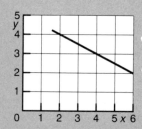

The first line has a gradient of $\frac{1}{2}$

The second line has a gradient of $\frac{-1}{2}$

4 across in the positive direction → and 2 up

4 across in the negative direction ← and 2 up

$\frac{2}{4} = \frac{1}{2}$

$\frac{2}{-4} = \frac{-1}{2}$

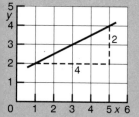 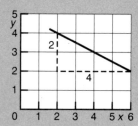

Find the gradients of these lines.

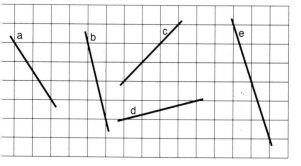

Find the gradient of a straight line passing through the points (2, 6) and (4, 2).

First make a sketch of the information.

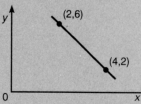

Use the sketch to help find the gradient

Across ⁻2, up 4

Gradient $= -\frac{4}{2} = {}^{-}2$

7 For each of these questions make a sketch and work out the gradient of the line passing through the coordinate points.

(a) (0, 4) and (4, 2)
(b) (1, 7) and (3, 1)
(c) (5, 2) and (7, 7)
(d) (⁻4, 7) and (⁻7, 4)
(e) (⁻1, 0) and (6, ⁻1)
(f) (1, 2) and (4, 4)
(g) (⁻1, ⁻3) and (2, 4)
(h) (4, 2) and (3, 4)
(i) (⁻2, 5) and (2, ⁻1)

8 (a) Find the gradients of the lines AB and BC.
(b) What would be the gradient of a line passing through the points AC?

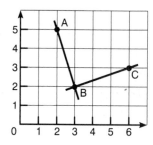

9 Mary works out the gradients of several lines. She puts her results in a table.

Line	a	b	c	d	e	f	g	h
Gradient	⁻3	$\frac{-5}{2}$	$\frac{1}{3}$	0·5	$\frac{3}{6}$	$\frac{-2}{5}$	$\frac{5}{2}$	0·4

(a) Which lines are parallel to each other?
(b) Which two lines are at right-angles to each other?

This is a graph of $y = x$.

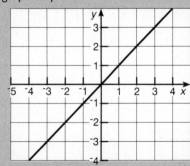

The line can be translated up.

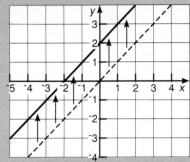

The equation of the line is now
$y = x$ moved up 2   or $y = x + 2$.

The line can be translated down.

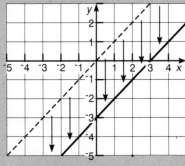

The equation of the line is now
$y = x$ moved down 3   or $y = x - 3$

10 The line AB is $y = 2x$. Write the equation of:
   (a) the line CD
   (b) the line EF.

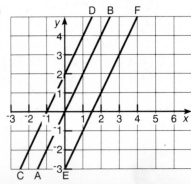

11 Write:
   (a) the gradient of
      the line a
   (b) the equation of
      the line a
   (c) the equation of
      the line b.

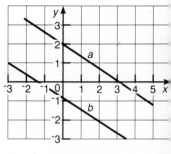
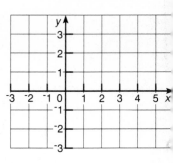

12 Make a copy of this
   diagram.
   (a) On your
      diagram draw
      the line
      $y = \frac{1}{2}x$.
   (b) Use this line to
      draw the line
      $y = \frac{1}{2}x - 3$.

13 Without drawing, write the gradient and amount of
   translation of these lines:
   (a) $y = 4x + 2$ (b) $y = {}^-5x - 2$
   (c) $y = \frac{3}{4}x - \frac{1}{2}$ (d) $y = 0{\cdot}6x + 0{\cdot}8$

14 The line $y = 5x + 12$ is a line of symmetry of two
   other lines. If one of the other lines is
   $y = 5x + 15$, write the equation of the other line.

15 Write the equation of each of these lines.

(a)   (b)

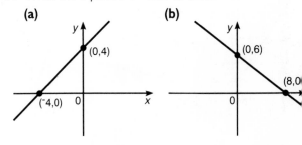

(c)   (d)

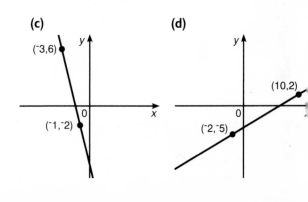

When an equation is written in the form $y = mx + c$ it is written in gradient intercept form, where m is the gradient and c is the amount of translation from $(0, 0)$ or where the line intercepts with the y-axis.

When you draw a graph the information can be presented in an alternative way.

To draw a graph of $3x + 2y = 6$
- find where the line cuts both axes
- where the line cuts the y-axis, x is 0 so
$$(3 \times 0) + 2y = 6$$
$$y = 3 \quad \text{giving the point } (0, 3)$$
- where the line cuts the x-axis, y is 0 so
$$3x + (2 \times 0) = 6$$
$$3x = 6$$
$$x = 2 \quad \text{giving the point } (2, 0)$$

Using these two coordinate points, the line $3x + 2y = 6$ can be drawn.

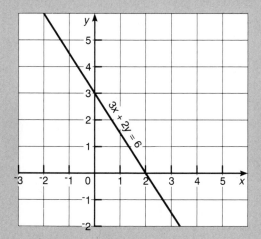

Substituting $x = 0$ and $y = 0$ into the equation sometimes gives values which are difficult to plot accurately on a graph.
- Draw the line $2x + 3y = 8$
When $x = 0 \qquad 3y = 8$
$$y = 2 \cdot 3333 \ldots$$
which may not be easy to plot accurately.
- It is better to try another value of x
Try $x = 1 \qquad 2 + 3y = 8$
$$3y = 6$$
$$y = 2$$
giving the point $(1, 2)$
- The second point can be found using the normal method.
When
$$y = 0$$
$$2x = 8$$
$$x = 4$$
giving the point $(4, 0)$ to plot.

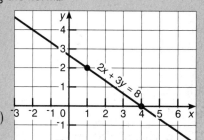

3 Draw the graph of these equations:
- **(a)** $3x + y = 2$ use $x = 0$ and $y = {}^-1$
- **(b)** $3x + 2y = 7$ use $x = 1$ and $y = {}^-1$
- **(c)** $5x - 4y = 1$ use $x = 5$ and $y = 1$
- **(d)** $4x - 3y = 11$ use $x = 2$ and $y = 3$
- **(e)** $2x + 5y = 12$ use $x = {}^-1$ and $y = 0$

4 (a) Draw the equation $x - y = 4$ by first using $x = 5$ to calculate y and then using $y = 2$ to calculate x.
- **(b)** Write any problems you may have had in trying to draw this equation.
- **(c)** Can you suggest better values of x and y to substitute into the equation?

When choosing values to substitute into an equation try to ensure that the two coordinate points you calculate are not too close otherwise it may be difficult to draw accurate graphs.

1 Using the above method draw graphs of:
- **(a)** $3x + 4y = 12$
- **(b)** $2x + 6y = 12$
- **(c)** $5x + 2y = 10$
- **(d)** $3x - 2y = 6$
- **(e)** $4y - 2x = 8$
- **(f)** $3x + 5y = 15$
- **(g)** $3x + 4y = {}^-12$
- **(h)** $4x - 2y = {}^-10$
- **(i)** $2x + 2y = 7$
- **(j)** $5y - 4x = 10$

2 (a) On the same graph draw these two lines $x + y = 3$ and $2x - y = {}^-6$
- **(b)** Write the coordinates where the two lines intercept.

5 Draw graphs of these equations.
- **(a)** $4x - 3y = 1$
- **(b)** $2x + 3y = 19$
- **(c)** $2x - 5y = 8$
- **(d)** $3x + 4y = 0$

Simultaneous equations 1

Find the x value and the y value which satisfy both these equations

$x + y = 3$ and
$2x - y = {}^-6$

These are known as **simultaneous equations**.

One method of finding the x and the y value is to draw the graph of both equations on the same pair of axes and find the coordinates where the two lines cross.

This is called solving simultaneous equations by **graphical methods**.

• Draw the equation $x + y = 3$

When $x = 0$,
  $y = 3$
giving the point
$(0, 3)$

When $y = 0$,
  $x = 3$
giving the point
$(3, 0)$

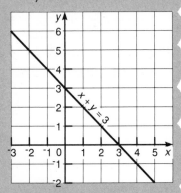

• Draw the equation $2x - y = {}^-6$

When $x = 0$,
  $y = 6$
giving the point
$(0, 6)$

When $y = 0$,
  $2x = {}^-6$
  $x = {}^-3$
giving the point
$({}^-3, 0)$

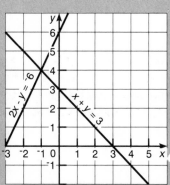

• From the graph, the point where the two lines cross is $({}^-1, 4)$. Always check that these coordinate values give the correct solution
${}^-1 + 4 = 3$ (correct)
${}^-2 - 4 = {}^-6$ (correct)
$x = {}^-1$ and $y = 4$ are therefore the correct solutions to the simultaneous equations
  $x + y = 3$ and
  $2x - y = {}^-6$

1 (a) On graph paper plot these two equations
    $x - y = 1$ and $x + 2y = 7$
  (b) Use your graph to confirm that the solution to the simultaneous equations
        $x - y = 1$
        $x + 2y = 7$
    is $x = 3$ and $y = 2$

2 Solve each of these pairs of simultaneous equations by drawing graphs.
  (a) $x + 3y = 0$ (b) $x - 2y = 1$
      $x - 3y = 6$ $2x + y = 2$
  (c) $x - y = 0$ (d) $4x - 2y = 7$
      $3x - y = {}^-2$ $x + 3y = 7$
  (e) $4x + 3y = 9$ (f) $5x + 3y = 1$
      $2x + 5y = 15$ $2x + 3y = {}^-5$
  (g) $2x + 3y = 29$ (h) $2x - 5y = 8$
      $3x + 2y = 16$ $3x - 7y = 11$

3 (a) Try to solve this pair of simultaneous equations
      $x + y = 4$ and $3x + 3y = 18$
  (b) Comment on what you notice.

4 (a) Try to solve these equations
      $2x + 3y = 12$ and $8x + 12y = 48$
  (b) Comment on what you notice.

When two lines are parallel to each other the equations are said to be inconsistent and will have no solutions.
In question **3** the equations are inconsistent because the first is $x + y = 4$ and the other $3x + 3y = 18$ or $x + y = 6$.
But $x + y$ cannot equal 4 and 6 at the same time.

When the two equations give the same line, as in question **4**, they are said to have an infinite number of solutions. Every point on the line fits both equations.

5 Study these pairs of simultaneous equations. Try to decide which will have 'one solution', which will have 'no solution' and which will have 'an infinite number of solutions'.
  (a) $3x + 2y = 18$ (b) $3x + 5y = 12$
      $9x + 6y = 54$ $12x + 20y = 48$
  (c) $3x + 4y = 24$ (d) $4x - 5y = 9$
      $x + 2y = 18$ ${}^-8x + 10y = {}^-18$

• Remember

Points in 2 dimensions are located and plotted using coordinates. The coordinates of this diagram are A(3, 2) B($^-$4, 1) C($^-$2, $^-$3) and D(5, $^-$3)

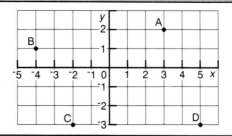

In this chapter the work on coordinates is extended into three dimensions.

In the diagram, point P is located in a 3D coordinate frame.

The coordinates of P are (5, 4, 3), so from the origin, O, P is

5 units along the x-axis OX,
4 units along the y-axis OY and
3 units up the z-axis OZ.

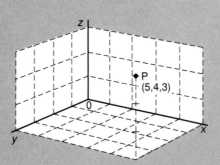

You need isometric paper and a cube.

1 The cube OABCDEFG of unit length is positioned within a 3D coordinate frame. The vertex, O, is at the origin (0, 0, 0) and the edges OA, OC and OE lie along the x, y and z axes respectively.

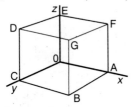

Write the coordinates of:

(a) the 8 vertices of the cube

(b) the centre of the cube.

2 OABCDEFG is a cuboid.
O is at the origin of the coordinates, and the edges OA, OC and OE lie along the x, y and z axes respectively.
OA = 4 units, OC = 3 units, OE = 2 units.

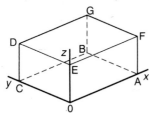

Write the coordinates of all 8 vertices.

3 ABCDEFGH is a cuboid with AB = 5 units, AD = 3 units and AF = 2 units. The coordinates of A are (4, 1, 2) and the edges AB, AD and AF lie parallel to the x, y and z axes respectively. Write the coordinates of the 8 vertices of the cuboid.

4 A cuboid has dimensions 3, 2 and 6 units. One of its vertices is at the point (1, 2, 4). Find all the possible coordinates of its other 7 vertices, given that the edges of the cuboid are parallel to the coordinate axes.

Flow diagrams

This diagram is a flow diagram.

Flow diagrams give a step-by-step instruction in order to solve a problem.

This flow diagram will square and then add 5 to any number.

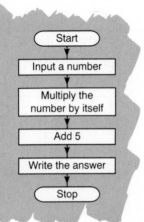

1 (a) Using this flow diagram write the output when:
   - A = 8 and B = 5
   - A = 12 and B = 2
   - A = ⁻2 and B = ⁻3

   (b) Write in your own words what this flow diagram does.

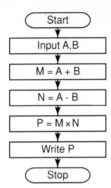

2 Write the output from this flow diagram when:
   (a) A = 10, B = 3, C = 2
   (b) A = 14, B = 10, C = 7
   (c) A = 20, B = 12, C = ⁻2

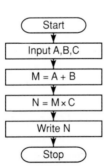

3 (a) Write the answer from this flow diagram when:
   - A = 10, B = 20
   - A = 17, B = 18
   - A = 14, B = 26
   - A = 32, B = 13

   (b) If the output from the flow diagram was 144 suggest the two numbers that may have been input.

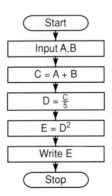

4 (a) Write the answer from this flow diagram when:
   - A = 6, B = 1
   - A = 570, B = 5
   - A = 136, B = 4

   (b) Suggest two numbers that will give an output of 10.

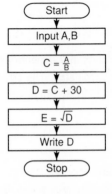

5 Draw flow charts:
   (a) to change a sum of money in £s and pence into pence
   (b) to add two numbers together and divide the result by 2
   (c) to add 3 numbers together and take away 12 from the answer
   (d) to add two numbers together, square the result and add this total to a third number
   (e) to multiply two numbers together, add 5 to the result, divide by 2 and then square root the answer.

Sometimes we need to ask a question within the flow diagram. The answers must be 'yes' or 'no'.

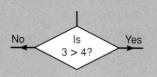

No ← Is 3 > 4? → Yes

5 This flow diagram will calculate all the square numbers less than 100.

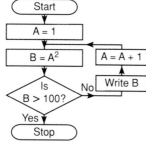

Start
A = 1
B = A² | A = A + 1
Is B > 100? — No → Write B
Yes ↓
Stop

Can you modify it so that:

(a) all the square numbers up to 200 are printed out
(b) only the first square number more than 50 is printed out?

6 (a) Write the output from this flow diagram.

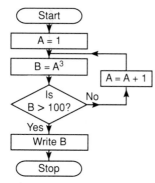

Start
A = 1
B = A³ | A = A + 1
Is B > 100? No
Yes ↓
Write B
Stop

(b) Modify the flow diagram so that only the cube numbers less than 100 are written.

7 Write the output from this flow diagram when:

(a) A = 25, B = 3
(b) A = ⁻2, B = 10

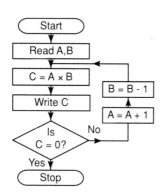

Start
Read A,B
C = A × B | B = B - 1
Write C | A = A + 1
Is C = 0? — No
Yes ↓
Stop

9 Mary invests £100 in the local building society. The society pays 8% interest per annum.

(a) Copy this table:

Number of years	Amount of money
0	100
1	
2	
3	
4	
5	

By following the instructions in the flow diagram complete your table.

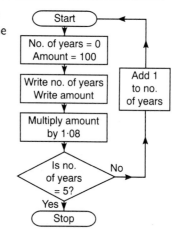

Start
No. of years = 0
Amount = 100
Write no. of years
Write amount | Add 1 to no. of years
Multiply amount by 1·08
Is no. of years = 5? — No
Yes ↓
Stop

(b) Modify the flow diagram so that the output is the number of years required to double the amount invested.

10 Draw flow diagrams:

• to work out all the multiples of 5 less than or equal to 50
• to work out all the factors of 100
• to input two numbers and print out the largest number
• to print out the first six consecutive numbers, starting with the number 1
• to print out the first six triangular numbers, starting with the number 1.

Pythagoras 1

The Theorem of Pythagoras

This theorem is one of the most important in mathematics. It is named after the Greek mathematician Pythagoras who lived from 580 to 500 BC.

In its simplest form it states that for any right-angled triangle

The area of the square drawn on the hypotenuse is equal to the sum of the areas of the squares drawn on the other two sides.

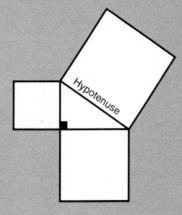

The diagram below shows a right-angled triangle BAC drawn on squared paper.

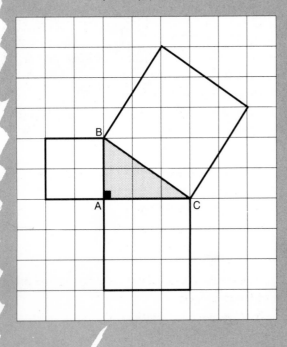

1 (a) On separate sheets of squared paper draw triangles ABC with the angle BÂC always equal to 90° and
   - AB = 1 unit   AC = 1 unit
   - AB = 4 units   AC = 1 unit
   - AB = 3 units   AC = 2 units
   - AB = 5 units   AC = 8 units
   - AB = 3 units   AC = 4 units

(b) Draw the squares on each of the three sides of each triangle. Calculate the area of each square and show that the area of the largest square is equal to the sum of the areas of the other two squares.

2 Calculate the area of each of the squares marked *x*.

(a)   (b)

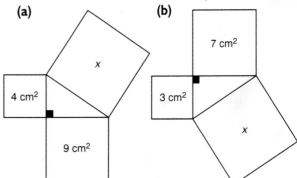

(c)   (d)

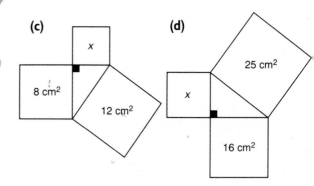

(e)

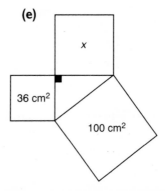

Pythagoras' theorem is usually written as:

$$a^2 + b^2 = c^2$$

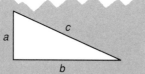

where a, b and c are the side lengths of a right-angled triangle, in which c is the longest side, or the hypotenuse.

3 Use Pythagoras' theorem to calculate the length of x in each triangle.

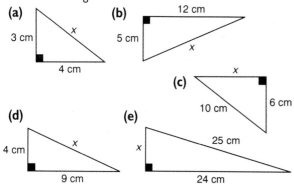

(a) 3 cm, x, 4 cm

(b) 12 cm, 5 cm, x

(c) x, 10 cm, 6 cm

(d) 4 cm, x, 9 cm

(e) x, 25 cm, 24 cm

4 In triangle ABC, $\widehat{BAC} = 90°$, AB = 12 cm, AC = 5 cm.
Calculate the length of BC.

5 In the triangle PQR the angle $\widehat{PQR} = 90°$, PQ = 7 cm, and PR = 25 cm.
Calculate the length of QR.

6 Marie walks 6 miles due north, and then turns clockwise through an angle of 90° and walks a further 10 miles due east, where she stops at a youth hostel. Calculate the shortest distance from her finishing point to her starting point.

7 The diagonal of a rectangular table is 15 cm. The shorter sides of the rectangle are both of length 12 cm. Calculate the length of the two longer sides of the table.

8 The length of the hypotenuse of a right-angled isosceles triangle is 10 cm. Calculate the length of the two equal sides.

9 A field PQR is in the shape of a triangle. The angle at P is 90°, the distance PQ is 300 metres and the area of the field is 120 000 square metres. Calculate the perimeter of the field.

10 Calculate the lengths of the sides marked with letters in each of the following.

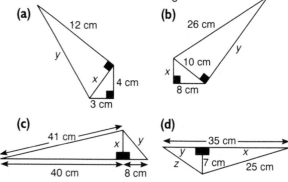

(a) 12 cm, y, x, 4 cm, 3 cm

(b) 26 cm, y, 10 cm, x, 8 cm

(c) 41 cm, x, y, 40 cm, 8 cm

(d) 35 cm, y, x, z, 7 cm, 25 cm

Find the diagonal of a cuboid.

The cuboid OABCDEFG has dimensions as shown.

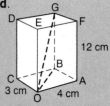

To find the length of the longest diagonal OG:

In triangle OAB

$$OB^2 = OA^2 + AB^2$$

so
$$OB^2 = 4^2 + 3^2$$
$$= 16 + 9$$
$$= 25$$

so $OB = 5$ cm

In triangle OBG

$$OG^2 = OB^2 + BG^2$$

so
$$OG^2 = 5^2 + 12^2$$
$$= 25 + 144$$
$$= 169$$

so $OG = 13$ cm

11 Calculate the length of the longest diagonal of a cuboid measuring:

(a) 3 cm by 6 cm by 10 cm
(b) 5 cm by 12 cm by 20 cm
(c) 8 cm by 8 cm by 15 cm.

12 Calculate the distance from the origin to the point with coordinates:

(a) (6, 8, 24)   **(b)** (3, 3, 3)
(c) (⁻3, 5, 7)   **(d)** (⁻5, 5, ⁻6)
(e) (1, 4, ⁻10)   **(f)** (⁻3, ⁻7, ⁻8)

Pythagoras 2

To calculate the distance, AB, between two points:

- draw the lines AM and BM, where M is the point horizontally across from A and vertically below B
- join AB
- from the diagram, AM = 8 units, BM = 6 units and the angle $A\hat{M}B = 90°$
- use Pythagoras' theorem

$$AB^2 = AM^2 + BM^2$$

so

$$AB^2 = 8^2 + 6^2$$
$$= 64 + 36$$
$$= 100$$

so

$$AB = 10 \text{ units.}$$

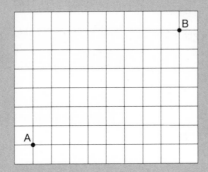

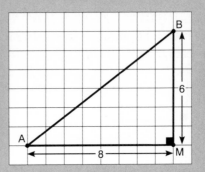

1 Calculate the distance between each of the pairs of points below.

(a)

(b)

(c)

(d)

2 Calculate the distance between:

(a) (3, 0) and (7, 3)   (b) (1, 1) and (13, 6)
(c) ($^-$2, 4) and (4, 12)   (d) ($^-$3, $^-$1) and (1, 7)
(e) ($^-$2, 7) and (3, 2)   (f) (5, $^-$1) and ($^-$5, 1)

3 Write a general expression for the distance between the points (x_1, y_1) and (x_2, y_2)

4 The distance between a point P and the origin is 13 units. Find at least 6 possible pairs of coordinates for P.

5 Show that points with coordinates (4, 6); (5, 5); ($^-$2, 6); ($^-$2, $^-$2) and (6, 2) all lie on a circle. Find the coordinates of:

(a) the centre of the circle
(b) 4 other points on the circle.

Here is a 3 by 7 grid with one of its diagonals drawn:

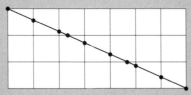

The diagonal makes 8 crossovers with the lines of the grid.

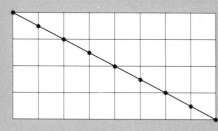

In a 4 by 8 grid, the diagonal makes 7 crossovers with the grid lines.

Investigate the relationship between the number of crossovers and the grid sizes.

You are advised to:

● **record your observations and comments**
● **make and test any conjectures**
● **form any generalisations, with appropriate explanations, justifications or proofs.**

To gain full credit, extend your enquiry in any way you wish, again offering comments, conjectures and generalisations with appropriate explanations, justifications or proofs.

Crossing polygons

Two diagonals have been drawn on this regular hexagon.

A diagonal of a polygon is a line which joins any two of its vertices and which is not a side of the shape.

1 Show that the regular hexagon has 9 diagonals.

2 Investigate the relationship between the number of diagonals and the number of vertices of a regular polygon.

3 Extend your investigation to:
   (a) irregular polygons
   (b) three-dimensional shapes.

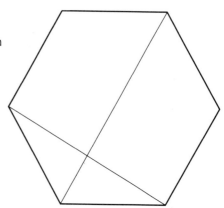

You are advised to:
● **record your observations and comments**
● **make and test any conjectures**
● **form any generalisations, with appropriate explanations, justifications or proofs.**

> Here are two proofs of Pythagoras' theorem. Both proofs have their failings but they will help you learn something about proof in general which is an important concept in investigative work.

Proof 1

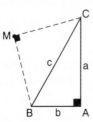

The right-angled triangle ABC is rotated 90° anti-clockwise about the point M. M is equi-distant from points B and C and lies along the perpendicular bisector of the hypotenuse.

This creates the figure

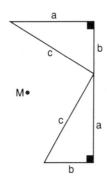

which is repeated twice more to create the shape

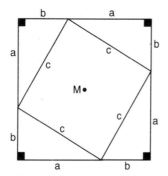

This shape is a square, all the sides are of length $a + b$ and the angles at the vertices are all 90°. Strictly speaking, we need to prove this fact.

The shape inside the large square is also a square, its sides are all of length c and the angles at its vertices are also all 90°. Again, strictly speaking, we need to prove this fact.

The area of the large square is:

$$(a + b)^2$$

which is, by standard algebraic multiplying out

$$a^2 + b^2 + 2ab$$

The larger square also consists of 4 identical (congruent) triangles each of area $\frac{1}{2}ab$ plus a square of area c^2.

The area of the larger square is also

$$4 \times \frac{1}{2}ab + c^2 = 2ab + c^2$$

So we have two algebraic forms each equal to the area of the larger square. In consequence they must be equal.

So

$$a^2 + b^2 + 2ab = 2ab + c^2$$

by cancelling the $2ab$ from both sides of this equation we are left with

$$\mathbf{a^2 + b^2 = c^2}$$

This is the classic, symbolic statement of Pythagoras' theorem.

Proof 2

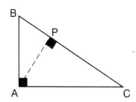

BC is a triangle right-angled at A. P is the point on
C with AP perpendicular to BC. Fundamental to this
roof is the fact that the three triangles BPA, APC and
BC are all similar.

We now

flect triangle BPA in the line AB
flect triangle APC in the line AC
flect triangle ABC in the line BC.

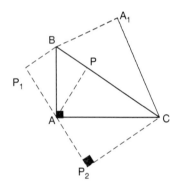

The triangles BP₁A, AP₂C, and A₁BC are also similar.

Also, since the areas of these 'reflected triangles' are
qual to the areas of BPA, APC and ABC and because

rea BPA + area APC = area ABC   then
rea BP₁A + area AP₂C = area A₁BC

o, if we draw similar right-angled triangles on the
hree sides, the area of the triangle on the hypotenuse
equal to the sum of the areas on the other two
des. This is actually the fuller Pythagoras' theorem
or which the 'squares' proof is a part.

We can double all the areas drawn on the sides.

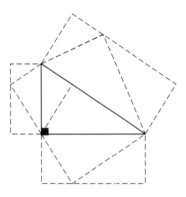

We can now divide each of these by four.

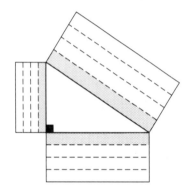

We can even construct semi-circles on the sides.

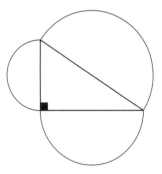

Each of the above and similar constructions do not
alter the basic statement that for any right-angled
triangle
*'If we draw similar shapes on the three sides then the area
of the shape drawn on the hypotenuse is equal to the sum
of the areas drawn on the other two sides.'*
This is the fullest statement of Pythagoras' theorem.

1 Write out these proofs using your own words.

Enlargements

Positive scale factors

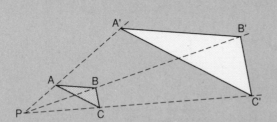

The triangle ABC has been enlarged, centred on P, with scale factor 3, to create the second triangle A'B'C'.

PA' = 3 × PA   PB' = 3 × PB
and   PC' = 3 × PC

Finding the centre and scale factor

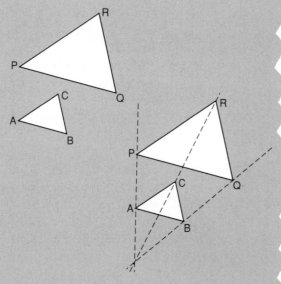

PQR is the enlargement of ABC.

To find the centre of the enlargement:
- draw the line P to A and extend it
- draw the line Q to B and extend it
- draw the line R to C and extend it.

The **centre** of the enlargement, X, is where these three lines meet.

The scale factor of the enlargement is the ratio

$$\frac{XP}{XA} \text{ or } \frac{XQ}{XB} \text{ or } \frac{XR}{XC}$$

1 You need tracing paper.

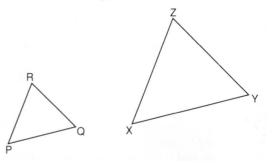

XYZ is an enlargement of PQR. Trace the two triangles PQR and XYZ.

(a) Find the centre of the enlargement and mark it with a C.

(b) Work out the scale factor of the enlargement.

You need squared paper.

2 (a) Plot the points A(3, 1), B(6, 1) and C(6, 3).
   (b) Draw the triangle ABC.
   (c) Draw the image A'B'C' of ABC transformed by an enlargement of scale factor 3 centred on the point (1, 1).
   (d) Write the coordinates of A', B' and C'.

Negative scale factors

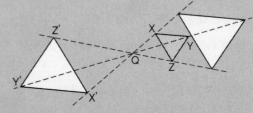

The triangle XYZ has been enlarged, centred on Q, with scale factor ⁻2, to create the triangle X'Y'Z'.

QX' = 2 × QX   QY' = 2 × QY
and   QZ' = 2 × QZ

3 (a) Plot the points X(1, 1), Y(4, 2) and Z(2, 4).
   (b) Draw the triangle XYZ.
      XYZ is transformed by an enlargement, scale factor ⁻4, centred on the origin to form the image X'Y'Z'.
   (c) Find the coordinates of X', Y' and Z'.
   (d) Draw the triangle X'Y'Z'.

Fractional scale factors

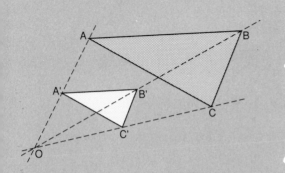

The triangle ABC has been enlarged, centred on O with scale factor $\frac{1}{2}$, to give the triangle A'B'C'

$$OA' = \frac{1}{2}OA \qquad OB' = \frac{1}{2}OB \qquad OC' = \frac{1}{2}OC$$

An enlargement of scale factor $\frac{1}{2}$ is essentially a **reduction by half**.

(a) Plot the points A(6, 3), B(12, 3) and C(12, 6).
(b) Draw the triangle ABC.
    ABC is transformed by an enlargement centred on the origin, scale factor $\frac{1}{3}$, to give A'B'C'.
(c) Draw the triangle A'B'C'.
(d) Write down the coordinates of A', B' and C'.
(e) On the same axes draw the image A"B"C" of ABC when it is transformed by an enlargement, scale factor $-\frac{1}{3}$, centred on the origin.

(a) Copy the diagram onto your squared paper. Draw the image P'Q'R' of the triangle PQR after PQR has been transformed by an enlargement of scale factor $\frac{3}{4}$, centred on the origin.

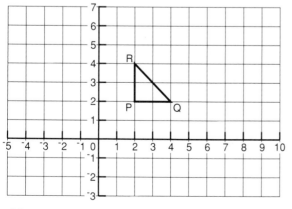

(b) Write the coordinates of P', Q' and R'.

6 ABC is an enlargement of LMN.

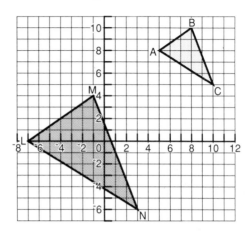

(a) Work out the coordinates of the centre of the enlargement.
(b) Work out the scale factor of the enlargement.

7 The vertices of a triangle ABC are the points A(4, 2), B(6, 2) and C(4, 6).
(a) Plot the points and draw the triangle.
(b) Calculate the area of ABC.
(c) Draw the image A'B'C' of ABC when it is transformed by an enlargement centred on the origin, of scale factor $\frac{1}{2}$.
(d) Calculate the area of A'B'C'.
(e) How does the area of A'B'C' relate to the area of ABC?
(f) Draw a second image A"B"C" when ABC is transformed by an enlargement centred on the origin, but this time of scale factor $\frac{1}{4}$.
(g) Calculate the area of A"B"C".
(h) How does the area of A"B"C" relate to the area of ABC?

8 (a) Plot the triangle PQR with verticles P(3, 3), Q(6, 3) and R(3, 6).
(b) Calculate the area of PQR.
(c) Draw the image P'Q'R' when PQR is transformed by an enlargement, centred on the origin of scale factor $\frac{1}{3}$.
(d) Calculate the area of P'Q'R' and state how it relates to the area of PQR.

9 Use the evidence of questions 7 and 8 to confirm the general statement that if a shape is enlarged by a scale factor $\frac{1}{k}$ then the area of the enlarged shape is $\left(\frac{1}{k}\right)^2$ the area of the original shape.

Lengths, areas and volumes

Rectangle

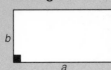

Perimeter = $2(a + b)$
Area = ab

Parallelogram

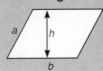

Perimeter = $2(a + b)$
Area = bh

I

(a) Find, in its simplest form, an expression using x for the perimeter of the rectangle.
(b) If the perimeter is 38 cm, find the value of x.
(c) Work out the area of the rectangle.

2 The area of a square, in square centimetres, is numerically equal to its perimeter in centimetres. Calculate:

(a) the length of a side of the square
(b) the length of a diagonal of the square.

Triangle

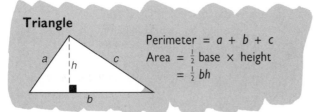

Perimeter = $a + b + c$
Area = $\frac{1}{2}$ base × height
= $\frac{1}{2} bh$

3 Do Worksheet I.

4 (a) Write down and simplify an expression in x for the perimeter of the triangle.

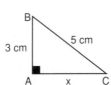

(b) If the perimeter is 31 cm, find the value of x.

5 (a) Find the length of the side marked x in the triangle ABC.
(b) Calculate:

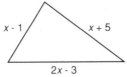

- the area of ABC
- the perimeter of PQR.

(c) The triangle ABC is enlarged by a scale factor of 3 to give a triangle PQR.
Calculate:

- the area of PQR
- the perimeter of PQR.

6 Do Worksheet 2.

7 Calculate the area of each parallelogram.

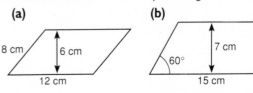

(a)   **(b)**

Trapezium

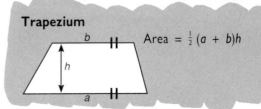

Area = $\frac{1}{2}(a + b)h$

8 Do Worksheet 3.

9 ABCD is a trapezium.
The sides AB and DC are parallel and the distance between them is 7 cm.
AB = 5·8 cm and DC = 11·4 cm
Calculate the area of the trapezium ABCD.

10 WXYZ is a trapezium with lengths of sides as marked, in centimetres.

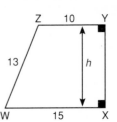

Calculate:

(a) the distance h between the parallel sides
(b) the area of the trapezium.

II Sharon wishes to fence off a rectangular garden using exactly 100 metres of fencing. Show that she will fence off a garden of maximum possible area if she makes it square.

Circle

Circumference $= 2\pi r = \pi d$

Area $= \pi r^2 = \dfrac{\pi d^2}{4}$

diameter $= 2 \times$ radius or $d = 2r$

12 Do Worksheet 4.

13 Calculate the area of a circle with radius 5 cm.

14 The area of a circle is 100 cm^2. Calculate:
  (a) the radius of the circle
  (b) the circumference of the circle.

15 The area of a circle, in square centimetres, is numerically equal to its circumference in centimetres.
  Calculate:
  (a) the radius of the circle
  (b) the area of the circle.

Cuboid

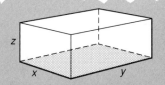

Surface area $= 2(xy + xz + yz)$
Volume $= xyz$

For a **cube** $x = y = z$
Surface area $= 6x^2$
Volume $= x^3$

16 Do Worksheet 5, The surface area of a cuboid.

17 Calculate the volume of a cube of side length 2·8 cm.

18 A cube has a volume of 80 cm^3. Calculate the length of a side of the cube.

19 A cube has a volume of 64 cm^3. Calculate:
  (a) the length of a side of the cube
  (b) the surface area of the cube
  (c) the length of one of the longest diagonals of the cube.

20 A crystal is in the shape of a cube. The length of one side of the crystal is 0·00032 cm.
Calculate the volume of the crystal.

■ Investigation

21 The volume of a cuboid is 72 cm^3. The length of each edge of the cuboid is an integer. Investigate the various possible values for the surface area of the cuboid.

22 This cuboid has a square base of side x cm. The height of the cuboid is h cm. The volume of the cuboid is 48 cm^3.

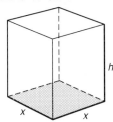

  (a) Show that $x = \sqrt{\dfrac{48}{h}}$
  (b) Calculate the value of x when $h = 2$
  (c) Calculate the value of h when $x = 4$.

23 The volume of a cube in cubic centimetres is numerically equal to its surface area in square centimetres.
Calculate the length of a side of the cube.

24 This cuboid has a height h cm. The base is a square of side length x cm.

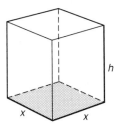

The volume of the cuboid is 50 cm^3. The surface area of the cuboid is 60 cm^2
  (a) Show that x satisfies the equation
    $$x^2 + \dfrac{100}{x} = 30$$
  (b) Find, by any means, an approximate solution to this equation. Comment on your solution.

Prism

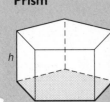

Surface area =
2 × Area of base
+ total Area of vertical faces.

Volume = Area base × height
= Area base × h

25 Do Worksheet 5, the surface area of a prism.

26 Here are a prism
and its base.
Calculate:
(a) the surface area of the prism
(b) the volume of the prism.

5 cm
6 cm
8 cm
12 cm

Wedge

Surface area =
area of two triangular faces
+ area of 3 rectangles.

Volume = $\frac{1}{2}$ volume of prism
= $\frac{1}{2} abc$ when angle
at base = 90°

27 Do Worksheet 6.

28 All the lengths of this wedge
are in centimetres. Calculate:
(a) the volume of the wedge
(b) the surface area of the
wedge.

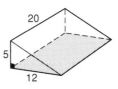
20
5
12

Pyramid

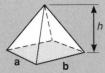

Volume =

$\dfrac{\text{area of base} \times \text{height}}{3}$

When the base of the pyramid is a rectangle
measuring $a \times b$

Volume = $\dfrac{abh}{3}$

29 Do Worksheet 7.

30 VABCD is a rectangular based pyramid. The
horizontal rectangular base ABCD has sides
AB = 5 cm and BC = 8 cm. The vertex V is
12 cm vertically above the mid-point of the base.
Calculate the volume of the pyramid.

31 This tetrahedron, VABC, has a triangular horizontal
base ABC, right-angled at A.
The vertex V is
vertically above A.

Calculate:
(a) the length BC
(b) the volume of the tetrahedron.

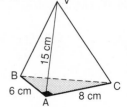
V
15 cm
B
6 cm
A
8 cm
C

Cylinder

Surface area = $2\pi rh + 2\pi r^2$
Volume = $\pi r^2 h$

32 Calculate:
(a) the surface area and
(b) the volume of a cylinder with base a circle
radius 5 cm and height 12 cm.

Cone

Volume = $\dfrac{\pi r^2 h}{3}$

33 Calculate the volume of a cone of height 12 cm
and base of radius 4 cm.

Sphere

Surface area = $4\pi r^2$
Volume = $\dfrac{4\pi r^3}{3}$

34 The radius of a sphere is 5 cm. Calculate:
(a) the surface area of the sphere
(b) the volume of the sphere.

Bell ringers produce peals of bells by ringing them in different orders.

One of the best known arrangements or permutations of the orders is called the Hunting Pattern. Here it is in diagrammatic form for 8 bells labelled A to H:

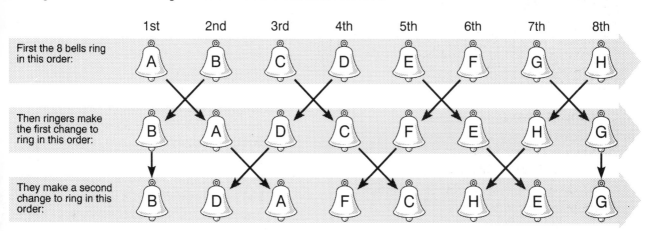

	1st	2nd	3rd	4th	5th	6th	7th	8th
First the 8 bells ring in this order:	A	B	C	D	E	F	G	H
Then ringers make the first change to ring in this order:	B	A	D	C	F	E	H	G
They make a second change to ring in this order:	B	D	A	F	C	H	E	G

Then they alternate the first change and the second change again and again.

1 Investigate the Hunting Pattern for various numbers of bells.

You are advised to look at:
- **the place in the order taken by each bell after each change**
- **the number of changes needed for the bells to return to their original order.**

2 Either:
- investigate other bell ringing patterns

or:
- investigate systematic changes in another ordered activity.

How probable?

There are seven pens in Mary's box. Three are red, and four are blue. If she selects one at random, the probability of it being a red pen is $\frac{3}{7}$, and the probability of it being a blue pen is $\frac{4}{7}$.

Probability of event =
$$\frac{\text{number of ways in which the event can occur}}{\text{number of ways in which all events can occur}}$$

She expects that if she selects 7 pens, 3 will be red, and 4 will be blue.
Mary takes out seven pens, one at a time, replacing each one after recording its colour. She finds that, of the seven pens, 4 are red, and 3 are blue! How can this be?

> Probability is used to estimate the **probable** outcome of events. Only a probability of 1 means that something is certain to occur.

Mary repeated the experiment ten times. She calculated how many times she would expect to select a red or a blue pen:

Number of selections = 70

Expected red pens $= 70 \times \frac{3}{7} = 30$

Expected blue pens $= 70 \times \frac{4}{7} = 40$

She selected 70 pens in turn. Her results were:
Red pens: 33   Blue pens: 37
The results were nearer her predicted figures.

1 Conduct your own experiment. You could:
  • take coloured counters from a bag
  • toss a coin
  • throw a dice.
  (a) Work with a partner; decide how many times you would like to repeat the task. Begin by calculating your expected outcomes.
  (b) Conduct your experiment, listing the results, and writing a conclusion.

(c) If others in the class have conducted the same experiment, combine your results and see what effect this has. Does extending the experiment to collect more data bring your results nearer to the predictions?

Collecting data

In order to calculate probability estimates, you need real data which you can use to calculate your initial estimates of probabilities.

You can obtain such data from:
  • existing records
  • questionnaires
  • observation records.

2 Here are some possibilities for you to work on:
  (a) Using existing records
      You could use school attendance records. Is the probability of someone being absent on a Monday higher than the probability of someone being absent on a Friday?
  (b) Using questionnaires
      You could design a questionnaire to help determine the number in each class who have been to a disco or party during the previous week. You could use this data to calculate the probability of a member of a class attending a disco or party per week.
  (c) Making and using observation records
      You could observe students leaving your school, and note down whether each student is leaving individually, in a pair, threes, or in a larger group. You could use the data to calculate the probability of a student belonging to one of these categories.

  (d) Using your own existing data
      You might have already collected some real data as part of a statistical survey which you could use to make some probability calculations.

Sometimes it is useful to use computers to simulate an experiment or a situation in real life, perhaps because it is quicker, or because it would be too expensive or dangerous to do it another way.

The probability of a coin showing heads when thrown is $\frac{1}{2}$. To do an experiment to test this probability estimate over 100 or 1000 repetitions would be time-consuming and tedious. We can use a computer, which will simulate random situations.

PROBABILITY PROGRAM

```
10   PRINT "NO. OF REPEATS"
20   INPUT REPEAT
30   PRINT "MAX NO. OF EVENTS (2–100)"
40   INPUT MAX
50   FOR COUNT = 1 TO REPEAT
60   LET X = INT(RND(1)*100)+1
70   IF X<1 OR X> MAX THEN 60
80   C(X) = C(X)+1
90   NEXT COUNT
100  FOR COUNT = 1 TO MAX
110  PRINT "NO. FOR"; COUNT; "IS"; C(X)
120  NEXT COUNT
130  END
```

1 (a) Use this program to simulate the throwing of a coin as many times as you wish. To use the program for coins the maximum number of events is just two: Heads and Tails.
Let Heads = 1, and Tails = 2.

(b) Set your results out in a table.

(c) How close does the simulation come to a probability of $\frac{1}{2}$ for Heads and $\frac{1}{2}$ for Tails?

2 Use the program to simulate these situations.

(a) To simulate the throwing of a single dice, use a maximum number of 6.

(b) To simulate the throwing of two dice, use a maximum number of 12, but ignore the 1s (do you know why?).

(c) To simulate Mary's pens situation, use the numbers 1, 2, & 3 for the red pens, and 4, 5, 6 & 7 for the blue pens (a maximum number of 7).

■ Investigation

3 Investigate these using the program:

(a) the throwing of an octagonal dice

(b) the selection of a card from a pack of playing cards:

♥ = 1,   ♦ = 2,   ♣ = 3,   ♠ = 4

or: Ace = 1, number cards 2–10,
picture cards 11–13.

(c) the rolling of a biased dice with the probabilities of each face set as follows:
the probability of 1: $\frac{1}{16}$
the probability of 6: $\frac{7}{16}$
the probability of other sides: $\frac{2}{16}$
Use the numbers 1 to 16 in the program.

Your school may have other programs which you can use to simulate situations in probability.

Ask me another

Statistics help to make decisions.
You may wish to test a **theory** like 'People think everybody should learn to swim'.
This is called a **hypothesis**.

To test a hypothesis you should design a questionnaire and carry out a survey. The questionnaire should:

- ask short questions
- not ask leading questions inviting certain responses
- be in a logical sequence
- provide tick answers.

A typical questionnaire to test this hypothesis is

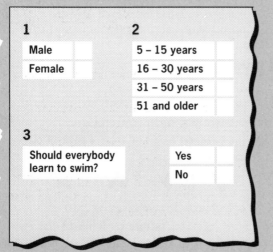

1		2	
Male		5 – 15 years	
Female		16 – 30 years	
		31 – 50 years	
		51 and older	

3			
Should everybody learn to swim?		Yes	
		No	

The questionnaire should be given to a sample of at least 50 people. The first two questions help to provide a **random sample** of different types of people.

If 50 people were asked the question, then the hypothesis 'People think everybody should learn to swim' should only be accepted if at least 30 people agreed.

1 Design a questionnaire to test the hypothesis 'The local community should provide more leisure activities'.

(a) Carry out a survey.

(b) Analyse the results to see whether the hypothesis is valid.

(c) Support your conclusion with statistical diagrams.

(d) Carry out another questionnaire to find out what leisure activities are requested.

(e) Illustrate your findings with statistical diagrams.

2 Design a questionnaire to test a hypothesis on a school issue.

(a) State the hypothesis.

(b) Carry out a survey.

(c) Analyse the results to see whether the hypothesis is valid.

(d) Support your conclusion with statistical diagrams and reasons.

3 Make a list of ten hypotheses you could design a questionnaire to test.

(a) Choose one of these hypotheses.

(b) Design a questionnaire to test this hypothesis.

(c) Carry out a survey.

(d) Analyse the results to see whether the hypothesis is valid.

(e) Support your conclusions with statistical diagrams and reasons.

Once data is collected it is usually arranged into a **frequency table**.

A frequency table displays data showing how many of each type there are.

A frequency table may help to test a hypothesis.

1 In a maths test 50 students from Class 4B obtained these marks.

```
27   8  16  21  29  31  18  42  35  29   7  37  38
12  27  23  14  31  23  11  15  28   5  29  11  31
22  16  27  43  21  17  45  23  33  28  21  29  21
18  25  23  26  41  28  35  27  44  17  38
```

(a) Copy and complete the frequency table.

Marks	Tally	Frequency
0–9		
10–19		
20–29		
30–39		
40–49		

(b) Use this table to help test the hypothesis 'Most students scored more than 29'.

2 In a survey the lengths of 50 horse chestnut leaves, in cm, were measured.

```
21·7  16·8  12·1  18·1  19·1  16·1  21·1  18·7
17·1  17·9  19·3  15·2  17·2  22·3  17·9  22·5
20·9  19·9  21·1  19·8  18·7  18·0  20·5  21·1
19·5  19·8  19·4  20·2  19·6  20·7  22·3  19·7
19·4  18·4  18·2  18·1  19·8  21·6  19·1  18·9
29·1  21·4  18·7  19·8  19·3  19·3  18·3  19·7
20·2  19·9
```

(a) Draw up a frequency table with class intervals of 1 centimetre, including tally and frequency columns.

(b) • Measure 50 leaves from a different tree of your choice.

• Construct frequency tables.

• Test the hypothesis that horse chestnut leaves are bigger than the other leaves you have chosen.

• Explain your conclusion with the help of statistical diagrams.

3 (a) Measure the heights of 50 boys and 50 girls, and record their measurements.

(b) Draw up two frequency tables with class intervals of 5 cm.

(c) Compare the two frequency tables by the use of statistical diagrams.

(d) Test the hypothesis 'Boys are taller than girls'.

(e) Is the hypothesis accepted or rejected? Explain your choice with reasons.

Around the middle

In statistics there are **three measures of average**.

The mean

The mean of a set of items is the **sum of the items** divided by the **number of items**.

$$\text{Mean} = \bar{x} \text{ ('x bar')} = \frac{\text{sum of the items}}{\text{number of items}} = \frac{\Sigma x}{n}$$

$\bar{x}$ is the symbol for the mean

Σx means the sum of the x-values

n means the number of items

The median

The median of a set of items is the **middle** item once the items are **arranged in ascending order**. If there is an even number of items the median is the mean of the two middle items.

The mode

The mode of a set of items is the **item which occurs most often**. If there are no repeated items then the mode does not exist.

The range

The range of a set of items is the **difference between the smallest and largest items** in the set.

The shopping bills for nine people were £28, £30, £34, £34, £40, £47, £52, £65, £120.

$$\text{Mean } \bar{x} = \frac{\Sigma x}{n} =$$

$$\frac{28 + 30 + 34 + 34 + 40 + 47 + 52 + 65 + 120}{9}$$

$$= \frac{450}{9} = 50$$

Mean   = £50

Median   = 28, 30, 34, 34, 40, 47, 52, 65, 120.

                        (middle item)

Median   = £40 ←

Mode   = 28, 30, 34, 34, 40, 47, 52, 65, 120

          = £34 ←

                 (most frequent item)

Range   = 120 – 28

          = £92

The mean can be distorted by extreme values (high or low). In this example 120 distorts the mean and gives an average of 50.

It is better to take the median because it describes the data more accurately and is not distorted by the extreme value.

The mode is easiest to calculate and eliminates the effect of extreme values. However, it does not always give a good average and is not often used.

---

1 **(a)** Find the mean, median, mode and range of the following:

- 2, 3, 4, 6, 8, 10, 14.
- 20, 24, 25, 27, 28, 29, 30, 35.
- 56, 57, 57, 58, 58, 60, 60, 62, 63.
- 4·6, 5·1, 5·4, 5·4, 5·4, 5·7, 5·8, 6·0, 6·3, 15·2.

(b) For each set state which average best describes the items and why.

2 The weight of 7 adults was

67 kg, 98 kg, 76 kg, 85 kg, 59 kg, 91 kg, 72 kg. Find the mean and median weights.

3 The temperature in degrees centigrade was measured at 1300 each day for ten days

22, 19, 27, 16, 21, 22, 18, 31, 23, 20

(a) Find:

- the mean
- the median
- the mode temperature.

(b) Which average best describes the temperature and why?

4 The heights of eleven students were measured.

157 cm, 182 cm, 162 cm, 159 cm, 173 cm, 169 cm, 174 cm, 152 cm, 168 cm, 191 cm, 175 cm.

Calculate:

(a) the mean   **(b)** the median height.

For data on a large number of items the number of times each item occurs can be counted and a **frequency table** obtained.

This data represents the number of people in each of 40 families.

```
8 4 2 5 3 3 2 6 7 3
3 2 4 5 6 2 3 5 4 3
5 3 2 4 7 3 6 3 2 4
4 4 3 2 5 4 3 3 4 6
```

Count the number of times 2, 3, 4, 5, 6, 7 and 8 occur and draw up a frequency table, from which the mean can be calculated.

No. of people in each family (x)	Frequency (f)	fx
2	7	14
3	12	36
4	9	36
5	5	25
6	4	24
7	2	14
8	1	8
	$\Sigma f = 40$	$\Sigma fx = 157$

mean x $= \dfrac{\Sigma fx}{\Sigma f} = \dfrac{\Sigma\ 157}{40} = 3\cdot925$

The median is found by adding the 20th and 21st numbers together and finding their average.

median $= \dfrac{4 + 4}{2} = 4$

The **mode** is the most common item, 3.

The data can be represented by a statistical chart.

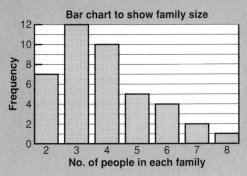

Bar chart to show family size

1 Louise carried out a survey to find the number of pets in 40 different families.

```
1 0 2 1 1 0 3 2 1 0
0 2 1 1 2 0 1 4 1 0
2 1 2 3 1 1 1 0 0 2
0 1 1 2 2 1 0 1 3 1
```

(a) Draw up a frequency table.
(b) Calculate:
  • the mean   • the median   • the mode.
(c) Illustrate the information with an appropriate statistical diagram.

2 Lee works in a clothing factory. He has cut 54 pieces of cloth of length:

```
169 167 169 171 174 172 172 170 168
173 166 170 171 172 169 171 168 170
169 171 174 170 172 169 168 173 167
171 174 170 169 172 171 170 168 174
170 170 169 171 167 169 170 173 170
169 170 165 170 171 166 168 172 170
```

(a) Draw up a frequency table.
(b) Calculate:
  • the mean   • the median   • the mode.
(c) Illustrate the data with a suitable statistical diagram.

3 (a) Find:
  • the mean   • the median
  • the mode from this frequency distribution.

x	10	11	12	13	14
f	1	3	6	9	15

x	15	16	17	18	19
f	13	8	4	2	2

(b) Illustrate the frequency distribution with a suitable statistical diagram.

Class marks

Class intervals are often used in statistics to group data.

In an examination, data for 80 candidates were grouped in class intervals with width 10.

Percentage mark	Number of candidates (frequency)
31–40	4
41–50	9
51–60	16
61–70	26
71–80	15
81–90	7
91–100	3

This type of table is called a **frequency distribution**.

A frequency distribution should have at least five classes but no more than twenty classes. This gives enough classes to reveal any pattern in the data, but not so many that the pattern disappears.

The information in the table can be represented by a **histogram** like this:

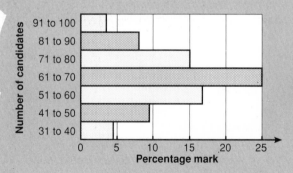

The mean (average) mark for the candidates can be estimated from the frequency distribution.

To calculate the estimate of the mean the half-way mark or centre of each class interval must be multiplied by the frequency.

The half-way mark for the class 31–40 is

$$\frac{31 + 40}{2} = 35.5$$

To calculate the estimate of the mean the table is completed:

Percentage mark	Number of candidates frequency (f)	Half way mark (x)	f × x
31–40	4	35·5	142
41–50	9	45·5	409·5
51–60	16	55·5	888
61–70	26	65·5	1703
71–80	15	75·5	1132·5
81–90	7	85·5	598·5
91–100	3	95·5	286·5
	80	Totals	5160

The estimated mean $(\bar{x}) = \dfrac{\text{sum of } f \times x}{\text{sum of frequency}}$

$$\bar{x} = \Sigma \, \frac{fx}{f}$$

$$\bar{x} = \frac{5160}{80}$$

$$\bar{x} = 64.5$$

I The frequency distribution shows the weights of 70 sheep.

(a) Form a frequency distribution table to include the half way mark, x, and the frequency, f, multiplied by the half way mark, x, called fx.

(b) Calculate an estimate of the mean using the rule

Estimate of mean, $x = \dfrac{\Sigma \, fx}{\Sigma \, f}$

(c) Illustrate the data with a histogram.

Weight in kg.	No. of sheep
20 to under 30	2
30 to under 40	5
40 to under 50	16
50 to under 60	25
60 to under 70	13
70 to under 80	6
80 to under 90	3

2 In a competition the marks obtained by 100 players
were:

Mark	No. of players
11–20	3
21–30	5
31–40	8
41–50	14
51–60	23
61–70	28
71–80	11
81–90	6
91–100	2

(a) Form a frequency distribution table to include x
and fx.

(b) Calculate an estimate of the mean using the rule

estimate of mean, $\bar{x} = \dfrac{\Sigma fx}{\Sigma f}$

(c) Illustrate the data with a histogram.

3 The time in hours that 100 electric light bulbs lasted
is shown in the frequency distribution table.

Time (Hours)	No. of bulbs
0 to under 200	1
200 to under 400	4
400 to under 600	7
600 to under 800	10
800 to under 1000	14
1000 to under 1200	33
1200 to under 1400	20
1400 to under 1600	6
1600 to under 1800	5

(a) Form a frequency distribution table which
includes x and fx.

(b) Calculate an estimate of the mean.

(c) Illustrate the data with a histogram.

4 The weekly wage of 100 young people in the
Midlands is given in the frequency distribution table.

Wage £	No. of people (f)
80 to under 90	1
90 to under 100	4
100 to under 110	9
110 to under 120	28
120 to under 130	37
130 to under 140	11
140 to under 150	7
150 to under 160	3

(a) Form a frequency distribution table which
includes x and fx.

(b) Calculate an estimate of the mean.

(c) Illustrate the data with a histogram.

5 A survey to find the age distribution of the members
of the Samurai Judo Club was carried out. The
results were:

Age	No. of members
0 – 9	20
10 – 19	64
20 – 29	52
30 – 39	21
40 – 49	2
50 – 59	1

(a) Form a frequency distribution table.

(b) Calculate an estimate of the mean.

(c) Illustrate the data with a histogram.

Frequency polygons

Frequency polygons can be used to illustrate data instead of histograms.
Frequency polygons are used to compare data.

To draw a frequency polygon:

- draw a histogram of the data
- plot the mid-points at the top of each bar of the histogram
- join the mid-points.

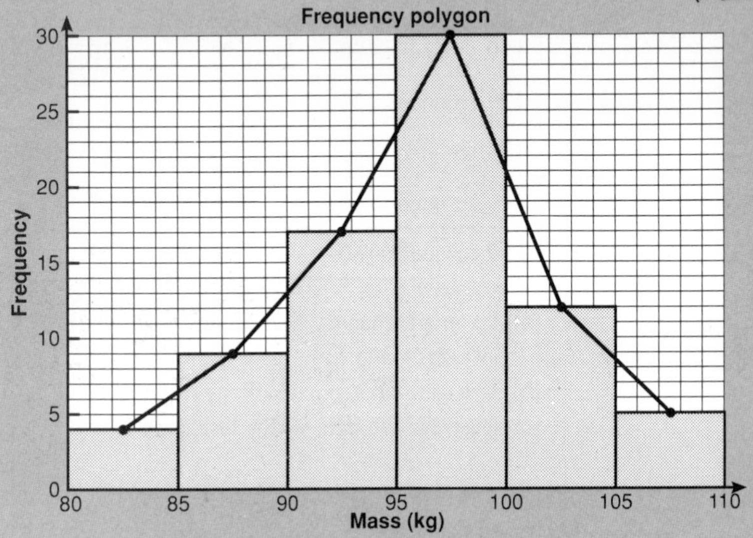

Frequency polygon

> Here is a frequency polygon showing the mass of a squad of rugby players.

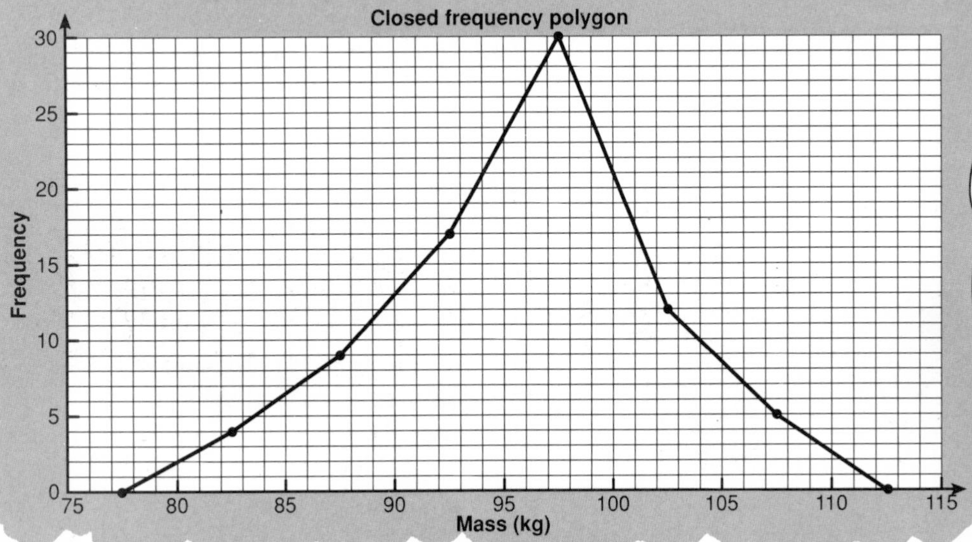

Closed frequency polygon

> The frequency polygon can be closed by joining the first and last mid-points in each bar to the horizontal axis.

1 In a sports competition the marks obtained by 110 competitors were:

Mark	1–10	11–20	21–30	31–40	41–50	51–60	61–70	71–80	81–90	91–100
No. of competitors	2	7	10	15	27	21	12	7	5	3

Illustrate this frequency distribution by drawing a frequency polygon.
(Remember to draw the histogram first).

2 The frequency distribution shows the age in years of 100 people.

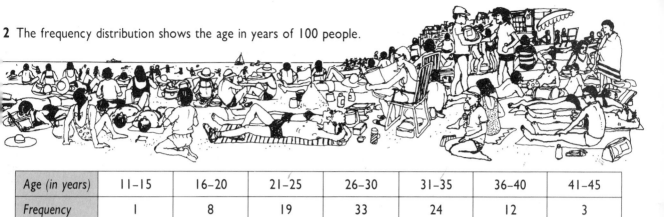

Age (in years)	11–15	16–20	21–25	26–30	31–35	36–40	41–45
Frequency	1	8	19	33	24	12	3

Illustrate this distribution by drawing a histogram and frequency polygon.

3 The frequency distribution gives the weekly sales of shirts in *Feeling Shirty* for one year.

No. of shirts sold	10–29	30–49	50–69	70–89	90–109	110–129	130–149
No. of weeks	2	4	18	19	11	7	1

Draw a closed frequency polygon to display the distribution.

4 This distribution gives the annual salary of 300 people at Central Telecom.

Annual salary (£)	1–5000	5001–10 000	10 001–15 000	15 001–20 000	20 001–25 000
No. of people	8	57	92	65	32

Annual salary (£)	25 001–30 000	30 001–35 000	35 001–40 000	40 001–45 000
No. of people	19	9	5	3

(a) Illustrate this information on a histogram.
(b) On the histogram draw the frequency polygon.

Scattered about

Some students are investigating the sizes of apples in 2 kg bags. One hypothesises that the median mass of the apples in a bag correlates with the number of apples in it.

They weigh some apples and tabulate their results.

Median mass of apples (to the nearest gramme)	72	87	96	105	110	125	136	142	147	159	174	192
Number of apples in the bag	20	21	15	16	18	14	14	15	16	11	13	10

They draw a scatter diagram to illustrate their data.

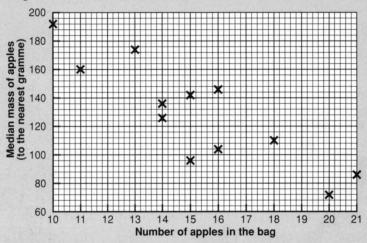

There is clear negative correlation so the hypothesis is verified.

Then one of the students asks whether the graph could be used to estimate the likely median mass of the apples in a bag if the apples were just counted. Another says that it would be useful to have a line to read off but where would they draw it?

They draw a **line of best-fit** so that it follows the trend of the plotted points. The line has an equal number of points on each side.

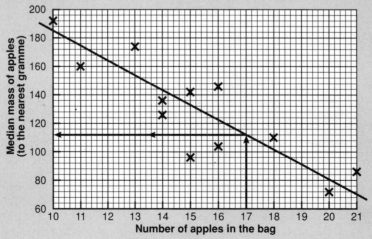

The arrowed line shows their estimate when there are 17 apples in a bag. Their estimate is 116 grammes.

In answering each of the following questions draw a scatter diagram, state the type of correlation, draw in a line of best fit and use it to estimate.

1

For 700 million years jellyfish have inhabited the seas, changing little with the passing millenia. Jellyfish have no brain, no bones, no heart and no lungs. Though they are simple in structure, some species are quite capable of killing a human. En masse they create serious problems. Millions of moon jellies

boat was long and low, and brightly painted. The hull was k with green rubbing strakes and a red gunnel. The panels on cabin sides were painted with roses - four flowers making a ond shape. A striped green and red pole stuck out of the From a distance it looked like a picture in a book, but close to, Helen saw that some of the paint was peeling, and there was a heap of dirty straw on the small semi-circular poop-deck.

No. of words per sentence	12	16	22	24	25	33	36	43	46	56
Mean no. of letters per word	5·1	5·3	4·9	5·4	5·1	5·2	4·7	4·9	4·6	4·7

From the table, estimate the mean number of letters per word, to one decimal place, in a sentence of 30 words.

2

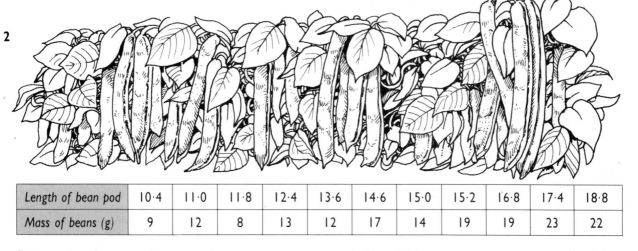

Length of bean pod	10·4	11·0	11·8	12·4	13·6	14·6	15·0	15·2	16·8	17·4	18·8
Mass of beans (g)	9	12	8	13	12	17	14	19	19	23	22

Estimate the mean mass of beans, to the nearest gramme, in a pod of length 14 cm.

3

Height of site above sea level (100 m)	2	4	6	8	9	12	16	17	21	24
Mean July midday temp. (°Celsius)	22	23	19	22	16	19	15	12	8	9

Estimate the mean July midday temperature of a site 1000 m above sea level.

The flow of things I

In a flow diagram:
- **circles** show the start and end points
- **rectangles** contain statements of fact (or where appropriate, the mathematical equations)
- **diamonds** occur where decisions have to be made and always have two ways out
- **boxes** with rounded ends contain activities.

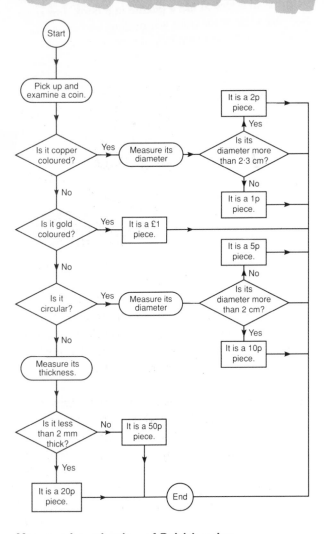

You need a selection of British coins.

1 The flow diagram above can be used to identify British coins by colour, shape and size.
Follow through the flow chart with each of the coins.

2 Draw another flow chart which does the same but uses different instructions. Ask a friend to test your flow chart with the seven different coins.

3 It is possible to program a robot to identify coins using measurement of distances and weight, although it is very difficult to make a robot recognise colour and shape.

Try to write a flow chart which identifies the coins, using measurement alone, which could be used as a basis for programming a robot.

4 A visitor from another planet does not know the names of mammals on our world. Help the visitor by drawing a flow chart which will identify as different; a dolphin, a chimpanzee, a bat, a lion, an elephant, a polar bear, a seal and a horse.

5 A refuse lorry takes rubbish to the recycling plant where it is sorted into different types. Before the rubbish goes into the incinerator, steel cans, aluminium cans, other metal objects, green, clear and brown bottles and plastic are removed. The rest is burnt to generate electricity. Draw a flow diagram to illustrate the sorting process.

6 You are offered £5 if you can be sure of guessing correctly each time, a whole number between 1 and 15 inclusive. You must ask a series of not more than four questions which will ensure that you get the right number. Draw a flow chart including the questions you will ask and what you will ask or say next.

7 Draw a flow chart illustrating how you could sort out your clothes into categories of your choice.

8 Draw a flow chart based upon attributes such as colour of hair, colour of eyes, gender, height etc, which would enable a new teacher to name each member of your class.

$$x^2 = 2$$
$$x^2 - 1 = 1$$
$$(x - 1)(x + 1) = 1$$
$$x - 1 = \frac{1}{x + 1}$$
$$x = 1 + \frac{1}{x + 1}$$

The first equation above states that the square of x is 2. So x must be the square root of 2. When the equation is changed into another form that is still the case.

The final equation is the basis for this flow diagram.

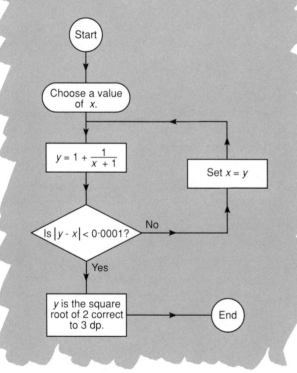

1 Use a calculator to follow through the flow diagram with starting figures of your own choice. Do you always arrive at 1·414 as a solution?

The flow diagram above has a loop in it. It needs the decision diamond to tell you when to stop.

2 Write a similar flow diagram to find the square root of 5 correct to 6 decimal places.

3 In the example in the panel, the algebra would have been simpler if both sides of the first equation had been divided by x to give $x = \frac{2}{x}$ and then $y = \frac{2}{x}$ used in the flow diagram.
Rewrite the flow diagram using $y = \frac{2}{x}$ and find out what happens when you use the following starting values for x:
1, 1·5, 2, 3.

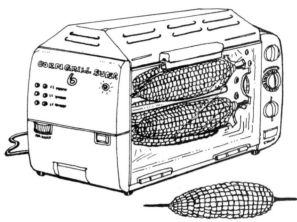

4 An automatic corn-on-the-cob roaster has to be loaded with 6 cobs. When the 'on' button is pressed the cobs are rotated next to a heating element. A detector checks the colour of the cobs every minute. When they are the correct shade of brown the heating element switches off and a bell rings. Draw a flow diagram to illustrate this process.

5 To check whether a number with many digits is divisible by three, find the sum of the digits to produce another number. If that number is greater than 10 add the digits again and keep repeating that process until you reach a single digit. If that digit is 3, 6 or 9 the original number is divisible by three. Draw a flow diagram to carry out that process.

6 Find out how to work out whether a positive integer is prime. Draw a flow chart to illustrate the process.

7 A random selection of 100 British coins are collected and have to be totalled in value. Draw a flow diagram to show how this can be done. Adapt the flow diagram on the previous page.

Jane is cycling along a level road.

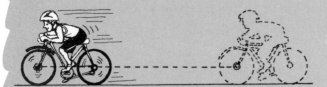

The dotted line shows the path taken by the mid-point of her cycle's front wheel. This is the collection of points through which the mid-point of the wheel passes.

This path (or collection of points) is called the **locus** of the mid-point of the front wheel.

You can model this situation by saying that it is equivalent to the one below.

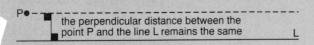

L is a fixed line and P a variable point. P can move, or take up, all the positions, in the plane of the paper, so that the perpendicular distance from P to the line L is a fixed distance.

Some of the positions of P are marked and joined below.

The **locus** of P is a straight line parallel to L.

Some examples of well-known loci are:

(i) The perpendicular bisector of a line segment

It is the locus of a point P which moves such that PA = PB.

(ii) The bisector of an angle

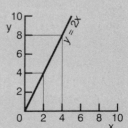

This is the locus of a point P which moves such that
the perpendicular distance from P to OA equals
the perpendicular distance from P to OB.

(iii) The circle

This is the locus of a point P which moves in the plane such that OP is a constant length.

A graph can be considered as a locus.

The graph of $y = 2x$ can be considered as the locus of a point P which moves such that the perpendicular distance from P to OX is twice the perpendicular distance from P to OY.

The path taken by any moving object can also be regarded as a locus, for example:

(i) A ship travels due North, turns and travels due East and then turns again and takes the shortest distance back to its starting point. The locus will look like this:

(ii) The flight of a rounders ball when hit hard could produce this locus.

1 Make accurate drawings of each of the loci of a point P which moves such that:

(a) its direction is 45° to the horizontal

(b) its distance from a fixed point is 5 cm

(c) its distance from a horizontal line is 2 cm

(d) its distance from point A equals its distance from point B, where A and B are two points 6 cm apart.

2

The diagram shows the horizontal and vertical axes H and V.

PH is the perpendicular distance from P to H, PV is the similar distance from P to V. On separate axes, draw the loci of a point P which moves such that:

(a) PH = PV   **(b)** PH = 3PV

(c) PH = $\frac{1}{2}$PV   **(d)** PH = $(PV)^2$

(e) PH × PV = 12   **(f)** PH + PV = 12

3 Express the graph of each of these equations as a locus in terms of PH and PV.

(a) $y = 3x$ **(b)** $y = 2x + 1$

(c) $y = x$ **(d)** $y = x^2$

(e) $xy = 24$ **(f)** $x + y = 10$

(g) $x^2 + y^2 = 25$

4 A rabbit enters a field at the top right hand corner. It is spotted by Rover the dog sitting by the gate on the other side of the field. The rabbit runs down the side of the field. Rover chases the rabbit in such a way that he is always running towards the rabbit.

Sketch the locus of Rover's path.

5 A and B are fixed points and P is a variable point in a plane.

$\overset{\bullet}{A}$ $\qquad\qquad\qquad\qquad$ $\overset{\bullet}{B}$

Draw the locus of P when:

(a) PA = 2PB   **(b)** PA + PB = 12 units

(c) PA − PB = 6 units   **(d)** Angle $A\hat{P}B = 90°$

6 A lighthouse, L, lies 10 kilometres due east of a harbour, H.

$\overset{\bullet}{H}$ $\qquad\qquad\qquad\qquad$ $\overset{\bullet}{L}$

A ship, S, sets sail from the harbour and travels along a bearing of 070°.

Construct an accurate scale drawing to show the positions of the ship when it is exactly 8 kilometres from the lighthouse. How far is the ship from the harbour at these points?

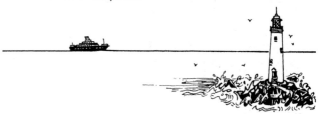

7 This coin rolls along the table top. P is a point on the circumference of the coin.

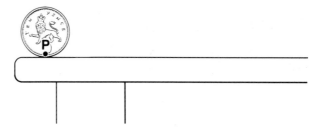

Sketch the locus of the point P.

Rectangles in a rectangle

Here is a 3 by 4 rectangular grid:

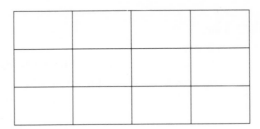

Inside the grid there are some rectangles. Here three of them are shaded:

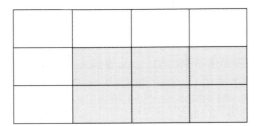

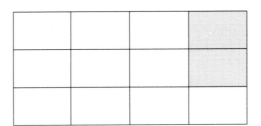

1 Show that the 3 by 4 grid contains 60 rectangles.

2 How many rectangles are there in a grid of size:
   (a) 2 by 3   **(b)** 3 by 5   **(c)** 4 by 5?

3 Investigate the relationship between the size of a
   grid and the number of rectangles it contains.

You are advised to:
- **record your observations and comments**
- **record your data, information and results**
- **explain your working**
- **make and test any conjectures**
- **form any generalisations, with appropriate
  explanations, justifications or proofs.**

In Manhattan the streets are all set out like straight lines on a grid. The houses and offices are like square blocks. As a diagram it looks like a grid.

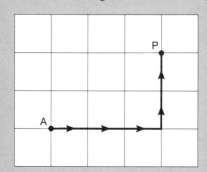

On the grid, the point P is 5 Manhattan blocks away from the point A.

You need squared paper.

1 Mark all the points P such that
PA = 5 Manhattan blocks
This is called the Manhattan locus of a point P such that
PA = 5 Manhattan blocks

In the following questions, A and B are fixed points and P is a variable point.

2 Find the following Manhattan loci:
(a) PA = 4 Manhattan blocks
(b) PA = 6 Manhattan blocks

(c) PA = c Manhattan blocks, where c is a constant. Compare each of these loci with the normal loci defined by PA = 4 units, PA = 6 units and PA = c units respectively.

3 (a) Find the Manhattan locus of a point P when:
• PA = 2PB
• PA = kPB, where k is a constant.
(b) Compare the Manhattan loci with the normal loci defined by PA = 2PB and PA = kPB respectively.

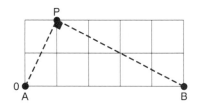

4 A and B are fixed points and P a variable point.
(a) Investigate the Manhattan locus such that PA + PB = a constant number of Manhattan blocks
(b) Compare this locus with the normal one defined by PA + PB = a constant.

You are advised to:
● **record your observations**
● **make and test any conjectures**
● **form any generalisations, with appropriate explanations, justifications or proofs.**

Bracketed together 1

Keith was given this sum in his homework: $4 + 3 \times 5$

Without brackets the meaning is not clear.
It could mean **either** $(4 + 3) \times 5$ **or** $4 + (3 \times 5)$

On a calculator when no brackets are shown
multiplication **takes precedence** over addition.
This means multiplication is done first, so the sum is:
$4 + (3 \times 5)$

You can overcome precedence on a calculator to
find $(4 + 3) \times 5$ in two ways:

- by pressing the $=$ button after pressing

  4 $+$ 3

- by using the calculator's bracket facilities like this:

Press $($ 4 $+$ 3 $)$ $\times$ 5 $=$

> The brackets facility on a calculator can save
> time and ensure accuracy.

1 Use the brackets on your calculator to answer these
questions.

(a) $(12 + 5) \times 3$ **(b)** $(2\cdot4 - 1\cdot7) \times 4\cdot6$

(c) $\dfrac{(36 + 14)}{2 \times 5}$ **(d)** $\dfrac{(5\cdot2 + 7\cdot8)}{(0\cdot5 \times 2\cdot4)}$

(e) $\dfrac{14\cdot25 + 2\cdot87}{3\cdot869 \times 29\cdot45}$ **(f)** $\dfrac{3\cdot05 - 0\cdot0768}{309 \times 0\cdot008465}$

2 Here is a famous formula for
finding the area of a triangle:

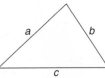

$s = \dfrac{a + b + c}{2}$

$\text{Area} = \sqrt{s(s - a)(s - b)(s - c)}$

This is called Hero's formula. Use it to find the
areas of these triangles:

(a) $s = 15$, $a = 5$, $b = 12$ and $c = 13$
(b) $s = 44\cdot8$, $a = 25\cdot7$, $b = 33\cdot5$ and $c = 30\cdot4$
(c) $s = 11\cdot88$, $a = 6\cdot47$, $b = 11\cdot36$ and $c = 5\cdot93$

3 The formula for finding
the cross-sectional area
of a pipe is:

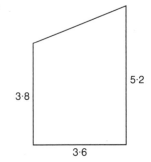

$A = 3\cdot142\,(R^2 - r^2)$

Find A when:

(a) $R = 3$ and $r = 2$
(b) $R = 6\cdot5$ and $r = 2\cdot25$
(c) $R = 12\cdot7$ and $r = 0\cdot125$

4 To change from degrees Fahrenheit (F) to degrees
Celcius (C) you can use the formula

$C = \dfrac{5(F - 32)}{9}$

Use the formula to change these temperatures from
Fahrenheit to degrees Celcius.

(a) 122   **(b)** 86   **(c)** 212
(d) 32   **(e)** 75   **(f)** ⁻16
(g) 450   **(h)** ⁻25   **(i)** 1000

5 You can find the area of
this trapezium by using
the formula

$\text{Area} = \dfrac{(a + b)}{2} \times w$

where a and b are the
two parallel sides and w
is the width. Find the
area of the trapezium.

6 This fence is made from four
trapezium-shaped panels.

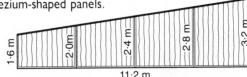

Find:

(a) the area of each panel
(b) the total area of the fence.

7 In physics this formula is used to find the distance
travelled by an accelerating object:

$s = ut + 0\cdot5\,at^2$

Find:

(a) s when $u = 2\cdot6$, $t = 5\cdot1$ and $a = 6$
(b) s when $u = 0\cdot6$, $t = 4\cdot7$ and $a = {}^-3\cdot2$

8 The Accuplas Company
make small plastic
cubes. The cost of each
cube is made up of a
fixed charge and a
variable charge which is
proportional to the
length of the cube.

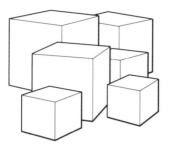

David, the works manager, uses this formula to
work out the cost of the cubes he sells.

Cost = $F + nx^2$

where F = the fixed charge

n = the number sold

x = the length of one side

(a) Find the cost of buying 1000 cubes that have
sides 2·4 cm long with a fixed charge of £156.

(b) At the end of the year Accuplas increase the
fixed charge by 10%. Find the increased cost of
500 cubes each with a volume of 27 cm³.

9 The membership fee to belong to 'The Cutting
Edge' skating club is:

The Cutting Edge

Children under 5........ £5·50 a year
Children 5 to 12........ £7·75 a year
Children 13 to 16........ £9·25 a year
Students 17 to 18........ £10·60 a year
Adults (over 18)...... £15·75 a year

Club membership for the year 1994 was:

Children under 5 25

Children 5 to 12 45

Children 13 to 16 .. 156

Students 17 to 18 ... 84

Adults (over 18) 234

(a) How many members did the club have in 1994?

(b) How much did the skating club receive in
membership fees for that year?

(c) What was the average (mean) membership fee
per member?

(d) The following year the club increased its fees.
The increase for each group was its percentage
of the total membership. Work out, to the
nearest penny, the new membership rates.

10 Derek is trying to solve this equation

$$4·25 = \frac{26·5}{2·2 + 3n}$$

He starts by substituting $n = 2$ and works out how
close this is. He uses his calculator to work out
$26·5 \div (2·2 + 3 \times 2)$ to get 3·23170317.

(a) What is the error, to 4 decimal places, if he
tries a value $n = 1·5$?

(b) Continue trying values of n until you get an
answer correct to 3 decimal places.

(c) In a table of results show all your workings.

11 Here is a 'simple' problem

$$\frac{16}{(3 + 5) \times 2}$$

(a) Work out the answer in your head.

(b) Work out the answer on your calculator by
entering the '16' first and then using the
brackets facilities.

12 Work out the value of the expression

$$\frac{125}{(2·6 + 3n)n} \quad \text{when}$$

(a) $n = 12$ **(b)** $n = 35$

13 Shaminder is trying to solve this equation.

$$4·0 = \frac{36}{(3·4 + n)n}$$

(a) Her first guess at a solution is $n = 2$. Work
out her result.

(b) What is the value of the expression when

• $n = 1·8$ • $n = 1·7$?

(c) Suggest a solution to this equation and check
it. Write down the error correct to two
decimal places.

14 During an experiment James has to work out the
value of this expression

$$\frac{(5·4 + 3·4) \times 2·7}{(8·1 - 3·6) \times 1·8}$$

Work out the value of the expression giving your
answer correct to 3 decimal places.

You've got the part

1 In the *Feeling Shirty* sale a shirt costing £12·15 is reduced by $\frac{2}{5}$.

(a) What fraction of the original price does the shirt now cost?

(b) What is the sale price?

2 During one week in August it was found that of all letters posted

Find:

(a) the fraction of letters that were posted correctly

(b) the minimum possible number of letters that were posted without a stamp.

3 This is the graph of $y = x^2$

The area under the curve can be found using the formula

$$\text{Area} = \left(\frac{a^3}{3} \right) - \left(\frac{b^3}{3} \right)$$

Find the area when:

(a) $a = 4$ and $b = 1$

(b) $a = 4$ and $b = 2$

(c) $a = 6$ and $b = 3$

4 The area under this curve can be found using the formula

$$\text{Area} = \left(\frac{a^4}{4} + 3a \right) - \left(\frac{b^4}{4} + 3b \right)$$

Find the area when:

(a) $a = 3$ and $b = 1$

(b) $a = 4$ and $b = 2$

(c) $a = 5$ and $b = 3$

(d) $a = \frac{1}{2}$ and $b = \frac{1}{4}$

5 If $r = \frac{1}{2}$, $s = \frac{1}{3}$, $t = \frac{1}{4}$ and $u = \frac{1}{5}$. Work out the value of:

(a) $r + s$ **(b)** $2s + u$
(c) $3u + t$ **(d)** $r + t + u$
(e) $4s - 3t$ **(f)** $t + s - u$

How many different combinations of r, s, t and u can you find that give a fraction less than $\frac{3}{4}$? For example, $2t + u = \frac{7}{10} > \frac{3}{4}$

6 Whilst working on a probability problem, Javed drew this tree diagram.

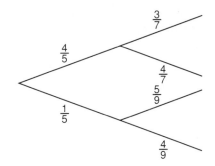

(a) Copy and complete the diagram.

(b) Solve the problem $\left(\frac{4}{5} \times \frac{4}{7} \right) + \left(\frac{1}{5} \times \frac{5}{9} \right)$

7 A class of 20 students take part in a sponsored walk. The walk is over a distance of 60 km. For each kilometre they walk they raise 50p each. Half of the students complete $\frac{3}{4}$ of the walk. $\frac{1}{5}$ of the students complete $\frac{1}{2}$ of the walk. $\frac{1}{4}$ of the students complete $\frac{2}{3}$ of the walk. The rest complete the full 60 km.

(a) How many students complete the total distance of 60 km?

(b) How much money did they raise altogether?

8 **(a)** What fraction of this circle has been shaded?

(b) What is the area of the whole circle?

(c) What is the area of the shaded part?

(d) What is the perimeter of the shaded part?

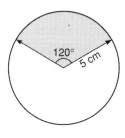

For this topic calculators cannot be used to answer any of the questions. Brain power only!

The decimal point on Sanjeev's calculator does not work.

To answer the question 2·496 × 8·77

He works out 2496 × 877 = 2188992

Because 2 × 8 = 16 and 3 × 9 = 27 he knows that the answer to 2·496 × 8·77 must be between 16 and 27.

2·496 × 8·77 must equal 21·88992

Copy each of the questions and 'answers'. Write the correct answer by including the decimal point.

(a) 3·5 × 2·4 = 84
(b) 5·5 × 7·13 = 39125
(c) 2·41 × 1·89 = 45549
(d) 10·65 × 12·77 = 1360005
(e) 3·4 × 5·1 × 4·8 = 83232
(f) 20·3 ÷ 5·6 = 3625
(g) 89·1 ÷ 17·2 = 5180232
(h) 4·46 ÷ 0·51 = 8745098
(i) (20·4 × 3·6) ÷ 8·57 = 8569428
(j) (16·4 × 5·8) ÷ 0·248 = 38354839

The area of a rectangle is 25·668 cm². One of the sides is 5·6 cm long. Sanjeev's calculator gives this sequence of numbers for the length of the other side.

458357 1429

(a) Write the length of the missing side correct to 2 decimal places.
(b) Estimate the perimeter of the rectangle.

Sanjeev's calculator gave the reading 158 1 13883 for the length of one side of this square.

(a) What is the length of one side of the square correct to 2 dp?

Area
250 cm²

(b) Use the information from **(a)** to find the length of one side of a square whose area is 25 000 cm².
(c) What is the length of one side of a square whose area is 2500 cm²?

Peter was trying to find the length of the missing side of this triangle.

He knew that if he could complete the calculation 0·47 × 5·3 it would give him the missing side.

Without his calculator, Peter had to estimate the answer.

He knew that 0·47 is approximately $\frac{1}{2}$ and 5·3 is approximately 5·0.

So an estimated answer would be $\frac{1}{2}$ × 5 = 2·5.

0·47 × 5·3 is approximately 2·5.

4 (a) Without using a calculator, work out the exact answer to Peter's problem.
(b) What is the difference between the exact answer and the estimated one?

5 Using fractions, work out an approximate answer to:
(a) 0·51 × 24·2   **(b)** 16·4 × 0·251
(c) 0·74 × 60   **(d)** 0·201 × 99·9
(e) 51·0 × 0·402   **(f)** 0·51 × 0·49
(g) 0·52 × 0·48 × 19·1
(h) 0·76 × 20·2 × 0·49
(i) (82 × 0·245) ÷ 4·0
(j) (0·99 × 56·3) ÷ 8·0
(k) (0·77 × 39·2) ÷ 2·0
(l) (0·77 × 39·2) ÷ 0·5

6 A strip of plastic measures 0·61 cm by 38·6 cm. Find the approximate area of the strip.

7 Before he retired, the Hyde family's milkman used to leave them 14 pints of milk each week. Their new milkman only delivers 1 litre cartons of milk. If 1 pint is approximately 0·568 litres, how many cartons should they order?

8 Jenny puts 6·25 gallons of petrol into her car. If 1 gallon is equal to 4·545 litres, how much petrol, in litres, did Jenny put into her car?

More than a guess 2

Kate was using the idea of proportion to estimate the width of this river. The calculation she used was

$$\frac{2 \cdot 8 \times 35 \cdot 9}{4 \cdot 1}$$

Without a calculator, Kate has to estimate the answer.

2·8 is approximately 3
35·9 is approximately 36
4·1 is approximately 4

An approximate answer is $\frac{3 \times 36}{4} = 27$

The river is approximately 27 metres wide.

1 Find approximate answers to:

(a) $\dfrac{4 \cdot 99 \times 20 \cdot 2}{9 \cdot 6}$

(b) $\dfrac{6 \cdot 2 \times 199 \cdot 4}{3 \cdot 89}$

(c) $\dfrac{2 \cdot 89 \times 15 \cdot 4}{4 \cdot 3}$

(d) $\dfrac{6 \cdot 78 \times 32 \cdot 7}{7 \cdot 9}$

(e) $\dfrac{0 \cdot 48 \times 29 \cdot 4}{2 \cdot 7}$

(f) $\dfrac{0 \cdot 28 \times 69 \cdot 3}{8 \cdot 4}$

(g) $\dfrac{0 \cdot 235 \times 36 \cdot 49}{0 \cdot 47 \times 8 \cdot 2}$

(h) $\dfrac{92 \cdot 8 \times 45 \cdot 6}{14 \cdot 5 \times 10 \cdot 7}$

(i) $(4 \cdot 76)^2 \times (3 \cdot 2)^2$

(j) $\dfrac{(2 \cdot 3)^2 + (6 \cdot 9)^2}{8 \cdot 9}$

2 (a) Estimate the approximate price of 375 of these teddy bears.

(b) Work out the exact price of the bears.

(c) What is the difference between the exact price and your estimate?

£7·15

3 (a) Estimate to the nearest whole number $(4 \cdot 5)^2$.

(b) Work out the exact answer to $(4 \cdot 5)^2$.

(c) What is the difference between your estimated answer and the exact answer?

4 For each of these numbers
  • $(5 \cdot 5)^2$ • $(6 \cdot 5)^2$ • $(7 \cdot 5)^2$

(a) make an estimate of the answer

(b) work out the exact value

(c) compare your estimate with the exact value

(d) write what you notice.
  Write the exact value of $(11 \cdot 5)^2$.

5 Avtar is using Pythagoras' rule to find the approximate length of the missing side. She uses this calculation

$$\sqrt{(3 \cdot 2)^2 + (3 \cdot 89)^2}$$

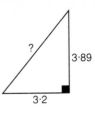

Estimate, to the nearest whole number, the length of the missing side.

6 A circle has a circumference of 24·5 cm. Estimate to the nearest whole number:

(a) the diameter   **(b)** the area.

7 A bus travels 45·2 km in 2 hours 30 minutes. Estimate its average speed in:

(a) metres per minute   **(b)** km per hour.

8 Estimate the number of complete revolutions this garden roller makes in rolling a piece of ground 86·8 m long.

0·45 m

9 Simon has to find the length of the side, x. He knows that the answer is the solution to this equation.

$$\frac{x}{0 \cdot 516} = \frac{6 \cdot 18}{0 \cdot 309}$$

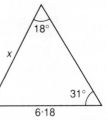

(a) Estimate the value of x correct to 1 decimal place.

(b) Check your answer using a calculator.

Look at this formula $a = bc + d$

Finding the value of a when $b = 4$, $c = 3$, $d = 9$ is easy. Just put the numbers into the formula.

$a = (4 \times 3) + 9$
$a = 21$

To find the value of c when $a = 3.4$, $b = 3.6$ and $d = 5.2$ put these numbers in the formula

$3.4 = (3.6 \times c) + 5.2$ or
$3.4 = 3.6c + 5.2$

By solving this equation the value of c is found

$3.4 - 5.2 = 3.6c$
$^{-}1.8 = 3.6c$
$\dfrac{^{-}1.8}{3.6} = c$
$^{-}0.5 = c$
$c = ^{-}0.5$

It is sometimes helpful to rearrange the formula first before putting in the numbers. Rearranging the formula is called 'making c the subject of the formula'.

$a = bc + d$
$a - d = bc$
$\dfrac{a - d}{b} = c$
$c = \dfrac{a - d}{b}$

I (a) Rearrange the formula $a = bc + d$ to make d the subject of the formula.
(b) Find the value of d when $a = 14.4$, $b = 8$ and $c = 0.25$

2 Rearrange these formulae to make the letter or number shown in the bracket into the subject.

(a) $a = 5c$ (c)   **(b)** $a = bc$ (c)
(c) $a = b + c$ (c)   **(d)** $a = 3b + c$ (c)
(e) $a = b - c$ (b)   **(f)** $a = b - c$ (c)
(g) $s = \dfrac{t}{u}$ (t)   **(h)** $s = \dfrac{t}{u}$ (u)

(i) $r = \dfrac{a}{p} - q$ (a)   **(j)** $r = m + \dfrac{a}{p}$ (p)

(k) $A = \dfrac{bh}{2}$ (h)   **(l)** $A = \dfrac{bh}{2}$ (2)

3 The volume of a cone is given by

$v = \dfrac{\pi r^2 h}{3}$

(a) Rearrange the formula to make h the subject.
(b) Find h when $v = 200$ and $r = 4.6$.

4 (a) Multiply out this bracket $a(b + c)$.
(b) Rearrange this formula to make b the subject $x = a(b + c)$.
(c) Find b when $x = 20$, $a = 32$ and $c = 0.4$.

5 Rearrange these formulae to make the letter in the bracket into the subject.
(a) $y = b(a + 3c)$ (c)   **(b)** $y = \dfrac{a}{b - 2c}$ (a)

(c) $x = \dfrac{a}{b} - 5c$ (c)   **(d)** $y = \dfrac{w + rx}{v}$ (v)

(e) $a = b(r + c)$ (r)   **(f)** $y = w(r - t)$ (t)
(g) $b = 2k(a - 4z)$ (z)   **(h)** $k = \dfrac{y}{r(w + t)}$ (t)

6 Rearrange these formulae to make the letter in the bracket into the subject.

(a) $s = at^2 + b$ (t)   **(b)** $A = r^2$ (r)
(c) $s = ut + gt^2$ (g)   **(d)** $A = \dfrac{4 r^3}{3}$ (r)
(e) $A = \pi(R^2 - r^2)$ (R)   **(f)** $y = a\sqrt{n} + c$ (n)

(g) $\dfrac{1}{v} = \dfrac{c}{b}$ (v)

(h) $\dfrac{1}{f} = \dfrac{1}{u} + \dfrac{1}{v}$ (f)

(i) $s = \dfrac{(u - v)t}{2}$ (u)

(j) $T = 2k \left(\sqrt{\dfrac{n}{g}} \right)$ (g)

7 The area of a trapezium is given by

$A = \dfrac{h(a + b)}{2}$

(a) Find the area when $h = 6.3$, $a = 4.4$, $b = 9.8$.
(b) Rearrange the formula to make a the subject.
(c) Find a when $A = 64$, $b = 6.6$, and $h = 12$.

8 Rearrange this formula to make k the subject

$4y = \dfrac{u}{kr + kt}$

Keep it in proportion 1

Asif is filling this cylinder with water. The water is being delivered from the tap at the rate of 150 ml/sec.

Asif times how long it takes to fill the cylinder.

Height of water (cm)	5	10	15	20	25	30
Time taken (sec)	1·2	2·4	3·6	4·8	6·0	7·2

1 (a) Draw a graph of height against time.
  (b) Use your graph to find the height of the water after 5 seconds.
  (c) How long does it take for the water to reach a height of 18 cm?

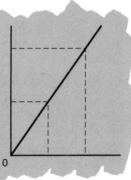

If a graph of two variables is a straight line through the origin then one variable is **directly proportional** to the other. This means that if one variable changes then the other also changes by the same ratio.

2 In which of these graphs is w directly proportional to t?

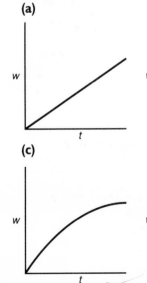

(a)

(b)

(c)

(d)

3 The height of a tree is directly proportional to the shadow it casts. At a certain time in the day, a tree, 5 m high, casts a shadow 8 m long.

  (a) Draw a graph to show this information.
  (b) Use your graph to find the height of a tree which casts a shadow of 12 m.
  (c) How long is the shadow of a tree 8 m tall?

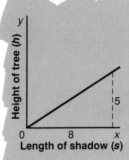

The gradient of a graph can be used to find the rule connecting the two variables.

$y = mx + c$ or
$h = ms + c$
$h = ms$ $c = 0$
$h = \dfrac{5s}{8}$

4 (a) Use the rule to find the height of a tree which casts a shadow 6·4 m long.
  (b) Rearrange the formula to make s the subject.
  (c) A tree is 18·5 m tall, how long is the shadow that it casts?

5 At a different time of day, a tree 10 m tall casts a shadow of 15 m.

  (a) Sketch a graph to show this information.
  (b) Find the rule connecting h and s.
  (c) Find h when s = 12·6.
  (d) Find s when h = 16·5.

6 Asif is filling a second cylinder with water. When the height reaches 14 cm the volume is 42 cm³. Given that the volume is directly proportional to the height:

  (a) • sketch a graph to show this relationship
     • find the rule connecting v and h.
  (b) What is the volume of water when the height is 32·4 cm?
  (c) What is the height of the water when the volume is 64·8 cm³?
  (d) Find h when v = 1·164.

Asif's sister, Parminder, has been given this problem to solve.

The weight of a metal bar is directly proportional to its length. A bar measuring 12 cm weighs 1·64 kg. How much does a bar measuring 8·4 cm weigh?

Parminder puts this information into a table.

Weight	1·64	?
Length	12	8·4

Parminder knows that the weight will increase or decrease by the same ratio as the length. The change ratio is

Weight	1·64	?
Length	12	8·4

↖ × 0·7 ↗

The weight of the bar is **1·64 × 0·7 = 1·148 kg**.

1 For each of these tables calculate the missing values to 1 decimal place:

(a)

w	6	9
h	8·4	?

(b)

h	12·0	16·8
s	24·5	?

(c)

p	7·8	?
s	6·8	17·6

(d)

y	14·4	10·2
x	?	23·9

2 Calculate, correct to 1 dp, the rule connecting the two variables for each of the tables in question **1**.

3 Mandeep shines a torch onto a wall 1·4 m away. The torch lights up a circle of diameter 4·2 cm. He backs away from the wall until the diameter of the circle is 21·6 cm.
  (a) Put this information into a table.
  (b) Use the table to find Mandeep's distance from the wall when the diameter is 21·6 cm.
  (c) Find the rule connecting the two variables.

4 Jane has an enlargement made of her favourite photograph. Unfortunately the enlargement gets torn.
  (a) Measure the length and width of the original.
  (b) Measure the length of the enlargement.
  (c) Put this information into a table.
  (d) Calculate the width of the enlargement.

5 The voltage across a resistor is directly proportional to the current flowing through it.
  (a) Write the readings of the two meters.
  (b) Calculate the current when the voltage is 6·8 volts.
  (c) Find the voltage when the current is 2·16 amps.

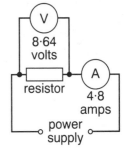

6 Carol obtains these readings from an experiment.

Voltage (v)	5	10	15	20	25	30
Current (i)	1·3	2·6	3·2	5·2	6·5	7·8

Unfortunately there is an error in her table.
  (a) Plot the points and draw a graph of voltage against current.
  (b) Which reading is wrong and what should it be?
  (c) Find the rule connecting v and i.
  (d) Find v when $i = 4·7$.
  (e) Calculate i when $v = 8·68$.

Bracketed together 2

Greg places 3 red and 2 blue counters on a table. He has $3r + 2b$ counters.

He decides he needs 2 lots of 3 red and 2 blue counters. That is $2(3r + 2b)$. He now has 6 red and 4 blue counters.

So $2(3r + 2b) = 6r + 4b$.

This is called **multiplying out brackets**.

Olivia is given 4 red and 6 blue counters. She wants to know how many sets of red and blue counters she has.

By arranging the counters in matching rows, Olivia can see that she has 2 sets of 2 red and 3 blue counters.

So $4r + 6b = 2(2r + 3b)$

This **reverse process** is called **factorising**.

---

1 How many counters, of each colour, will Greg have if he wants:

(a) 3 lots of 4 red and 3 blue

(b) 2 lots of 6 red and 5 blue

(c) 5 lots of $(4r + 3b)$

(d) 3 lots of $(2r + 3b + 4y)$

(e) $4(5r + 6b)$

(f) $7(2r + 5b + 3y)$

(g) $5(2r + 8b + 7y + 2g)$?

2 Multiply out these expressions.

(a) $2(p + q)$ (b) $3(a + 2)$

(c) $4(3b + 4)$ (d) $r(3 + b)$

(e) $r(2y + 3g)$ (f) $a(a + 3)$

(g) $x(x + y)$ (h) $y(x + y)$

(i) $m(2m - 3)$ (j) $x(4x - 2y)$

(k) $^-2(r + y)$ (l) $^-4(2r - 3y)$

(m) $^-1(x - 3y)$ (n) $^-x(x - xy)$

3 (a) Find the area of these rectangles.

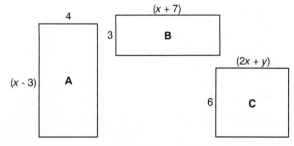

(b) What is the total area of rectangle A and rectangle B?

(c) What is the total area of A and C?

(d) What is the total area of all three rectangles?

4 Write the largest number of sets equivalent to the following counters. Set out your answer in the same form as above

$4r + 6b = 2(2r + 3b)$

(a) 3 red and 6 blue   (b) 2 red and 8 blue

(c) 4 red and 10 yellow   (d) 5 green and 10 red

(e) 9 red and 12 yellow   (f) 4 red and 8 green

(g) $6r + 9b$ (h) $12y + 10b$

(i) $18g + 12b$ (j) $24r + 32g$

Debbie was given these two piles of counters. In symbols this can be written as $gr + br$.

Both piles have a red counter. This is the common factor that is brought outside the brackets.

So $gr + br = r(g + b)$

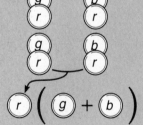

5 Factorise:

(a) $ac + bc$ (b) $pt + 3p$

(c) $2r + gr$ (d) $br - 2gr$

(e) $3ab - 2ac$ (f) $12x - 18y$

(g) $x^2 + 3x$ (h) $a^2b - 2a$

(i) $2rb + 3rw - 4rb$ (j) $a^2x + bx$

(k) $x^2 - 6xy$ (l) $4y^2 - 6y$

(m) $ay^2 + ay$ (n) $r^2b + rb^2$

(o) $24r^2b + 16rb^2$ (p) $12y^3 - 6y^2 + 8y$

The area of this rectangle is $3 \times 5 = 15$ sq units.

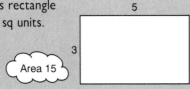

Area 15

1 What is the area of these rectangles?

(a)

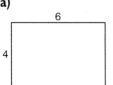

6

4

(b)

2

7

(c)

10

3

(d)

35

20

This rectangle has a length of $(x + 3)$ and a width of $(x + 2)$. Its area must be $(x + 3)(x + 2)$

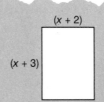

$(x + 2)$

$(x + 3)$

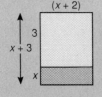

$(x + 2)$

3

$x + 3$

x

The area can by found by splitting the rectangle in two.

The area of the first rectangle is $x(x + 2)$

The area of the second rectangle is $3(x + 2)$

$(x + 2)$

x

3

$(x + 2)$

The total area is $\qquad x(x + 2) + 3(x + 2)$

So $(x + 3)(x + 2) = x(x + 2) + 3(x + 2)$
$= x^2 + 2x + 3x + 6$
$= x^2 + 5x + 6$

2 If $(x + 3)(x + 7) = x(x + 7) + 3(x + 7)$ draw rectangles to show this information.

3 Make a copy of these rectangles. Split each one into two smaller rectangles. Find:
  (a) the area of each small rectangle
  (b) the total area of each large rectangle.

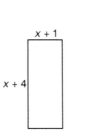

$x + 1$

$x + 4$

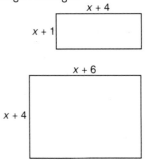

$x + 4$

$x + 1$

$x + 6$

$x + 4$

4 Make a copy of these rectangles.

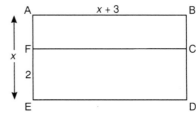

A $\qquad x + 3 \qquad$ B

F $\qquad$ C

x

2

E $\qquad$ D

  (a) Find:
    • the length AF in terms of x
    • the area of rectangle ABDE
    • the area of rectangle CDEF.
  (b) Work out $(x - 2)(x + 3)$ and so find the area of rectangle ABCF.

5 Sketch rectangles with these dimensions and so find the area of each:
  (a) $(x + 4)$ and $(x + 8)$
  (b) $(p + 7)$ and $(p + 2)$
  (c) $(y - 2)$ and $(y + 4)$
  (d) $(w + 3)$ and $(w - 9)$
  (e) $(x - 5)$ and $(x - 6)$

6 Multiply out each of these:
  (a) $(x + 4)(x + 5)$ **(b)** $(a + 4)(a - 2)$
  (c) $(x - 3)(x + 6)$ **(d)** $(p - 4)(p - 7)$
  (e) $(y + 4)(y + 4)$ **(f)** $(2x + 1)(x + 5)$
  (g) $(3x - 2)(x + 5)$ **(h)** $(3r + 2)(2r - 1)$
  (i) $(ax + b)(cx + d)$ **(j)** $(ar - 2)(br + 2)$
  (k) $(ax - 5)(ax + 7)$ **(l)** $(5x + y)(y^2 - x)$

7 Draw rectangles to explain the result of multiplying out these expressions:
  (a) $(x + 3)(x - 3)$ **(b)** $(y + 5)^2$
  (c) $(y + 0)(y + 6)$ **(d)** $(x - 2)(x - 3)$

Simultaneous equations 2

1 Solve graphically the simultaneous equations
$3x + 3y = 15$ and $3x + 2y = 12$

It is sometimes difficult to solve simultaneous equations accurately using graphical methods and to decide the scale to use for the x and y axes.

An alternative method is to **calculate** the value of x and y.

Let the first equation be (1) $\qquad 3x + 3y = 15$
and the second equation (2) $\qquad \underline{3x + 2y = 12}$

Subtract (2) from (1) $\qquad\qquad\qquad \underline{y = 3}$

Put $y = 3$ into equation (1) $\qquad 3x + 9 = 15$
$\qquad\qquad\qquad\qquad\qquad\qquad \underline{3x = 6}$
$\qquad\qquad\qquad\qquad\qquad\qquad \underline{x = 2}$

This gives the solutions $x = 2$ and $y = 3$

Check using equation (2) $\qquad\qquad 6 + 9 = 15$

This method is called **the method of elimination**, (the aim is to eliminate one of the unknowns).

2 By subtracting the two equations solve these simultaneous equations:

(a) $2x + 2y = 6$ $\qquad$ **(b)** $3x + 21y = 45$
$\quad\ \ 2x + y = 0$ $\qquad\qquad\ \ 3x + 4y = 11$
(c) $3x + 2y = 7$ $\qquad$ **(d)** $4x + 12y = 28$
$\quad\ \ 2x + 2y = 6$ $\qquad\qquad\ \ 4x - 2y = 7$

Sometimes you need to add the two equations together in order to eliminate one of the unknowns.

$\qquad\qquad\qquad$ (1) $\qquad 2x - 2y = 2$
$\qquad\qquad\qquad$ (2) $\qquad \underline{x + 2y = 7}$

Add (1) and (2) $\qquad\qquad\qquad 3x \quad\ = 9$
$\qquad\qquad\qquad\qquad\qquad\qquad \underline{x = 3}$

Put $x = 3$ into (2) $\qquad\qquad 3 + 2y = 7$
$\qquad\qquad\qquad\qquad\qquad\qquad 2y = 4$
$\qquad\qquad\qquad\qquad\qquad\qquad \underline{y = 2}$

This gives the solution $x = 3$ and $y = 2$

Check using equation (1) $\qquad\qquad 6 - 4 = 2$

3 Solve these simultaneous equations by adding to eliminate one of the unknowns:

(a) $3x + 2y = 10$ $\qquad$ **(b)** $x + 2y = 7$
$\quad\ \ 8x - 2y = 12$ $\qquad\qquad 3x - 2y = {}^-3$
(c) $^-x + y = {}^-1$ $\qquad$ **(d)** $^-4x + 3y = 26$
$\quad\ \ \ x + y = 3$ $\qquad\qquad 4x - 10y = {}^-12$

4 Solve these simultaneous equations by adding or subtracting to eliminate one of the unknowns:

(a) $x + 5y = 17$ $\qquad$ **(b)** $5x + y = 11$
$\quad\ \ x + 2y = 8$ $\qquad\qquad 3x + y = 7$
(c) $3x - 2y = {}^-6$ $\qquad$ **(d)** $4x - 3y = 11$
$\quad\ \ x + 2y = 6$ $\qquad\qquad 2x - 3y = 7$
(e) $^-3x + 2y = {}^-17$ $\qquad$ **(f)** $2x + y = 5$
$\quad\ \ 3x + 2y = 1$ $\qquad\qquad 2x - y = 3$

5 This diagram shows the lines $2x + y = 8$ and $x - y = 1$

Without drawing these lines, solve the simultaneous equations and write down the coordinates of the point where the two lines cross.

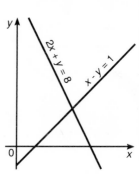

6 Without drawing, find the point of intersection of the two lines $x + y = 13$ and $3x - y = 19$

7 It is known that a certain straight line passes through the points (1, 5) and (3, 11).
The equation of the line is of the form
$y = mx + c$

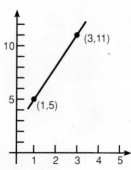

(a) Explain the meaning of the expression
$5 = 1m + c$.
(b) Write a second equation involving m and c.
(c) By solving the two simultaneous equations find the value of m and c and write the equation of the line.

1 A student was given these two simultaneous
equations (i) $4x - 2y = 14$ and
(ii) $3x + 3y = 24$ to solve.

(a) Add the two equations together.

(b) Subtract (ii) from (i).

(c) Subtract (i) from (ii).

In question **1** neither of the two unknowns was
eliminated by adding or subtracting. Before solving
simultaneous equations by this method **one
unknown must be eliminated**.

However, if we multiply (i) by 3 and (ii) by 4 the
x coefficients will be the same

Multiply (i) by 3	$12x - 6y = 42$
Multiply (ii) by 4	$12x + 12y = 96$
Subtract (ii) from (i)	$^-18y = ^-54$
	$y = 3$
Put $y = 3$ into (i)	$4x - 6 = 14$
	$4x = 20$
	$x = 5$

This gives the solution $x = 5$ and $y = 3$

Check in (ii) $15 + 9 = 24$

---

2 Show that the equations given in question **1** can be
solved by multiplying equation (i) by 3 and equation
(ii) by 2.

3 Solve these simultaneous equations.

(a) $\quad x + 2y = 4 \quad$ multiply by 2
$\quad 2x + y = 5 \quad$ multiply by 1

(b) $5x + 2y = 2 \quad$ multiply by 3
$\quad 2x + 3y = ^-8 \quad$ multiply by 2

(c) $3x - 2y = 4 \quad$ multiply by 3
$\quad 2x + 3y = ^-6 \quad$ multiply by 2

(d) $4x + 3y = 9 \quad$ multiply by 5
$\quad 2x + 5y = 15 \quad$ multiply by 3

(e) $3x - 5y = ^-21$ multiply by 1
$\quad x + y = 1 \quad$ multiply by 3

(f) $3x - 5y = ^-21$ multiply by 1
$\quad x + y = 1 \quad$ multiply by 5

4 Solve these simultaneous equations.

(a) $5x - 4y = 18$
$\quad 2x + y = 2$

(b) $3x + 4y = 11$
$\quad 2x - y = 0$

(c) $5x + 2y = 9$
$\quad 4x - y = 2$

(d) $4x - y = ^-11$
$\quad 3x + 4y = 6$

(e) $3x - 4y = 5$
$\quad 2x - 5y = 8$

(f) $7x - 4y = 37$
$\quad 2x + y = 17$

(g) $6y = 2x + 9$
$\quad 3y = ^-4x + 12$

(h) $5y = 3x + 11$
$\quad 7y = 2x - 3$

(i) $4x = 3y$
$\quad 8x = 9y - 12$

(j) $5x = 2y - 14$
$\quad x = 5y - 12$

(k) $8h + 4k = 7$
$\quad 6h - 8k = 41$

(l) $4h + 2k = ^-8$
$\quad 6h - 2k = ^-27$

5 Find the point of intersection of the lines
$$x - 2y = 18$$
and $\quad 3x - 4y = 66$

6 The line of the equation $y = mx + c$ passes through
the points $(^-2, 2)$ and $(0, 4)$.

(a) Explain the equation $2 = ^-2m + c$.

(b) Find a second equation in m and c.

(c) Find the value of m and c.

(d) Write down the equation of the line.

7 (a) Write the
perimeters of the
rectangle and
triangle in terms of
a and b.

(b) Solve the two
equations you have
written to find the
value of a and b.

(c) Write the lengths of
the three sides of
the triangle.

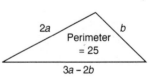

● **Remember**

Average speed = $\dfrac{\text{distance travelled}}{\text{time taken}}$

Distance travelled = average speed × time taken

Time taken = $\dfrac{\text{distance travelled}}{\text{average speed}}$

1 (a) Find the time taken for a car to travel 80 km at an average speed of 20 km/h.

(b) What is the average speed of a car which travels 125 km in 2 hours?

(c) Find the distance travelled by a car in 3 hours at an average speed of 65 km/h.

(d) How far will a car travel in 5 hours with an average speed of 70 km/hour?

(e) A car travels 100 km in 2 hours 30 minutes. What is the average speed of the car?

(f) How long will it take to travel 500 km at an average speed of 80 km/h?

This graph shows the progress of a car which travels 300 km in 5 hours.

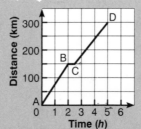

To find the average speed for the first part of the journey

From the graph
the distance travelled = 150 km
the time taken = 2 hours

Average speed = $\dfrac{\text{distance travelled}}{\text{time taken}}$ = $\dfrac{150}{2}$ = 75 km/h

2 (a) Find the average speed of the car for the part of the journey C to D.

(b) Give a possible explanation for the part of the journey B to C.

(c) What was the average speed of the car for the whole journey?

(d) The car returns home in 3 hours. Copy the travel graph and show the return journey on your graph.

3 This distance/time graph is for a train. Find the average speed:

(a) for the first 5 minutes

(b) between the 10th and 15th minutes

(c) for the whole journey.

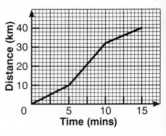

4 Kate decides to cycle to see her friend, Ruth. She cycles 14 km in 2 hours. She then rests for 30 minutes before completing her journey to Ruth's house by cycling a further 20 km in 2·5 hours.
After spending 3 hours with Ruth, Kate returns directly home at an average speed of 6 km/h.

(a) Show this information on a travel graph.

(b) Use your graph to find her average speed:

- before she rested

- after she had rested

- for the whole of her journey to Ruth's house.

5 Lara is hiking in the Lake District. This graph shows her progress one morning.

(a) How far did Lara walk?

(b) How long did it take her to complete the walk?

(c) How far had she walked before taking a rest?

(d) For how long did she rest?

(e) Find Lara's average speed for:

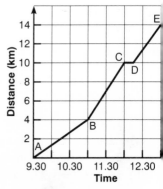

- each of the three walking stages of her journey

- the whole journey.

6 Jaswinder cycles at an average speed of 8 km/h for 45 minutes. She then stops for a 15 minute rest before returning home at an average speed of 9 km/h.

(a) Show this information on a time/distance graph.

(b) How far did Jaswinder cycle altogether?

(c) What was her average speed for her total journey?

Two towns, Adbury and Budley, are 120 km apart. Thomas leaves Adbury at 11.00 am to drive to Budley at an average speed of 80 km/h. 30 minutes later Carrie leaves Budley to drive to Adbury at an average speed of 90 km/h.

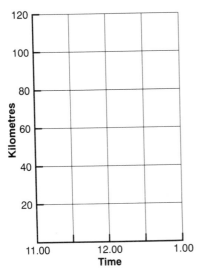

(a) Make a copy of the grid and show the progress of both motorists.
(b) Use your graph to find how far from Budley the two motorists are when they pass.
(c) Find the time that Thomas and Carrie reach their destinations.

8 Richard, a salesman, leaves home at 10.00 am and returns at 5.30 pm. The distance he travels from home is shown on this graph.

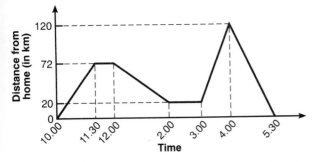

(a) Calculate his average speed between 10.00 am and 11.30 am.
(b) Calculate how far Richard travels during the day.
(c) How many times during the day does he travel towards his home?
(d) What was his average speed for the whole day?

9 This diagram shows part of a journey made by the Redruth Ramblers. Copy the diagram.

(a) What was the average speed of the ramblers before they had a rest?
(b) For how long did they rest?
(c) At 2 pm they set off again and completed their 20 km walk in a total time of 3 hrs 30 mins. Show this last part of the walk on your graph.
(d) What was their average speed for the whole of the journey?

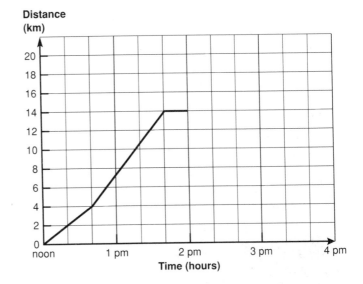

10 A racing cyclist, Clare, leaves Catford at 8.00 am to cycle to Darby, a distance of 200 km. She cycles at an average speed of 25 km/h for 5 hours and then stops for a 45 minute rest. She continues her journey and arrives at Darby at 5.00 pm.

(a) Draw a distance/time graph of her journey.
(b) Calculate her average speed for the final part of her journey.
(c) Calculate her average speed for the whole of the journey.
(d) At 2.00 pm Jonathan leaves Darby and drives to Catford at an average speed of 60 km/h. Show Jonathan's progress on your graph.
(e) How far from Catford are they when they pass each other?
(f) What time is it when they pass each other?

Trial and improvement

To solve $x^2 = 30$

- $5^2 = 25$ less than 30
  $6^2 = 36$ greater than ?

> The solution to $x^2 = 30$ must be between 5 and 6.

- Try $x = 5.5$
  $5.5^2 = 30.25$ greater than 30

> The solution to $x^2 = 30$ must be greater than 5 and less than 5.5.
> Because $5^2 = 25$ and $5.5^2 = 30.25$, the solution is likely to be closer to 5.5 than it is to 5.

- Try $x = 5.4$
  $5.4^2 = 29.16$ less than 30

We now have
$5.4^2 = 29.16$ less than 30
$5.5^2 = 30.25$ greater than 30

> The solution to $x^2 = 30$ must be between 5.4 and 5.5.

- Try $x = 5.45$
  $(5.45)^2 = 29.7025$
  $5.45 < x < 5.5$

A good approximation is $x = 5.455$
(Note $(5.455)^2 = 29.757$)

This process of trial and improvement can be continued **to any degree of accuracy**.

---

1 Solve each of these equations by trial and improvement.

   (a) $x^2 = 40$ (b) $x^2 = 60$ (c) $x^2 = 90$
   (d) $x^3 = 18$ (e) $x^4 = 30$ (f) $3x^2 = 100$

2 Show that the equation

$$x^2 + 2x = 30$$

has a solution between $x = 4$ and $x = 5$

Use the method of trial and improvement to find an estimate for the solution correct to 2 dp.

3 Solve the equation

$$x^2 - 3x = 14$$

by trial and improvement.

4 (a) Show that the equation

$$x^2 + \frac{3}{x} = 12$$

     has a solution in the range $3 < x < 4$.
  (b) Find a final estimate for the solution.
  (c) Use a trial and improvement technique to obtain
     x correct to 2 dp.

5 (a) Draw the graphs of

$$y = x^2 + 1 \text{ for } 0 < x < 2$$

     and

$$y = \frac{5}{x} \text{ for } 0.5 < x < 2$$

     at intervals of 0.2
  (b) Show that the graphs intersect when x lies
     between 1 and 2.
  (c) Write a first approximation to the solution of
     the equation

$$x^2 + 1 = \frac{5}{x}$$

  (d) Use two successive trial and improvements to
     improve on this first approximate solution.

Over the centuries two problems have been of particular concern to the human race.

One of these was the problem of creating an instrument to record the time of day. Early civilisations knew that the lengths of shadows varied according to the height of the sun in the sky.

The other problem was a military one, a problem of defending fortifications against attack.

When a cannon in the castle was pivotted it had to be able to cover the full width of the harbour otherwise any marauding ships could pass on either side of the cannon's angle of fire and the castle would be defenceless. Also, if the castle's cannon could only fire shots within a limited distance then attacking ships could sit out of range. If the ships' cannons were more powerful than the castle's then the ships could bombard the castle with no fear of retaliation.

Attempts to solve these two problems led to the study of **trigonometry**.

Mathematicians of the time saw the military problem as being that of finding the relationships between the chord length AB, the distance AM and the angle at the centre of the circle.

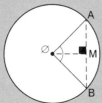

This is where we start trigonometry.

You need two geo-strips.

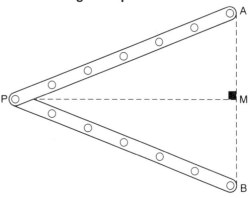

1 Work in pairs.

Vary the angle between your geo-strips from 0° to 180°.

(a) For at least 5 different angles measure and record the length:

• AB, between the ends of the strips

• PM, from the pivot to the mid-point of AB. Record your results in a table.

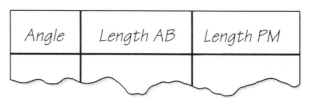

Angle	Length AB	Length PM

(b) Plot graphs of:

• AB against the angle and PM against the angle

• PM against the angle and AM against the angle. Write down any observations about these graphs.

2 Measure the length of your geo-strip. For at least five different angles work out the value of:

$$(AM)^2 + (PM)^2$$

Check that in each case this is more or less equal to (the length of the geo-strip)^2.

3 Explain why, in theory

$$(AM)^2 + (PM)^2 = (AP)^2$$

4 For what value of the angle $A\hat{P}M$ does AM = PM?

Trigonometry 1

Imagine an arm, OA, of length 1 unit, free to rotate in the plane about a pivot O.

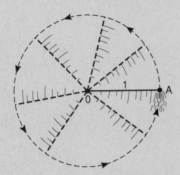

When it completes one whole rotation, the tip A of the arm will describe a circle.
Imagine that we take a picture at one point in the circle when the arm has turned an angle $x°$, anti-clockwise from the horizontal.

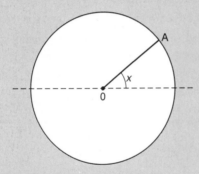

We now draw the line AB from A to the horizontal and draw the tangent AT where T is also on the horizontal.

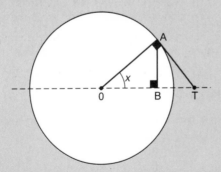

The distance OA is 1 unit.
The distance AB is defined as Sine x.
The distance OB is defined as Cosine x.
The distance AT is defined as Tangent x.

These are the **three basic trigonometric ratios** for the angle x.

You can use your scientific calculator to work out the sine, cosine and tangent of any angle.

To work out the sine of any angle:
• input the angle, say 30°
• press the Sine or Sin function button.
For 30° your calculator will read Sine 30 = 0·5

To find x when Cosine x = 0·6428
• input 0·6428
• press the inverse or second function button
• press the Cosine or Cos button.
Your calculator will record an angle of 40°.

1 Use your calculator to complete the following table:

Angle	Sine	Cosine	Tangent
36			
50			
60			
88			
100			
120			
175			
200			
250			
300			

2 Use your calculator to find the angle x when:
   (a) Sine x = 0·866   (b) Cosine x = 0·866
   (c) Tangent x = 1   (d) Tangent x = 0·5
   (e) Cosine x = 0·342   (f) Sine x = 0·4432
   (g) Cosine x = 0·1145   (h) Tangent x = 3·7321
   (i) Sine x = 0·9863   (j) Tangent x = 0·3739

3 (a) Use your calculator to work out the Sine, Cosine and Tangent of the angles from 0° to 90° at intervals of 10°.
   (b) Plot the graphs of the Sine, Cosine and Tangent functions for angles from 0° to 90°.

4 On your calculator, input any angle x. Find the values of Sine, Cosine and Tangent of x.

Show that $\dfrac{\text{Sine } x}{\text{Cosine } x} = \text{Tangent } x$

Repeat this for three other angles.

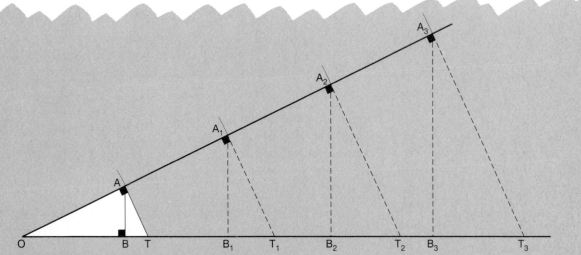

The diagram shows the same unit arm OA and the points B and T, but the lengths from O have been extended by scale factors 2, 3, etc to create the points A_1, B_1, T_1, A_2 etc.

Now $AB = \text{Sin } x$
so since $A_1B_1 = 2AB$
then $A_1B_1 = 2\text{ Sin } x$

5 Write expressions for OB_1 and A_1T_1 in terms of the basic trigonometric ratios.

6 In the diagram the angle $B\hat{O}A$ is $40°$. The figure has been enlarged by scale factor 4 to give OP, OQ and PR.

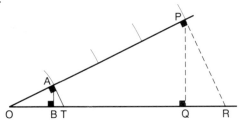

(a) Write the lengths of:
OA, OB, AT
(b) Calculate the lengths of:
OP, OQ, PR

7 Repeat question **6** for:
   (a) angle $B\hat{O}A = 50°$ and scale factor 10
   (b) angle $B\hat{O}A = 70°$ and scale factor 8
   (c) angle $B\hat{O}A = 60°$ and scale factor $\frac{1}{2}$.

8 Use the original diagram to find the acute angle x for which:

(a) Sine x = Cosine x (b) Tangent x = 1

Try to explain the results.

Trigonometry 2

Sine, Cosine and Tangent, can be abbreviated to sin, cos and tan.

They are defined as follows:

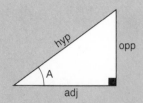

opp = side opposite A
adj = side adjacent to A
hyp = hypotenuse

$\sin A = \dfrac{opp}{hyp}$ or opp = hyp × sin A

$\cos A = \dfrac{adj}{hyp}$ or adj = hyp × cos A

$\tan A = \dfrac{opp}{adj}$ or opp = adj × tan A

Remember SOH   CAH   TOA

Sin = Opposite over Hypotenuse
Cos = Adjacent over Hypotenuse
Tan = Opposite over Adjacent

Examples

• Calculate the length of the side marked x.

x = opp   10 = hyp
use sin

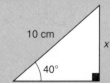
10 cm

40°

opp = hyp × sin 40
x = 10 × sin 40
x = 10 × 0·6428
x = 6·428 cm

• Calculate the angle marked x.

opp = 3   adj = 8
use tan

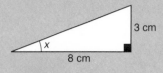
3 cm

8 cm

$\tan x = \dfrac{opp}{adj}$

$\tan x = \dfrac{3}{8}$

$\tan x = 0·375$
x = 20·6°

• Calculate the length of the side marked x.

x = adj   8 = hyp
use cos

70°
8 cm

adj = hyp × cos 70
x = 8 × cos 70
x = 8 × 0·342
x = 2·736 cm

1 These questions are all about Sine. All lengths are in centimetres. Calculate either the side or the angle marked x.

(a)

x
10
30°

(b)

8
x
40°

(c)

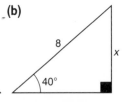
x
70°
12

(d)

x
22°
7

(e)

$x°$
10
6

(f)

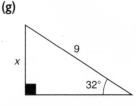
12
$x°$
15

(g)

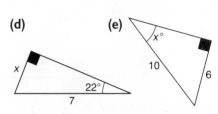
9
x
32°

(h)

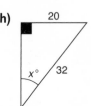
20
$x°$
32

(i)

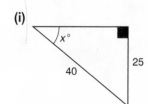
$x°$
40
25

2 These questions are all about Cosine. All lengths are in centimetres. Calculate either the side or the angle marked *x*.

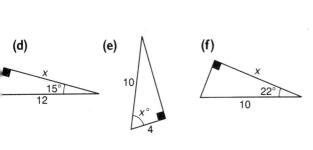

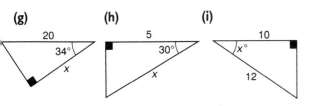

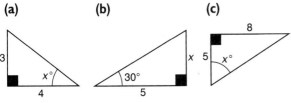

3 These questions are all about Tangent. All lengths are in centimetres. Calculate either the side or the angle marked *x*.

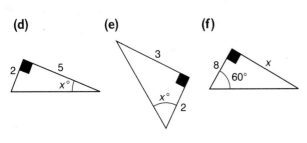

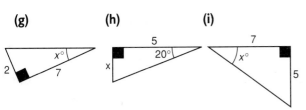

The following questions are a mixture about Sine, Cosine and Tangent.

4 Calculate the angles marked A below, all lengths are in cm.

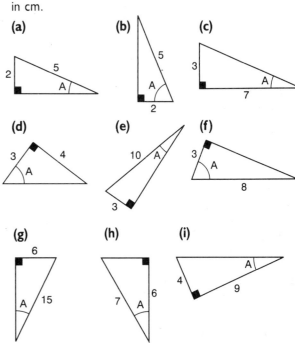

5 Calculate the length of the sides marked *x* in each of the following; all the given lengths are in centimetres.

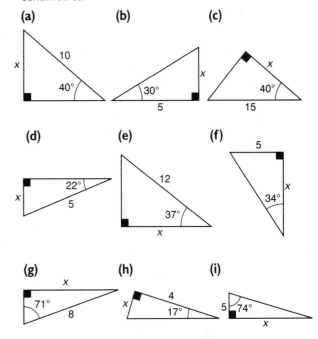

6 A flag pole of vertical height 16 metres casts a shadow of length 20 metres on level ground. Calculate the angle of elevation of the sun.

7 The sun makes an angle of elevation of 20°. The length on level ground of the shadow of a television aerial is 70 m. Calculate the vertical height of the aerial.

8 As it comes in to land, an aeroplane descends at a uniform angle. It travels 2000 m and descends 200 m. Calculate its angle of descent.

9 This is the cross-section of a valley.

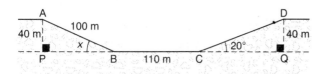

Calculate:

(a) the angle x **(b)** the distance PB
(c) the distance CQ   **(d)** the distance PQ
(e) the distance CD
(f) the angle of elevation of A from C
(g) the angle of depression of B from D
(h) the distance BD

10 In the village of Preble, the post office is 240 m from St Mary's church spire, which is 100 m high. Calculate the angle of elevation of the top of the spire from the post office.

11 Sarah rides 300 m up a hill and finds she has gained 20 m in altitude. Calculate the angle the hill makes with the horizontal.

12 On the sea front at Parkstone the beach slopes down at a constant angle of 9° to the horizontal. Asif is 1·7 m tall. How far can he walk out to sea before the water just covers his head?

13 The length of this clock's pendulum is 50 cm and its total angle of swing is 80° (40° each way). What is the difference in height of the bottom of the pendulum at the lowest and highest points in its swing?

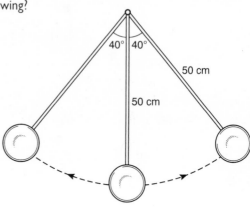

14 A box ABCD is held on a trailer by a rope. The rope passes over the box and is secured at two points P and Q.

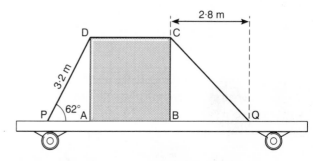

Calculate:

(a) the height of the box
(b) the length CQ
(c) the angle BĈQ.

15 In this equilateral triangle M is the mid-point of AB.

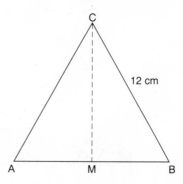

(a) Calculate the height, CM, of the triangle.
(b) Calculate the area of the triangle.

The area of any triangle is given by

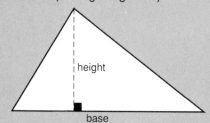

height

base

Area $= \frac{1}{2}$ base $\times$ height

This formula can be expanded using trigonometry.

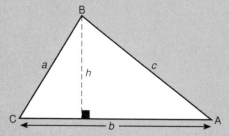

In this triangle the base is length b, the height is h and the angle at C is known.

Area $= \frac{1}{2}bh$

$\frac{h}{a} = \sin C$

or $h = a \sin C$

Area $= \frac{1}{2}ba \sin C$

or Area $= \frac{1}{2}ab \sin C$

The area of a triangle is half the length of one side multiplied by the length of another side, multiplied by the sine of the angle between these two sides.

To calculate the area of the triangle:

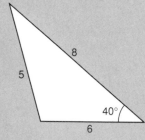

Area $= \frac{1}{2} \times 6 \times 8 \times \sin 40$

$= 24 \times 0.6428$

$= 15.43$ sq units

---

1 Calculate the area of each of these triangles.

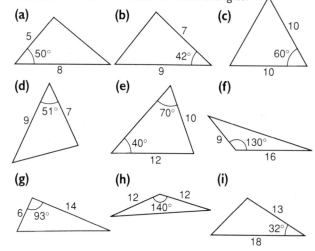

2 Jeff fences off a triangular building plot PQR. The length of PQ is 32 m. The length of PR is 56 m. The angle at P is 80°.
Calculate the area of the plot.

3 The angle between the two equal sides of an isosceles triangle is 142°.
The equal sides are of length 12 cm.
Calculate the area of the triangle.

4 Calculate the area of the quadrilateral ABCD.

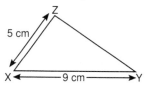

5 The area of the triangle XYZ is 13 cm².

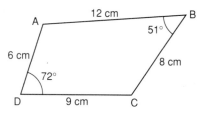

Calculate the value of the angle YX̂Z.

6 The area of the triangle PQR is 73·5 cm²

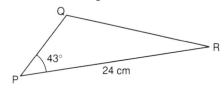

Calculate the length of PQ.

Similar figures

Two shapes are **similar** if one is an enlargement of the other.

The ratio of the lengths of corresponding sides is equal to the scale factor of the enlargement.

These two right-angled triangles are similar.

The ratio of their corresponding sides is 2:1

When two shapes are **similar** not only are their corresponding sides in a given ratio but also **corresponding angles are equal**.

This means that these two triangles must be similar.

The two triangles ABC and PQR are similar

 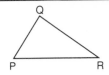

The two triangles ABC and PQR are similar

means $\dfrac{AB}{PQ} = \dfrac{BC}{QR} = \dfrac{AC}{PR}$

that is **corresponding sides are in a common ratio**.

The two triangles ABC and PQR are similar, with given lengths in cm.

To find the lengths QR and AC

$\dfrac{AB}{PQ} = \dfrac{4}{8} = \dfrac{1}{2}$

For the triangle PQR, the lengths are double the corresponding lengths of those in ABC, and the lengths in ABC are half those in PQR.

QR = 2 × BC = 2 × 6 = 12 cm and

AC = $\dfrac{1}{2}$ × PR = $\dfrac{1}{2}$ × 7 = $3\dfrac{1}{2}$ or 3·5 cm

I For each pair of similar triangles, calculate the lengths of the sides x and y. All lengths are in cm.

(a)

(b)

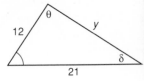

(c)

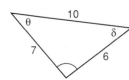

(d)

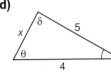 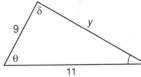

(e)

 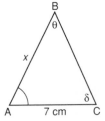

2 Triangles ABC and PQR are similar.

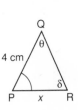

Calculate the value of x.

3 Triangles XYZ and RST are similar.

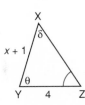 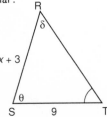

Calculate the value of x.

● **Remember**

Choose corresponding sides from corresponding angles.

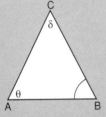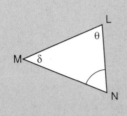

These triangles are similar because their corresponding angles are equal.

The sides opposite the δ are AB and LN.
The sides opposite the θ are BC and MN.
The sides opposite the ⌒ are AC and LM.

The equal ratios are

$$\frac{AB}{LN} = \frac{BC}{MN} = \frac{AC}{LM}$$

4 Do Worksheets 8 and 9.

5 In each pair of similar triangles, the corresponding equal angles are indicated by identical marks. The given lengths are in cm. Calculate the lengths of sides x and y.

(a)

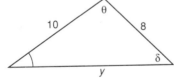

(b)

(c)

(d)

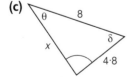

6 Do Worksheet 10.

7 Chords and/or tangents have been drawn on these circles. The given lengths are in cm. In each case calculate the length x.

(a)

(b)

(c)

(d)

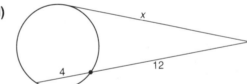

(e)

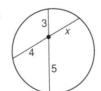

8

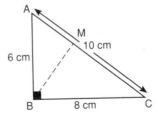

In the right-angled triangle ABC, BM is the perpendicular from B to AC. Calculate the length of BM.

9 Do Worksheet 11.

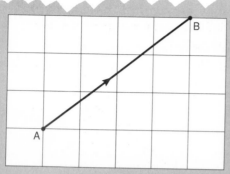

The movement from point A to point B is a **translation**.

It is 4 spaces to the right
    3 spaces upwards

It is shown by $\overline{AB} = \begin{pmatrix} 4 \\ 3 \end{pmatrix}$ and is called a **vector**.

The 4 and 3 are the horizontal and vertical **components** of the vector.

The length of $\overline{AB}$ is
    (length of $\overline{AB}$)^2 = $4^2 + 3^2$ (Pythagoras)
        = 16 + 9 = 25
    so length AB = $\sqrt{25}$
        = 5 units

The angle AB makes with the horizontal is

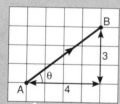

$\tan \theta = \frac{3}{4} = 0.75$

$\theta = 36.87°$

1 You need squared paper.
Sketch each of the vectors below. For each one, find its length and calculate the angle it makes with the horizontal.

(a) $\begin{pmatrix} 3 \\ 4 \end{pmatrix}$ (b) $\begin{pmatrix} 8 \\ 6 \end{pmatrix}$ (c) $\begin{pmatrix} 12 \\ 5 \end{pmatrix}$

(d) $\begin{pmatrix} 3 \\ 3 \end{pmatrix}$ (e) $\begin{pmatrix} ^-4 \\ 3 \end{pmatrix}$ (f) $\begin{pmatrix} ^-2 \\ 1 \end{pmatrix}$

(g) $\begin{pmatrix} ^-5 \\ 2 \end{pmatrix}$ (h) $\begin{pmatrix} ^-4 \\ ^-6 \end{pmatrix}$ (i) $\begin{pmatrix} 5 \\ ^-12 \end{pmatrix}$

(j) $\begin{pmatrix} 24 \\ ^-7 \end{pmatrix}$ (k) $\begin{pmatrix} ^-5 \\ 5 \end{pmatrix}$ (l) $\begin{pmatrix} 6 \\ 0 \end{pmatrix}$

(m) $\begin{pmatrix} 0 \\ 3 \end{pmatrix}$ (n) $\begin{pmatrix} 0 \\ ^-4 \end{pmatrix}$ (o) $\begin{pmatrix} ^-5 \\ 0 \end{pmatrix}$

2 The rectangle ABCD has its vertices at the points with coordinates
A(1, 1), B(4, 1), C(4, 3), D(1, 3)
Sketch the rectangle.
Write the vectors:

(a) $\overline{AB}$ (b) $\overline{CD}$

(c) $\overline{AC}$ (d) $\overline{DB}$

(e) AM, where M is the mid-point of ABCD.

Addition of vectors

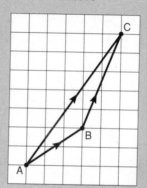

From the diagram
$\overline{AB} = \begin{pmatrix} 3 \\ 2 \end{pmatrix}$ $\overline{BC} = \begin{pmatrix} 2 \\ 5 \end{pmatrix}$ and $\overline{AC} = \begin{pmatrix} 5 \\ 7 \end{pmatrix}$

$\overline{AC} = \overline{AB} + \overline{BC}$ ←

the addition of two vectors

Subtraction of vectors

From the same diagram

$\overline{AB} = \begin{pmatrix} 3 \\ 2 \end{pmatrix}$ $\overline{BC} = \begin{pmatrix} 2 \\ 5 \end{pmatrix}$

$\overline{AB} - \overline{BC} = \begin{pmatrix} 3 \\ 2 \end{pmatrix} - \begin{pmatrix} 2 \\ 5 \end{pmatrix} = \begin{pmatrix} 1 \\ ^-3 \end{pmatrix}$ ←

the subtraction of two vectors

Equal vectors

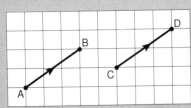

The vectors $\overline{AB}$ and $\overline{CD}$ have different start points and different end points.

However, $\overline{AB} = \begin{pmatrix} 3 \\ 2 \end{pmatrix}$ and $\overline{CD} = \begin{pmatrix} 3 \\ 2 \end{pmatrix}$

> $\overline{AB}$ and $\overline{CD}$ are equal

Two vectors are equal if they are of the same length, parallel, and the translations (from start to finish) are in the same direction.

3 The points A, B, C, and D are the four vertices of a parallelogram.
Their coordinates are
A(2, 1), B(6, 3), C(7, 6), D(3, 4)
(a) Sketch the parallelogram.
(b) Write the vectors:
$\overline{AB}$, $\overline{BC}$, $\overline{AD}$, $\overline{BC}$
(c) Show that $\overline{AB} + \overline{BC} = \overline{AC}$
(d) Show that $\overline{AB} - \overline{BC} = \overline{DB}$

4 A vector $\begin{pmatrix} p \\ q \end{pmatrix}$ has length 13 units.

It makes an acute angle of θ with the horizontal.
Tan $\theta = 2\cdot 4$. Find all the possible integer values of p and q.

5 $\overline{AB} = \begin{pmatrix} 4 \\ -1 \end{pmatrix}$ and $\overline{BC} = \begin{pmatrix} 6 \\ 9 \end{pmatrix}$

(a) Calculate $\overline{AC}$.

(b) Calculate $\overline{BC} - \overline{AB}$.
(c) Calculate the length of $\overline{AB} + \overline{BC}$ and the angle this vector makes with the horizontal.
(d) Calculate the length of $\overline{BC} - \overline{AB}$ and the angle this vector makes with the horizontal.

Multiplication of a vector by a scalar (a number)

If $\overline{AB} = \begin{pmatrix} 4 \\ 3 \end{pmatrix}$ then $2\overline{AB} = 2\begin{pmatrix} 4 \\ 3 \end{pmatrix} = \begin{pmatrix} 8 \\ 6 \end{pmatrix}$

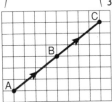

The vector $2\overline{AB}$ is parallel to $\overline{AB}$ and twice the length of $\overline{AB}$. Also, $\frac{1}{2}\overline{AB}$ is $\begin{pmatrix} 2 \\ 1\frac{1}{2} \end{pmatrix}$ and is a vector parallel to $\overline{AB}$ and half its length.

> If λ is any number and $\overline{AB}$ any vector then $\lambda\overline{AB}$ is a vector parallel to $\overline{AB}$ and of length λ times that of $\overline{AB}$.

$(^-1)\,\overline{AB}$ is the negative of $\overline{AB}$. It is a vector parallel to $\overline{AB}$, the same length but going in the opposite direction.

$(^-1)\,\overline{AB}$ can be written as $\overline{BA}$

6 Two vectors, x and y have components

$x = \begin{pmatrix} p \\ q \end{pmatrix}$ $y = \begin{pmatrix} r \\ s \end{pmatrix}$

Write expressions using p, q, r, s for:
(a) $x + y$ (b) $y - x$ in component form
(c) $3x$ (d) $5y$
(e) $3x + 5y$ in components
(f) the length of x
(g) the tangent of the angle $x - y$ makes with the horizontal.

7 Two vectors, a and b, are given by

$a = \begin{pmatrix} 4 \\ 3 \end{pmatrix}$ $b = \begin{pmatrix} 6 \\ -8 \end{pmatrix}$

(a) Show that a and b are perpendicular.
(b) Calculate $a - \frac{1}{2}b$.
(c) Calculate the area of a square whose side is equal in length to the length of $a - \frac{1}{2}b$.

8 OABC is a parallelogram. $\overline{OA} = a$, $\overline{AB} = b$. In terms of a and b write the vectors:
(a) $\overline{OB}$ (b) $\overline{OC}$ (c) $\overline{AC}$

Take a chance

When two events occur that do not affect each other they are said to be **independent events**. If one of the events happens, the probability that the other event will happen is not affected.

Notation

The probability of throwing a 6 on a dice is written P(throwing a 6).

$$P(\text{throwing a 1}) = \frac{1}{6}$$

$$P(\text{throwing a 2}) = \frac{1}{6}$$

$$P(\text{throwing a 3}) = \frac{1}{6}$$

$$P(\text{throwing a 4}) = \frac{1}{6}$$

$$P(\text{throwing a 5}) = \frac{1}{6}$$

$$P(\text{throwing a 6}) = \frac{1}{6}$$

So $P(\text{throwing a 1 or 2}) = \frac{1}{6} + \frac{1}{6} = \frac{2}{6} = \frac{1}{3}$

P(throwing a number less than 6)

$$= \frac{1}{6} + \frac{1}{6} + \frac{1}{6} + \frac{1}{6} + \frac{1}{6} = \frac{5}{6}$$

P(throwing an even number)

$$= \frac{1}{6} + \frac{1}{6} + \frac{1}{6} = \frac{3}{6} = \frac{1}{2}$$

A spinner can be weighted so that it has a bias.

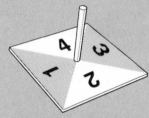

This spinner has been weighted so that the probabilities of throwing each number are:

$$P(1) = \frac{1}{4}, \ P(2) = \frac{1}{8},$$

$$P(3) = \frac{1}{4}, \ P(4) = \frac{3}{8}$$

P(throwing an even number)

$$= P(2) + P(4) = \frac{1}{8} + \frac{3}{8} = \frac{4}{8} = \frac{1}{2}$$

P(throwing a 1 or a 4)

$$= P(1) + P(4) = \frac{1}{4} + \frac{3}{8} = \frac{5}{8}$$

1 Jason's spinner has eight numbers, 1 to 8. He spins the spinner and records the score.
What is the probability of Jason spinning:

(a) an even number

(b) a number more than 4

(c) a number less than 3

(d) a 2, 3 or 4?

2 Megan's bag contains eight coloured marbles: 3 blue, 3 green, and 2 white. She picks out one marble.
What is the probability of her selecting:

(a) a blue or green

(b) a white or blue

(c) a green or a white marble?

3 Andy selects a card at random from a set of one thousand cards numbered 1 to 1000. Find the probability that the number on the card he selects is:

(a) divisible by 10

(b) an odd number

(c) divisible by 10 or an odd number.

4 A tank contains 8 goldfish, 4 grey fish, and 13 multi-coloured fish. One fish is netted. Calculate the probability that the fish is:

(a) gold or grey

(b) gold or multi-coloured

(c) grey or multi-coloured.

5 Stewart chooses a letter at random from the letters in the word HEINEMANN. Find the probability that the letter he chooses is:

(a) H or E   **(b)** M or N

(c) E or N   **(d)** a vowel.

6 A computer is programmed to generate the letters
A, B, C, X, Y, Z according to the following
probabilities:

$P(A) = \frac{5}{32}$, $P(B) = \frac{3}{32}$, $P(C) = \frac{8}{32}$,

$P(X) = \frac{4}{32}$, $P(Y) = \frac{7}{32}$, $P(Z) = \frac{5}{32}$.

The computer is asked to select a letter. Calculate
the probability that the letter selected is:

(a) A or C **(b)** X or Z **(c)** B or Y
(d) C or X **(e)** A or B or C **(f)** X or Y or Z.

7 An amusement arcade game is made to show
symbols according to these probabilities.

What is the probability of getting:

(a) a cherry or a plum
(b) a strawberry or a banana
(c) a plum or a BAR
(d) any fruit
(e) a plum, BAR or strawberry?

8 A robot arm is told to select snooker balls
according to these probabilities.

What is the probability that the ball selected will be:

(a) red or yellow **(b)** pink or black
(c) blue or green **(d)** red or black
(e) two reds **(f)** three reds
(g) two reds and a pink?

9 The probability of Angela selecting a particular type
of card from a pack of playing cards is:

$P(\text{ace}) = \frac{1}{13}$,
$P(\text{any number card 2–10}) = \frac{1}{13}$,
$P(\text{picture card}) = (\frac{3}{13})$.
What is the probability that she will select:

(a) an Ace or a 2
(b) a number card
(c) an Ace or a picture card
(d) a picture card or an even numbered card?

10 $\frac{3}{5}$ of the cards in a box are red, $\frac{1}{5}$ are blue, $\frac{1}{10}$
yellow and $\frac{1}{10}$ green. One card is picked at random
from the box. What is the probability that the card
will be:

(a) red or blue **(b)** blue or yellow
(c) green or red **(d)** not green?

11 A spinner is weighted so that the probability of
throwing each letter is:
$P(A) = P(B) = x$, $P(F) = z$
$P(C) = P(D) = P(E) = y$
Write down an expression
for the probability that
you will score:

(a) A or B **(b)** F or D
(c) C or A **(d)** A or D or E
(e) Not F **(f)** Not A

12 An electrical board has built into it twelve
integrated circuits: 3 of type A, 3 of type B, 2 of
type C, and 4 of type D. The probability of each
type of circuit having a fault is w, x, y and z
respectively.
Write an expression for the probability that the
following circuits will have a fault:

(a) any A or any B
(b) any C or any D
(c) any of type A
(d) any of type D
(e) any other than A.

Guess what ?

United is about to play City.

We've won three matches out of every four we've played! UNITED

We've won one match out of every four played.

What is the probability that United will beat City?
This question is impossible to calculate on these figures, since there are many other factors which need to be taken into account: the 'home' advantage; sickness and injury of key players; the weather; overall performance leading up to the game.

Any probability would have to be decided **subjectively**. That is, it needs to be an informed estimate, taking into account the calculated probability estimate, but also with an element of human judgement.

If we play you at home, we'll probably win. The probability might be $\frac{3}{4}$ or more...

...but if you play at City, the probability of you winning might be far less — maybe less than $\frac{1}{2}$ — in fact you'll probably lose!!

1 For each situation described below, state whether or not the probability is subjective, giving a reason for each answer.

(a) The probability of a car exceeding the speed limit on a busy road.

(b) The probability that a number picked at random from 1 to 100 will be even.

(c) The probability that it will snow on Christmas Day.

(d) The probability that an egg selected on a farm from a batch of 1000 is bad.

(e) The probability that a record produced by your favourite group will make number 1 in the charts.

(f) The probability that it will take more than a month to build a house.

(g) The probability that a calculator picked at a factory from a batch of 500 is faulty.

(h) The probability that six dice thrown together will give six 6s.

Repeated probability

Using a dice:
The probability of throwing a 6 on a dice is $\frac{1}{6}$. The probability of throwing a 6, followed by another 6, is $\frac{1}{6} \times \frac{1}{6} = \frac{1}{36}$

Using a dice and a coin:
The probability of throwing a head is $\frac{1}{2}$
The probability of throwing a 6 is $\frac{1}{6}$
The probability of throwing a head on a coin followed by a 6 on a dice is

$\frac{1}{2} \times \frac{1}{6} = \frac{1}{12}$

Now $\frac{1}{12} < \frac{1}{2}$, and $\frac{1}{12} < \frac{1}{6}$

There is less chance of throwing a head on a coin and a 6 on a dice than throwing **both** a head on a coin and 6 on a dice.

2 (a) Is it always the case that there is less probability of two events happening than the probabilities of either event individually?

(b) If so, can you explain why?

The **cumulative frequency** is the running total of the frequency up to a particular class boundary.

This frequency table shows the distribution of marks in a test.

Marks	0	1	2	3	4	5	6	7	8	9	10
Frequency	1	3	4	17	25	30	23	19	15	2	1

This means that 1 + 3 + 4 + 17 + 25 students obtained a mark of 4 or less.

The cumulative frequency may be displayed in a cumulative frequency table.

Marks	Frequency	Cumulative frequency
0	1	1
1	3	4
2	4	8
3	17	25
4	25	50
5	30	80
6	23	103
7	19	122
8	15	137
9	2	139
10	1	140

The cumulative frequency is **always** up to the class boundary.

The cumulative frequency of a grouped frequency table can also be calculated.

This table gives the height of 100 people.

Height (cm)	Frequency	Cumulative frequency
100 to < 110	2	2
110 to < 120	5	7
120 to < 130	9	16
130 to < 140	16	32
140 to < 150	27	59
150 to < 160	19	78
160 to < 170	12	90
170 to < 180	7	97
180 to < 190	3	100

1 Make a cumulative frequency table for this data about shoe size.

Shoe size	4	5	6	7	8	9	10	11	12
Frequency	2	7	16	30	45	26	14	8	2

2 Copy and complete the cumulative frequency table for this frequency distribution.

Examination mark	Frequency	Cumulative frequency
0–5	3	3
6–10	8	11
11–15	15	
16–20	28	
21–25	37	
26–30	45	
31–35	23	
36–40	16	
41–45	4	
46–50	1	

3 Copy and complete the cumulative frequency table for this frequency distribution.

Weight (kg)	Frequency	Cumulative frequency
100 to < 110	4	4
110 to < 120	19	23
120 to < 130	39	
130 to < 140	60	
140 to < 150	53	
150 to < 160	34	
160 to < 170	16	
170 to < 180	3	
180 to < 190	2	

Cumulative frequency curves 1

A cumulative frequency curve can be drawn by plotting the cumulative frequency data on a graph.

To draw the cumulative frequency curve for this cumulative frequency table:

- choose a suitable scale for each axis

- draw the axis.
  Cumulative frequency is always the vertical axis.
  Mark is the horizontal axis.

- plot the points (Mark, Cumulative frequency)
  (0, 1), (2, 4), (2, 8), (3, 25), (4, 50), (5, 80),
  (6, 103), (7, 122), (8, 137), (9, 139), (10, 140).

- draw a smooth curve through the points.

Marks	Frequency	Cumulative frequency
0	1	1
1	3	4
2	4	8
3	17	25
4	25	50
5	30	80
6	23	103
7	19	122
8	15	137
9	2	139
10	1	140

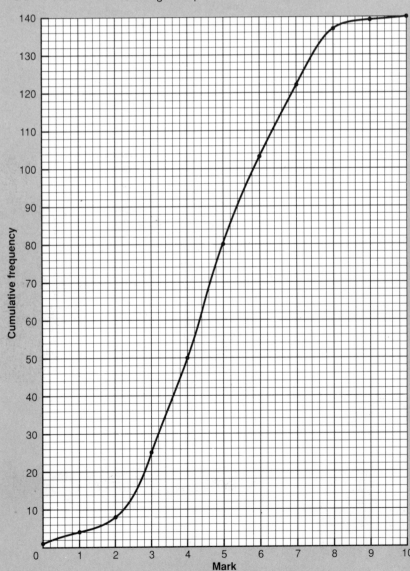

The curve is an **S-shape**.
Another name for a cumulative frequency curve is **ogive**.

You need graph paper.

1 (a) Copy and complete the cumulative frequency
table.

Marks	Frequency	Cumulative frequency
10	2	2
11	9	11 (= 9 + 2)
12	21	
13	45	
14	81	
15	53	
16	34	
17	15	
18	7	
19	3	

(b) Plot the cumulative frequency table on a graph,
and draw the cumulative frequency curve. Label
the axes and give your graph a title.

2 The weights of 100 students were recorded to the
nearest kilogram and shown in the frequency table.

Weight (kg)	Frequency
20–29	8
30–39	13
40–49	41
50–59	20
60–69	14
70–79	3
80–89	1

(a) Draw up a cumulative frequency table for this
data.
(b) Draw a cumulative frequency curve.

3 The heights of 288 students were measured to the
nearest centimetre, and shown in the frequency
table.

Height (cm)	Frequency
130–135	2
136–140	5
141–145	13
146–150	22
151–155	36
156–160	57
161–165	87
166–170	37
171–175	21
176–180	7
181–185	1

(a) Draw up a cumulative frequency table for this
data.
(b) Draw a cumulative frequency curve.

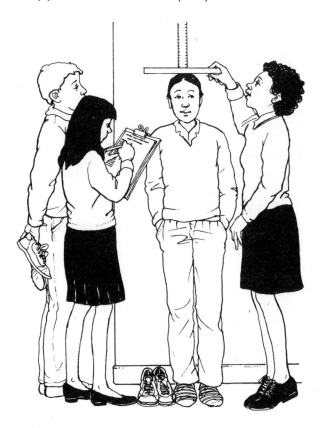

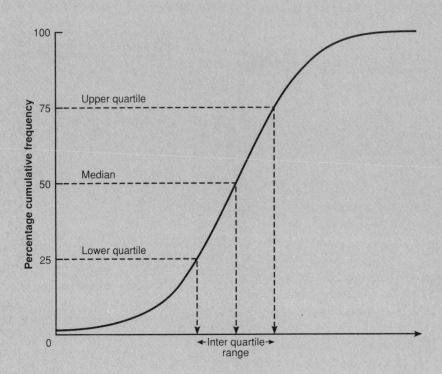

A **cumulative frequency graph** can be used to estimate useful statistical measures.

Median

The **median** is the middle value of a distribution. To find an estimate of the median from a cumulative frequency graph:

- find the halfway value on the cumulative frequency axis
- draw a horizontal line from this point to meet the cumulative frequency curve
- where this horizontal line meets the curve draw a vertical line to meet the horizontal axis
- read off the value on the horizontal axis where the vertical line meets the horizontal axis.

Lower quartile

- The **lower quartile** is the value one quarter of the way into the distribution.

To find an estimate of the lower quartile from a cumulative frequency curve:

- find one quarter way up the cumulative frequency axis
- draw a horizontal line from this point to meet the cumulative frequency curve
- where this horizontal line meets the curve draw a vertical line to meet the horizontal axis
- read off the value on the horizontal axis where this vertical line meets the horizontal axis.

Upper quartile

The **upper quartile** is the value three quarters of the way into the distribution.

You can find an estimate of the upper quartile from a cumulative frequency curve in a similar way to finding the lower quartile.

Inter quartile range

The **inter quartile range** is the difference between the **upper quartile** and the **lower quartile**.

Inter quartile range = Upper quartile – Lower quartile

This measure gives the range of the middle half of the data. It is useful as it is **not distorted by extreme values** at either end of the distribution, which may be the case for the range. It shows the way in which the distribution clusters around the median.

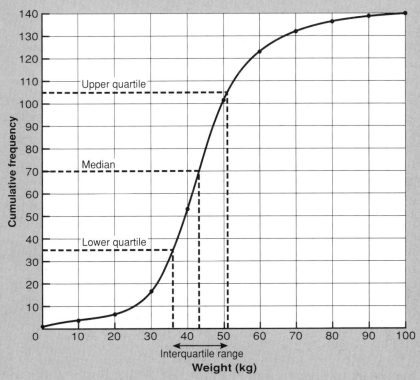

In this example of a cumulative frequency graph:

Median

The median is found by going across horizontally half-way at 70, then vertically down to where it meets the curve to the horizontal axis.

Median = 43 kg

Lower quartile

The lower quartile is found by going across horizontally quarter of the way at 35, then vertically to where it meets the curve to the horizontal axis.

Lower quartile = 36 kg

Upper quartile

The upper quartile is found by going across horizontally three quarters of the way at 105, then vertically to where it meets the curve to the horizontal axis.

Upper quartile = 51 kg

The inter quartile range

Inter quartile range = upper quartile – lower quartile

$$= 51 - 36$$
$$= 15 \text{ kg}$$

Cumulative frequency curves 2

1 Make a cumulative frequency table for the data below.

Length (km)	Frequency
1–5	5
6–10	41
11–15	77
16–20	58
21–25	39
26–30	17
31–35	3

(a) Draw a cumulative frequency curve.
(b) Use the cumulative frequency curve to find an estimate for: • median • lower quartile • upper quartile • inter quartile range

2 The table shows the ages, to the nearest year, of 200 people.

Age (years)	Frequency
0–10	5
11–20	19
21–30	47
31–40	79
41–50	32
51–60	15
61–70	2
71–80	1

(a) Draw up a cumulative frequency table.
(b) Construct a cumulative frequency curve.
(c) Find estimates for: • median • lower quartile • upper quartile • inter quartile range

3 The frequency table shows the weight to the nearest kg, of 300 students.

Weight (kg)	Frequency
30–39	3
40–49	11
50–59	24
60–69	56
70–79	123
80–89	70
90–99	13

(a) Draw up a cumulative frequency table.
(b) Construct a cumulative frequency curve.
(c) Find estimates for: • median • lower quartile • upper quartile • inter quartile range.
(d) What percentage of students weigh 56 kg or less?
(e) What percentage of students weigh more than 72 kg?

4 This frequency distribution shows the age distribution in India's population.

Age (years)	Frequency (millions)
0–8	71
9–16	110
17–24	186
25–32	131
33–40	88
41–48	52
49–56	25
57–64	7

(a) Draw up a cumulative frequency table.
(b) Construct a cumulative frequency curve.
(c) Find estimate for: • median • lower quartile • upper quartile • inter quartile range
(d) What percentage of the population is 49 years or older?
(e) What percentage of the population is less than 25 years old?
(f) What percentage of the population is aged between 9 and 32 inclusive?

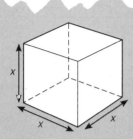

This cube has side of length x units.

Its volume, V, is

$V = x^3$ cubic units.

The surface area, S, of the cube is

$S = 6x^2$

In the above formula for the surface area:

> 6 is a **dimensionless** number
> x, the length of the side of the cube, has **dimension 1**
>
> x^2 has **dimension 2**
>
> x^3 has **dimension 3**

Volume of a cone

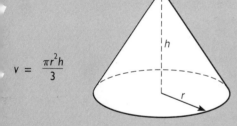

$v = \dfrac{\pi r^2 h}{3}$

In the formula for the volume of a cone, its dimension is 3, because

$$\underset{\text{dim 1}}{\boldsymbol{r}} \quad \times \quad \underset{\text{dim 1}}{\boldsymbol{r}} \quad \times \quad \underset{\text{dim 1}}{\boldsymbol{h}}$$

The dimensions of a formula will never tell you if it is exactly right. They can, however, tell you if you have chosen the wrong one and help to distinguish between formulae.

> For a volume the **dimension is always 3**.
> For an area the **dimension is always 2**.
> For a length the **dimension is always 1**.

1 Give the dimensions of the following.

(a) Area of a rectangle

$A = ab$

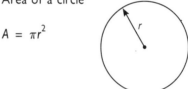

(b) Perimeter of a rectangle

$P = 2(a + b)$

(c) Area of a circle

$A = \pi r^2$

(d) Volume of a sphere

$V = \dfrac{4\pi r^3}{3}$

(e) Surface area of a sphere

$S = 4\pi r^2$

2 Write as many of the other standard formulae for lengths, areas and volumes as possible. In each case check that the dimensions are correct.

3 In this question the numbers and greek letters are dimensionless but the other letters are all lengths. Determine whether the expressions give lengths, areas or volumes.

(a) πr **(b)** $\lambda a^2 b$ **(c)** $\mu(a + b)$

(d) $2(xy + xz + yz)$ **(e)** $\pi(R^2 - r^2)$

(f) $a^2 + b^2$ **(g)** $x^2 h$

Question time 1

A **hypothesis** is a form of generalisation which needs data to justify it.

For example, you might hypothesise that rhubarb grows taller more quickly if it is grown under buckets. To test the hypothesis you would have to carry out experiments and gather data.

When a hypothesis concerns discrete data, a questionnaire is used to collect the data. Where the data are continuous, experiments involving measurement are carried out.

At this level of work your questionnaires should contain opportunities for respondents to list preferences and your experiments should be designed to deal effectively with several variables which might affect the results.

If you illustrate your results using graphs they should be appropriate to the data. It is likely that you will need to use scatter diagrams, frequency polygons or cumulative frequency graphs to match the level of sophistication required. This should be kept in mind when making a hypothesis.

Discrete data – questionnaires

HYPOTHESIS:
People choose to shop at a specific supermarket because they prefer its range of products rather than for any other reason.

To test this hypothesis a questionnaire has been designed.

- As many different responses as possible have been anticipated.
- To ensure that there is not another overwhelming reason an 'other reason' category has been included.
- To anticipate bias, the questionnaire includes some questions about the respondents themselves. Gender, age, home address and number of children might throw light on trends.
- To ensure a fair spread of opinion, the survey would need to be conducted at all the possible supermarkets in a town.

SUPERMARKET QUESTIONNAIRE

Supermarket _ _ _ _ _ _ _ _ _ _ _ _ _   Time _ _ _ _ _ _

Tick the box which describes yourself:

Gender: Female ☐   Male ☐

Age: 18-25 ☐   26-35 ☐

36-50 ☐   Over 50 ☐

Fill in the spaces:

Home town ☐

Number of children ☐

Put the numbers 1 to 6 next to the statements below to give their order of importance to you. Use the number 1 for your most important reason for shopping here.

Prices are lower
It's easy to park
The range of products is better
It's closest to home
It's easy to get to
It's close to other shops

If you have another reason more important than your number 1 write it here: ☐

Thank you for your help and time.

Questionnaire design

You should always take into account these points:

- Anticipate all possible responses and have 'boxes' to receive the results.
- Each question must be unambiguous and require a simple answer or list of preferences.
- Each person's response must fall into one category for each question. Two answers for one question should be avoided. Force the respondent to make a choice.

- Demonstrate that you know how bias can arise when constructing your questionnaire.
- Be able to explain how your way of conducting a survey has been chosen by considering how bias can be eliminated.
- Demonstrate understanding of how bias could have arisen in your survey results. Be critical of your results and describe any limitations in their reliability.

Design a questionnaire to test the hypothesis that cheese and onion flavoured crisps are more popular the older the student in your school.

You may like to consider the following in your survey.

- Does the popularity vary with gender?
- Does the popularity of cheese and onion flavoured crisps correlate with age?

Data analysis

To test a hypothesis you need to analyse your data.

In the supermarket example, a crude way to approach this would be to count up the number of times each of the six responses has the number 1 in its box. If 'The range of products is better' receives the most 1's then your hypothesis would be justified for that particular supermarket. But is it the same for all the supermarkets? You might be able to comment upon the results for each supermarket.

A more sophisticated approach might be to add up all the numbers next to each response and then the response with the lowest total could be said to be the most popular. People might not put 'The range of products is better' as their number one choice but it might be high on everyone's list. You could then argue that your hypothesis had been justified by the data but you should explain that other responses were more frequent in many cases. Graphs could then be used to show the responses by gender, age, home town, number of children and individual supermarket.

You might want to record the time at which the supermarket questionnaire was completed to see if that had any effect on the responses.

You also need to decide how you will select the people to ask. Do you need to select a representative group? Will you catch them as they leave the supermarket? Will you approach them in the car park? Is the coffee shop a good place to do the survey?

The last two ways might introduce a bias towards car drivers or people who stop for a snack.

2 Make a hypothesis about the relative popularity of two subjects which all your class study. Design a questionnaire, carry out a survey and write about your results, being careful to describe the reasons for the data justifying, or not, your hypothesis.

3 Describe in detail how you would use a questionnaire in a survey to test the hypothesis that students do better in subjects that they enjoy most. Your answer should include a questionnaire and your reasons for including every detail of it.

Give details of how you would illustrate the data and how you would respond to possible outcomes in terms of how they do or do not justify the hypothesis.

4 Make a hypothesis about some preferences which might be held by the students in your class. Write a questionnaire, carry out a survey, illustrate the data using graphs and try to justify your hypothesis.

Question time 2

HYPOTHESIS:
Rhubarb grows taller more quickly if it is grown under up-turned buckets.

To test this hypothesis an experiment can be undertaken.

Care must be taken to ensure that the only difference between growing conditions of plants under test is whether or not they are under buckets. So **the effects of all other variables must be reduced to as low a level as possible**.

That will mean:

- testing several plants with the same mass of roots so that averages can be taken
- making sure that the plants are all grown in the same soil with the same moisture content
- making sure that the plants are all at the same temperature
- ensuring that watering and supply of fertilizer are the same for all
- using buckets which do not restrict the rate of growth.

My hypothesis is that there's a correlation between the height of students in this form and the distance round their heads.

I reckon there's a closer correlation between someone's height and the distance from their middle finger up to their nose when their arm is stretched out horizontally.

1 **(a)** Describe in detail how you would carry out an experiment to investigate the hypothesis that bean seeds grow more rapidly to a height of three centimetres in damp sand than in damp soil.

Pay particular attention to the amount of water available in both cases and the effects of the amount and length of exposure to light, and how you would consider variations in temperature.

(b) Describe how you would analyse the results in terms of which measures of average and spread you would use and why.

(c) Which form of graph would you use to illustrate your results and why is your choice appropriate?

2 Carry out an experiment on the other students in your class to find out which hypothesis is more justified. Are there any other hypotheses of a similar kind which you can make, and test?

3 **(a)** Design an experiment to investigate whether reaction times are faster when students in your class respond to sound rather than sight.

(b) Describe in detail what steps you will take to ensure that the effects of any other variable are minimised. For instance, are you going to let them practice before the test run? How are you going to ensure that each test is exactly the same?

(c) Carry out the experiment and analyse the results. What are your conclusions? How could the experiment be refined to give greater reliability?

4 Ask your teacher to supply a method of working out the reading age of a piece of writing.

Design an experiment to test the hypothesis that students in your class find pieces with a lower reading age easier to understand.

This grid has 11 spaces.
2 of them are empty,
3 contain grey counters,
3 contain black counters and
3 contain white counters.
This is the starting position
for the game.

This is the situation at the end of
the game.

The rules determining the movement of the counters are:

• at the start and end of the game counters of different colours must be
separated by an empty space

• a counter can slide either left or right to move into an empty adjacent space

• a counter can jump over exactly one counter of another colour to land
in an empty space.

xamine the game strategies and investigate the relationship between the
umber of counters and the minimum number of moves required to go from
he starting position to the finish.

ou are advised to:

record your observations and comments

explain your game strategies

make and test any conjectures

**form any generalisations, with appropriate explanations,
justifications or proofs.**

Hopping about

Row 1

Row 2

Here are 4 counters on Row 1 of a rectangular grid. They are to be moved to Row 2.

The rules governing their movement are:

- Counters can only move up or down like this:

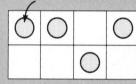

or

- A counter can only move if the one on its immediate right is in Row 1 and all of the others to its right are in Row 2.

So this counter
can move . . .

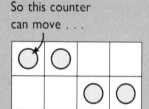

. . . but this counter
cannot move.

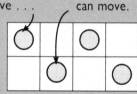

This counter
can move.

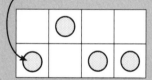

This counter
cannot move . . .

. . . but this one
can move.

- Whether a counter can move or not **does not** depend on the positions of the counters to the left of it. So the counter on the far right can always move.

1 Show that it takes a minimum of 10 moves to get all four counters from Row 1 to Row 2.

2 Investigate the relationship between the number of counters and the number of moves needed to get all the counters from Row 1 to Row 2.

You are advised to:

- **record any observations**
- **outline clearly any game strategies you employ**
- **form conjectures and ways of testing them**
- **offer any generalisation with appropriate explanations, justifications or proofs.**

You can obtain the neatest formal symbolic generalisation by expressing your results in something other than ordinary base ten notation and by using the idea of a Geometric Progression. Information about Geometric Progressions can be found in many of the standard textbooks for 'A' level mathematics.

6 spinners have three equal sectors, white, black and grey.

These 6 spinners are set out as a 2 by 3 rectangular grid. The starting positions for the spinners always have grey at the top.

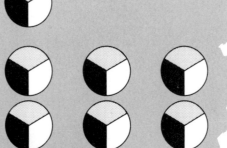

The spinners can be spun around through 120° in a clockwise direction but only according to the rule that either a whole row or a whole column must be spun at the same time.

This is the effect of spinning the first column. It is called a finishing pattern.

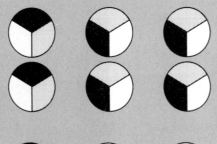

Spinning the second row gives this finishing pattern.

The act of spinning the first column and then the second row can be written as $C_1 * R_2$

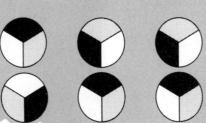

Record the finishing patterns for the following combinations of spins:

(a) C_2 (b) $R_2 * C_3$ (c) $C_2 * R_2 * R_1$

(d) $C_1 * R_2 * R_2 * C_2$ (e) $C_2 * C_2 \; (= C_2^2)$

(f) $C_1^2 * R_2^2$

Investigate the relationship between the number of finishing patterns and the number of spinners in the rectangular grid.

You are advised to:

   record any observations and comments

   outline any techniques or strategies you use

   form and test any conjectures

● **state any generalisations with appropriate explanations, justifications or proofs.**

3 Investigate the algebraic properties of combinations of spins:

   You are advised to look in particular at:

   • **the existence of an identity element**

   • **the existence of the inverse of an element**

   • **the commutativity of the operation of combining spins**

   • **the associativity property**

   • **ways of simplifying combinations**

   • **ways of solving equations such as $C_i * R_j * X = C_k$.**

The cowboy's dilemma

A cowboy has been given exactly 600 metres of rope. He has been told by the trail boss to rope off a piece or pieces of land in which the cows can graze.

Strangely, the trail boss insists that any piece of land used for grazing must be triangular in shape.

Each cow requires ten square metres of grazing land.

1 Investigate the various pieces of land the cowboy could rope off.
Help him to advise the trail boss on the maximum number of cows they can have with 600 metres of rope.

2 Investigate the way in which the solutions to the cowboy's problem vary if the length of the rope varies.

3 What is the minimum length of rope required for 5000 cows?

You are advised to:
● **record your observations and comments**
● **make and test any conjectures**
● **form any generalisations, with appropriate explanations, justifications or proofs.**

You are likely to gain more credit if your answers are clear, well-constructed and thorough.

This enquiry lends itself well to the application and use of computers and spreadsheets.

This is one possible arrangement of five equal-sized regular hexagons.

Here are two other arrangements.

Investigate the relationship between the number of arrangements of a collection of equal-sized regular hexagons and the number of hexagons in the collection.

You are advised to:
- **record your observations and comments**
- **make and test any conjectures**
- **form any generalisations, with appropriate explanations, justifications or proofs.**

You could extend your investigation by considering hexagonal tiles which have different colours on either side, or in any other way of your own choosing.

Some special numbers

The triangular numbers

T_1
$= 1$
$= 1$

T_2
$= 1 + 2$
$= 3$

T_3
$= 1 + 2 + 3$
$= 6$

1 (a) Show that the fourth triangular number, T_4 is $T_4 = 10$.

(b) Work out the values of T_5, T_6 and T_7.

(c) Work out the values of $T_7 - T_6$, $T_6 - T_5$, $T_5 - T_4$, $T_4 - T_3$, $T_3 - T_2$.
What do you notice about the result?

(d) Write down a general result for $T_{n+1} - T_n$ in terms of n.

(e) Given that $T_{100} = 5050$, calculate the values of T_{101} and T_{102}.

(f) What can you say about $T_{n+2} - T_n$?

(g) $T_3 + T_4 = \boxed{}$

(h) Generalise the result in part **(g)**.

(i) Show that

$$T_n = \frac{n(n + 1)}{2}$$

(j) Calculate the value of T_{200}.

The square numbers

S_1
$= 1 \times 1$
$= 1$

S_2
$= 2 \times 2$
$= 4$

S_3
$= 3 \times 3$
$= 9$

(a) Work out the values of S_4, S_5 and S_6.

(b) Write the values of any three square numbers of your own choosing.

(c) Find the values of $S_6 - S_5$, $S_5 - S_4$, $S_4 - S_3$ and make a statement about the results.

(d) Write a general result for $S_{n+1} - S_n$ in terms of n.

(e) Given that $S_{100} = 10\,000$, calculate the values of S_{101} and S_{102}.

(f) Check that $S_7 - S_5 = 24 = 12 \times 2 = (7 + 5) \times (7 - 5)$.

(g) Can you generalise the result in part **(f)**?

The tetrahedral numbers

H_1	H_2	H_3
$= T_1$	$= T_1 + T_2$	$= T_1 + T_2 + T_3$
$= 1$	$= 1 + 3$	$= 1 + 3 + 6$
$= 1$	$= 4$	$= 10$

(a) Calculate the values of H_4 and H_5.

(b) Use the ideas in questions **1** and **2** to find a general result for $H_{n+1} - H_n$ in terms of n.

(c) If $H_{10} = 220$, calculate the values of H_{11} and H_{12}.

The pyramid numbers

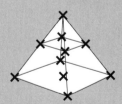

P_1	P_2	P_3
$= S_1$	$= S_1 + S_2$	$= S_1 + S_2 + S_3$
$= 1$	$= 1 + 4$	$= 1 + 4 + 9$
$= 1$	$= 5$	$= 14$

Investigate the pyramid numbers. Try to give a general result for $P_{n+1} - P_n$ in terms of n.

The cube numbers are given by

$C_1 = 1 \times 1 \times 1 = 1$ $C_2 = 2 \times 2 \times 2 = 8$ etc.

(a) Say why these numbers are called the cube numbers.

(b) Experiment with the sums and differences of the cube numbers and try to find some general results similar to those found in the previous questions.

The number of people who watched Kidchester Football Club for the first 5 matches of the new season were:

(13 400) (12 300) (8 200) (14 700) (9 800)

Each attendance was rounded to the nearest 100 spectators.

Since each attendance was recorded to the nearest 100, the actual attendance for the first match could have been anywhere between 13 350 and 13 450.

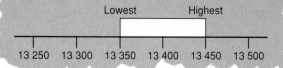

Lowest   Highest

13 250   13 300   13 350   13 400   13 450   13 500

1 Write down the lowest and highest possible attendances for the other 4 matches.

2 (a) If the actual attendance for all five matches was the smallest possible for each of the 5 games, what was the total number of spectators who watched all 5 games?

(b) If the actual attendance for all five matches was the highest possible for each of the 5 games, what was the total number of spectators who watched all 5 games?

(c) What is the difference between the highest possible and lowest possible totals of spectators who watched all 5 games?

3 The attendances for the five matches to the nearest 10 were

(13 360) (12 350) (8 230) (14 670) (9 800)

(a) Using this information, what was the smallest possible number of spectators who watched all five games?

(b) What was the highest possible total?

(c) What is the difference between the highest and lowest possible attendances?

4 A manufacturer makes rods to be used in practical maths equipment.

A yellow rod is said to be 5·0 cm long. In practice this means that the actual length can be anywhere between 4·95 cm and 5·05 cm.

5·0 cm

If these yellow rods were placed end to end, what are the smallest and longest possible total lengths for:

(a) 2 rods   **(b)** 10 rods?

5 A black rod is said to be 7·0 cm long.

(a) If a black rod and a yellow rod are placed end to end what are the minimum and maximum possible total lengths?

(b) If a black rod and a yellow rod are placed side by side, what are the possible values of the differences in length?

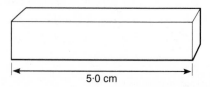

DARBYE 12 km   MEDING 8 km

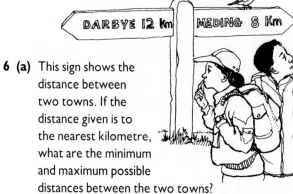

6 (a) This sign shows the distance between two towns. If the distance given is to the nearest kilometre, what are the minimum and maximum possible distances between the two towns?

(b) Two hikers meet at the signpost. One sets off to Darbye and the other to Meding. What are the minimum and maximum possible differences in the distance they have to walk?

7 At the school sports day Darren wins the 100 m race. If the time given was 13 seconds, what were the slowest and fastest possible times?

A length of pipe is laid on the floor and Osman, Leroy and Shamain are all asked to measure it.

Osman measures the pipe and gives its length as 2 metres.
This means that the lower and upper limits are 1·5 m and 2·5 m respectively.

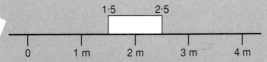

Leroy gives his answer as 2·0 metres. This means that the lower and upper limits are 1·95 m and 2·05 m respectively.

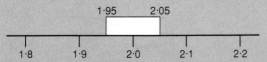

Shamain gives her answer as 2·00 metres. This means that the lower and upper limits are 1·995 and 2·005 respectively.

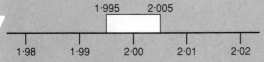

When you round off a number, you are really giving an **interval approximation**. This interval approximation should be meaningful and realistic.

1 Who do you think gave the most realistic interval approximation when measuring the length of the pipe, Osman, Leroy or Shamain? Give a reason for your answer.

2 (a) The population of Darbye is given as 5000 to 3 sig fig. What is the interval approximation?
  (b) If the population was given as 5000 to the nearest 100, what is the approximation interval?
  (c) Which approximation gives the most useful information, and why?

3 The population of Meding is 456 000 to the nearest thousand. The population of Kidchester is 342 000 to the nearest thousand.
  (a) Write the interval approximation for the population of Kidchester.
  (b) What is the interval approximation for the total population of the two cities?
  (c) Write the minimum and maximum differences between the populations of the two cities.

4 This information appears in many text books.

Basic unit	Equivalent unit
1 inch	2·54 cm
1 yard	91·4 cm
1 litre	1·76 pints
1 ton	1·016 tonnes
1 km	0·621 miles
1 mile	1609 metres

Write down an interval approximation for each of the equivalent units in the table.

5 The sides of a rectangle are measured as 5·6 cm and 4·8 cm.
  (a) Write the interval approximations for these two measurements.
  (b) Calculate the minimum and maximum values for the perimeter of the rectangle.
  (c) Calculate the minimum and maximum values for the area of the rectangle.

6 A car travelled a distance of 120 m measured to the nearest metre. It took 25 seconds to the nearest second.
  (a) Using this information calculate the average speed of the car.
  (b) Write the interval approximation for the distance travelled.
  (c) Write the interval approximation for the time taken.
  (d) Calculate the maximum possible average speed.
  (e) Calculate the minimum possible average speed.

Tolerating the difference

Rotator Ltd makes a rotor arm for use in the car industry. The rotor arm is produced by a machine and should be 5·6 cm long. In practice it is difficult to make the rotor arm exactly 5·6 cm long, but it can still be used if the actual length is in the interval 5·55 cm to 5·56 cm.

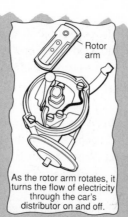

Rotor arm

As the rotor arm rotates, it turns the flow of electricity through the car's distributor on and off.

The difference between the upper and lower limit is called the tolerance. In this case the tolerance is 5·65 − 5·55 = 0·1 cm.

The tolerance can be written as 5·6 ± 0·05. This means that:

• the length required is 5·6 cm
• the lower limit is 5·6 − 0·05 = 5·55 cm
• the upper limit is 5·6 + 0·05 = 5·65 cm

1 Motopart & Co. can produce the same rotor arms with a tolerance of ± 0·03.
   (a) What is the shortest possible length of the rotor arm?
   (b) What is its longest possible length?

2 Write down the lower and upper limit of:
   (a) 5·6 ± 0·05   (b) 5·6 ± 0·02
   (c) 5·6 ± 0·025   (d) 5·6 ± 0·01

3 (a) Heather places two metal bars end to end. The first has a length of 5·2 cm ± 0·05 and the second bar has a length of 7·5 cm ± 0·025. Find the minimum and maximum possible total lengths.

   (b) If she places the same two bars side by side, what are the minimum and maximum possible differences in their two lengths?

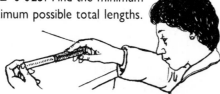

4 Gerry makes bolts and screws. One of the bolts he makes is 4·2 ± 0·05 cm long and has a diameter of 1·4 ± 0·05 cm.
   Sheila sells drills. All the drills that she sells have a tolerance of ± 0·025 cm.
   (a) If Gerry buys a drill from Sheila with a nominal diameter of 1·4 cm, for use with the bolts that he makes, what problems may he experience?
   (b) What can Gerry do to solve any problem that he may have?

5 The Evertite Ball Bearing Company make ball bearings for use in industry and technical work. In their catalogue one item is listed as

The Evertite Ball Bearing Co.

Item	Nominal Diameter	Tolerance	Price
Ball bearing	2·2 cm	0·05	25 p
	2·2 cm	0·025	50 p
	2·2 cm	0·02	75 p
	2·2 cm	0·01	£2·00

   (a) Match the possible types of ball bearings required for these applications:
      • precision engineering
      • general engineering
      • home and domestic use
      • car manufacturing.
   (b) Give a possible explanation for the variations in the cost of the ball bearings.

6 Small squares are punched out of a metal sheet. The squares have a length of 12·0 ± 0·02 cm.
   (a) What are the minimum and maximum lengths of one side of the square?
   (b) What are the minimum and maximum areas of one square?
   (c) Express the perimeter in the form $a ± b$.

7 If the lower limit of a tolerance is 55·975 and the upper limit 56·025 express this information in the form $a ± b$.

1 Multiply out these brackets:

(a) $(x + 2)(x + 10)$ (b) $(x + 1)(x + 9)$
(c) $(x + 5)(x + 5)$ (d) $(x - 2)(x - 3)$
(e) $(x + 7)(x - 3)$ (f) $(x - 6)(x + 7)$

2 Factorise:

(a) $x^2 + 4x$ (b) $5x + 20$
(c) $x^2 + 3x$ (d) $6x + 18$
(e) $x^2 - 5x$ (f) $3x - 15$

This rectangle has an area of $x^2 + 7x + 12$. What are the lengths of its sides?

$x^2 + 7x + 12$

To find the length of the sides reverse the process of multiplying out the brackets.

$$x^2 + 7x + 12 = x^2 + 4x + 3x + 12$$
$$= x(x + 4) + 3(x + 4)$$
$$x^2 + 7x + 12 = (x + 3)(x + 4)$$

So the lengths are $(x + 3)$ and $(x + 4)$

This is also called factorising.

To factorise, notice this number pattern

$$x^2 + 7x + 12 = x^2 + 4x + 3x + 12$$
$4x + 3x = 7x$
$4 \times 3 = 12$

3 Split the x term into two so that the expression is in the same form as above.

$$x^2 + 7x + 12 = x^2 + 4x + 3x + 12$$

(a) $x^2 + 8x + 12$ (b) $x^2 + 7x + 10$
(c) $x^2 + 11x + 24$ (d) $x^2 + 5x + 4$
(e) $x^2 + 6x + 9$ (f) $x^2 + 9x + 20$
(g) $x^2 + 9x + 18$ (h) $x^2 + 16x + 39$
(i) $x^2 + 20x + 100$ (j) $x^2 + 15x + 54$

4 If each of the expressions in question **3** is the area of a rectangle, find the length of each side.

5 Factorise:

(a) $x^2 + 11x + 30$ (b) $y^2 + 12y + 27$
(c) $r^2 + 10r + 16$ (d) $f^2 + 14f + 48$
(e) $x^2 + 17x + 60$ (f) $y^2 + 15y + 56$
(g) $h^2 + 21h + 110$ (h) $x^2 + 25x + 156$

This rectangle has an area of $x^2 + 3x - 28$

$x^2 + 3x - 28$

To find the length of its sides use the same method.

$$x^2 + 3x - 28 = x^2 + 7x - 4x - 28$$
$7x - 4x = 3x$
$7x \cdot {}^-4 = {}^-28$

$$x^2 + 3x - 28 = x(x + 7) - 4(x + 7)$$
$$x^2 + 3x - 28 = (x - 4)(x + 7)$$

So the lengths are $(x - 4)$ and $(x + 7)$

6 Factorise:

(a) $x^2 + 2x - 8$ (b) $x^2 + 6x - 27$
(c) $y^2 + y - 56$ (d) $p^2 + 4p - 21$
(e) $p^2 - 7p + 12$ (f) $x^2 - 11x + 24$
(g) $w^2 - 13w + 36$ (h) $x^2 - 4x - 5$
(i) $y^2 - 16y + 63$ (j) $r^2 - 5r - 50$
(k) $m^2 - m - 90$ (l) $m^2 + m - 30$
(m) $x^2 + 11x - 60$ (n) $x^2 + 23x + 132$
(o) $y^2 - 9$ (p) $x^2 - 16$
(q) $x^2 - 64$ (r) $x^2 - 100$

7 Find the length of the missing side of each rectangle.

(a) $(x + 7)$ — area equals $x^2 + 9x + 14$
(b) $(x + 5)$ — area equals $x^2 + 2x - 15$
(c) $(x - 8)$ — area equals $x^2 - 14x + 48$
(d) $(x - 7)$ — area equals $x^2 - 49$

8 This rectangle has an area of $3x^2 - 7x - 20$. The width is $(x - 4)$. Find the height.

$(x - 4)$ $3x^2 - 7x - 20$

9 Factorise these expressions:

(a) $2x^2 + 5x + 2$ (b) $3x^2 + 14x + 8$
(c) $4x^2 + 11x + 6$ (d) $4x^2 + 10x + 6$
(e) $2x^2 - 5x - 3$ (f) $6x^2 + 8x - 8$

Keep it in proportion 3

Jill volunteers for a charity walk. She is given 50p for each km.
If Jill doubles the distance she walks, she doubles the money she collects.
This is an example of direct proportionality.

$$m \alpha d$$

the money collected ↑ distance walked
is proportional to

The symbol α means 'is proportional to'.

Not all proportionality is direct.

1 A car travelling at 50 km/h takes 4 hours to complete a journey. If the speed of the car:

(a) increases, what happens to the time taken
(b) doubles, how long does it take to complete the journey
(c) halves, how long does the journey take?

In question 1 the speed is **inversely proportional** to the time.

A table can still be used to solve problems but this time three rows are needed.

Time (t)	4	?
$\frac{1}{t}$	0·25	?
Speed	50	100

The speed doubles to 100, $\frac{1}{t}$ doubles to 0·5 and $\frac{1}{0·5}$ = 2. The journey time is halved.

Check your answers to question 1 before continuing.

2 Copy, complete and explain:

Time (t)	4		
$\frac{1}{t}$	0·25	0·4	
Speed	50		60

3 Copy and complete this table:

Time (t)	8·0		
$\frac{1}{t}$		0·045	
Speed	0·5		12·4

4 Weather balloons are used to find out information about the weather at different heights in the atmosphere. The pressure inside a balloon is inversely proportional to its diameter.
Here are two weather balloons. The pressure inside balloon 1 is 1000 millibars.
What is the pressure inside balloon 2? You will need to measure the balloons.

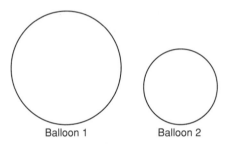

Balloon 1   Balloon 2

5 In an experiment Jonathan obtains these results:

Wavelength (metres)	0·1	0·2	0·3	0·4	0·5
Frequency (hertz)	1650	820	550	410	350

He suspects that the relationship between the frequency f and the wavelength w is

$$f \alpha \frac{1}{w}$$

This is his conjecture.

(a) Draw a graph of f against $\frac{1}{w}$
(b) Was Jonathan's conjecture correct?
(c) Use your graph to find f when $w = 0·35$
(d) Write the law connecting w and f

6 The density of a quantity of gas is inversely proportional to its volume. It is known that when the density is 1·6 kg/m the volume is 2·1 m³. Find:

(a) the density when the volume is 2·4 m³
(b) the volume when the density is 0·6 kg/m
(c) the rule connecting the density and the volume.

There are several different types of proportionality.

$$h \alpha\ t^2, \qquad v \alpha\ r^3, \qquad l \alpha\ \sqrt{a}, \qquad k \alpha\ \frac{1}{l^2}$$

1 The surface area of a sphere is proportional to the radius squared. A certain sphere has a surface area of 452 mm^2 and a radius of 6 mm.

(a) Copy and complete this table:

r	6	4	
r^2	36		
y	452		100

(b) Find the surface area of a sphere with a radius of 10 mm.

2 A ball is thrown into the air with a speed of u m/s and reaches a height (h). It is known that $h \alpha\ u^2$. Given that $h = 60$ when $u = 36$ find:

(a) h when $u = 42$
(b) u when $h = 90$

3 The handbrake of a car fails and the car rolls down a hill. The velocity it reaches is proportional to the square root of the distance travelled. If it reaches a velocity of 12 m/s after it has travelled 20 m, find:

(a) the velocity it reaches after 30 m
(b) the distance it has travelled when it reaches a speed of 25 m/s.

4 Ken has two similar measuring jugs in his kitchen. The smaller one is 11·5 cm tall and holds 600 ml when full. The larger jug is 13·3 cm tall. Calculate how much it will hold when full.

5 The energy (E) stored in an elastic string varies as the square of the extension (T). If the extension is 4 cm when the string stores 96 joules, find:

(a) E when the extension is 3·2 cm
(b) the rule connecting E and T.

The inverse square law states that the force of gravity acting on an object is proportional to the inverse of the square of the distance measured from the Earth's centre.

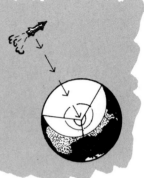

6 An object on the Earth's surface is 6400 km away from the centre of the earth. Find:

(a) the distance from the centre of the Earth when the gravity is $\frac{1}{4}$
(b) the gravity on a spacecraft 10 000 km above the Earth's surface.

7 The resistance (R) of a length of wire is inversely proportional to the diameter (d). If the resistance is 4·75 ohms for a diameter of 1·5 mm, find:

(a) the resistance when the diameter is 2 mm
(b) the diameter when the resistance is 12 ohms
(c) the rule connecting the two variables.

8 These are the results of a number of experiments. Work out the type of any proportionality, and hence the rule connecting the two variables.

(a)

t	2	5
a	12	75

(b)

t	2	8
a	2	0·5

(c)

t	4	9
a	12	18

(d)

t	2	4	6
a	10	14	18

9 If $A = \frac{1}{B}$, what is the percentage change in A when:

(a) B increases by 20% **(b)** B decreases by 50%
(c) What is the percentage change in B when A decreases by 75%?

10 If $P = Q^3$, what is the percentage change in P when:

(a) Q increases by 10% **(b)** Q decreases by 25%
(c) What is the percentage change in Q when P increases by 50%?

On the graph the line $2x + 3y = 12$
When x is zero, $3y = 12$ and $y = 4$ (0, 4)
When y is zero, $2x = 12$ and $x = 6$ (6, 0)
Plotting these two points, the line $3x + 2y = 12$
can be drawn.

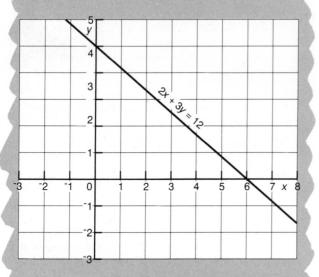

The line $2x + 3y = 12$ divides the plane into two
regions.
Above the line is the region $2x + 3y > 12$
Below the line is the region $2x + 3y < 12$

To check the first statement choose a point above
the line, say (2, 3), and show that the statement
$2x + 3y > 12$ is true
$(2 \times 2) + (3 \times 3) > 12$
$4 + 9 > 12$ True

1 (a) From the graph choose any coordinate point
   below the line and show that it satisfies the
   statement $2x + 3y < 12$
   (b) Calculate the value of $2x + 3y$ for the
   coordinate point (3, 2). Write a statement
   satisfied by this point.

2 Calculate the value $2x + 3y$ at each of these
   coordinate points and state if they are in the region
   $2x + 3y > 12$, $2x + 3y < 12$ or on the
   line $2x + 3y = 12$
   (a) ($^-$1, 4)   (b) (6, 2)   (c) (8, $^-$1)
   (d) (9, $^-$2)   (e) ($^-$3, 2)   (f) (2·1, 2·9)

3 The line $x - 2y = 6$ divides the plane into two
   regions.

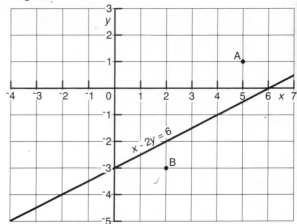

   (a) Write the coordinates of point A.
   (b) Calculate the value of $x - 2y$ for the
   coordinate of point A.
   (c) Write an inequality for the region containing:
   • point A   • point B.

4 Write an inequality which describes each shaded
   region. Show at least one test point.
   (a)

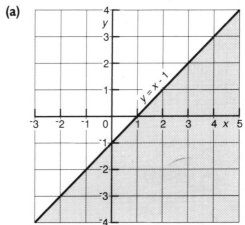

   (b)

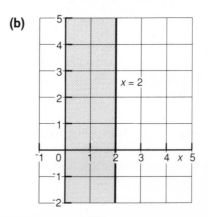

When drawing lines, draw a solid line if the line is included in a region, for ≤ or ≥, and a dotted line if it is not, < or >.

To show the region described by the inequalities $y - x < 3$ and $2x + 3y < 6$:

- draw the line $y - x = 3$
- use a test point to work out which side is $y - x < 3$

Shade out the part not required.

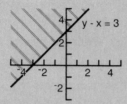

- draw the line $2x + 3y = 6$
- use a test point to work out which side is $2x + 3y < 6$

Shade out the part not required.

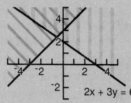

The region left unshaded satisfies both inequalities $y - x < 3$ and $2x + 3y < 6$.

Draw diagrams to show the region described by these inequalities.

(a) $y > x$ and $x + y > 4$
(b) $x > 4$ and $x + 2y \leq 8$
(c) $y - x \geq 2$ and $3x + 2y < 12$
(d) $y \leq 2x$ and $y \geq \frac{1}{2}x$

The lines $x + y = 3$ and $y = x - 2$ divide the plane into four regions, A, B, C, D.

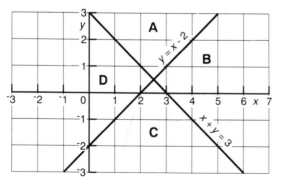

Write two inequalities which describe each region.

To shade the region described by the inequalities $y > \frac{1}{2}x$, $3x + 4y > 12$ and the line $y < 3$:

- draw the three lines $y = \frac{1}{2}x$, $3x + 4y = 12$ and $y = 3$

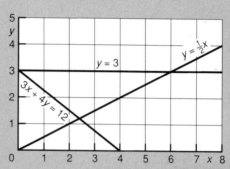

- work out, using a test point, the region where: $y < \frac{1}{2}x$, $3x + 4y > 12$ and $y < 3$
- shade the region common to all three inequalities

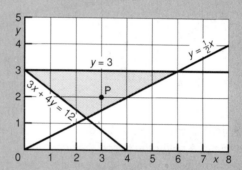

- pick a test point, from within the shaded area and check that it satisfies all three inequalities. For example (3, 2)

$y < \frac{1}{2}x \ldots 2 > \frac{1}{2} \times 3$ (correct)
$y < 3 \ldots 2 < 3$ (correct)
$3x + 4y > 12 \ldots (3 \times 3) + (4 \times 2) > 12$ (correct)

7 (a) Write the equations of the three lines on each of these diagrams.

(b) Describe the shaded regions in terms of three inequalities.

(c) Choose a test point from the shaded region and show that it satisfies your inequalities.

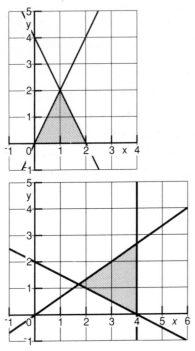

8 For each of these inequalities draw a coordinate diagram and shade the region they describe. Choose, check and show a test point in each case.

(a) $x \geq 0$, $y \geq 1$, $x + y \leq 8$

(b) $x \geq 1$, $y \geq 0$, $2x + 3y < 12$

(c) $y \leq x$, $y \geq \frac{1}{2}x$, $4x + 3y > 12$

(d) $x \geq 0$, $x + 3y \geq 6$, $x + y \leq 6$

(e) $y - x > 0$, $x \geq {}^-2$, $y < {}^-2x$

(f) $x + y < 6$, $3y - 2x > 6$, $y - 6x < 6$

(g) $y - x \leq 3$, $2x + y \leq 4$, $y \geq {}^-2$

(h) $3x + 5y < 15$, $y - x \geq 2$, $y < 2$, $x > {}^-3$

9 (a) Draw a diagram to show the region described by these inequalities:

$x > 6$, $y > 6$, $x + y > 13$, $x + y < 18$

(b) Write all the integer coordinates included within the region.

10 (a) Draw a graph of $y = x^2 - 1$ for values of x from $^-3$ to 3.

(b) On the same axes draw the line $y = 2x + 3$.

(c) Describe the region bounded by the two lines.

11 Mary has been given £30 to buy prizes for the school raffle. She decides to buy boxes of chocolates and bottles of perfume.

c represents the number of boxes of chocolate and p represents the number of bottles of perfume.

(a) Write the meaning of the inequality

$2c + 5p \leq 30$.

Mary also decides to buy at least 3 bottles of perfume. This can be represented by the inequality $p \geq 3$.

(b) Draw both inequalities on a graph, shading the region required.

(c) Write all the different combinations of prizes Mary can now buy.

(d) What is the largest number of prizes she can buy?

(e) What is the maximum amount of money Mary can spend?

12 Florence makes two types of designer lamp shades. She makes a wire frame over which she puts the shade. A standard shade requires 2 metres of wire and takes 1 hour to make. The de-luxe shade requires 2·5 metres of wire and takes 2 hours to make. Florence has 20 metres of metal in stock and works for a maximum of 8 hours.

Let s represent the standard shade and let d represent the de-luxe shade.

(a) Explain the meaning of these two inequalities:

$2s + 2 \cdot 5d \leq 20$ and $s + 2d \leq 8$

(b) On squared paper draw these two inequalities, shading out the region **not** required.

(c) If a standard shade sells for £12 and a de-luxe shade for £18, how much money is represented by the point (3, 4)?

(d) What combination of standard and de-luxe shades is best for Florence to make the most money?

The diagram shows two planes cutting 3D space.

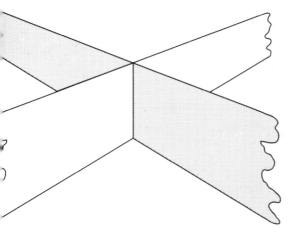

If these planes were extended infinitely in each direction they would divide 3D space into four distinct regions.

Into how many distinct regions do 5 planes divide 3D space?

Investigate the relationship between the number of planes and the number of regions into which they divide 3D space.

You are advised to:
● **record your observations and comments**
● **record your strategies**
● **make and test any conjectures**
● **form any generalisations, with appropriate explanations, justifications or proofs.**

Consecutive powers

It is well-known that:

Result A

$3^2 + 4^2 = 5^2$ The sum of these two squares equals a third square.

It is less well-known that:

Result B

$10^2 + 11^2 + 12^2 = 13^2 + 14^2$ The sum of these three squares equals the sum of the next two squares.

It is not so well-known that:

Result C

$3^3 + 4^3 + 5^3 = 6^3$

Investigate whether Results A, B and C are isolated flukes or particular cases of general results.

You are advised to:
● **record your observations and comments**
● **make and test any conjectures**
● **form any generalisations, with appropriate explanations, justifications or proofs.**

Trigonometry 4

The cuboid ABCDEFGH has volume 240 cm^3.

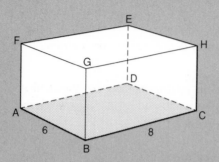

The base ABCD is a rectangle measuring 6 cm by 8 cm.
To calculate:

- **the height of the cuboid**

  Volume = area of base × height (h)

  $240 = 6 \times 8 \times h$

  $240 = 48 \times h$

  $h = 240 \div 48 = 5$ cm

- **the length of AC**

  Looking at the base

By Pythagoras

$AC^2 = 6^2 + 8^2$

$= 36 + 64$

$= 100$

AC = 10 cm

- **the angle AĈB**

  Looking at the base again

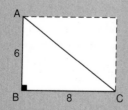

Tan ACB $= \dfrac{\text{opp}}{\text{adj}} = \dfrac{6}{8} = 0.75$

AĈB = 36·87°

- **The length of AH**

  Looking at triangle ACH

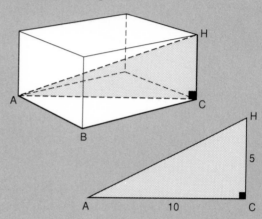

AĈH = 90°

By Pythagoras

$AH^2 = AC^2 + CH^2$

$AH^2 = 10^2 + 5^2$

$= 100 + 25$

$= 125$

AH = 11·18 correct to 2 decimal places (dp)

- **The angle EB̂D**

  Looking at the triangle EDB

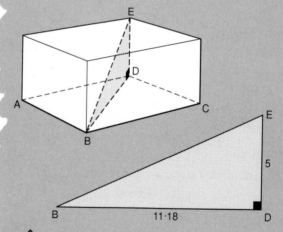

ED̂B is 90°

length ED = height = 5 cm

length DB = length AC = 10 cm

Tan EBD $= \dfrac{\text{opp}}{\text{adj}} = \dfrac{ED}{DB} = \dfrac{5}{10} = 0.5$

Tan EBD $= 0.5$

EB̂D = 26·57° correct to 2dp

1 PQRSTUVW is a cuboid.
QP = 8 cm, QR = 12 cm and QV = 5 cm

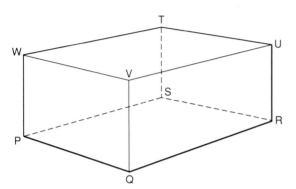

Calculate:

(a) the volume of the cuboid
(b) the length of PV, QU, QS
(c) the angle UŜR
(d) the length of QT
(e) the angle TQ̂S

2 ABCD is a flat rectangular roof. A vertical television aerial VA stands in the corner A. The aerial is held in place by three tight guide ropes VB, VC and VD.

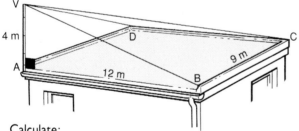

Calculate:

(a) the distance from A to C
(b) the lengths of the guide ropes VB, VC, VD
(c) the angles VBC, VCA, DVA

3 A cuboid has dimensions x, y and z units.

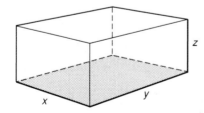

Find an expression in terms of x, y and z for the lengths of each of the diagonals of the cuboid.

4 ABCDEF is a wedge. ABC and DEF are right-angled triangles. The other three faces of the wedge are all rectangles, all lengths are in cm.

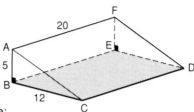

Calculate:

(a) the angle AĈB
(b) the length of FD
(c) the distance AC
(d) the angle FĈE
(e) the volume of the wedge.

5 VABC is a tetrahedron. The base ABC is a horizontal triangle which is right-angled at A. The vertex, V, is vertically above A.

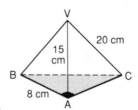

Calculate:

(a) the length of VB
(b) the length of AC
(c) the length of BC
(d) the angle AV̂B
(e) the angle AĈV

6 VABCD is a square based pyramid. The square base ABCD is horizontal and the vertex, V, is vertically above M, the centre of the base. N is the mid point of AD.

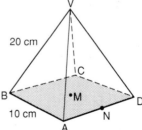

Calculate:

(a) the length of BD
(b) the length of VM
(c) the angle BV̂A
(d) the distance VN
(e) the angle VN̂M

● Remember

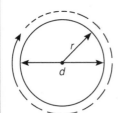

$$\text{Circumference} = 2\pi r$$
$$= \pi d$$

$$\text{Area} = \pi r^2$$
$$= \frac{\pi d^2}{4}$$

Arc length

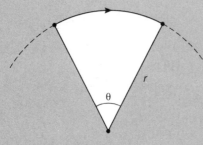

The arc is $\frac{\theta}{360}$ of the distance all round the circle.

$$\text{Arc length} = 2\pi r \times \frac{\theta}{360} \text{ or } \pi d \times \frac{\theta}{360}$$

$$= \frac{\pi r \theta}{180} \quad \text{or} \quad \frac{\pi d \theta}{360}$$

To calculate the length of the arc of this circle

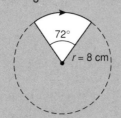

$$\text{Arc length} = \frac{\pi r \theta}{180}$$
$$= \frac{3 \cdot 14 \times 8 \times 72}{180}$$
$$= \textbf{10} \cdot \textbf{048 cm}$$

The area of a sector

The sector is $\frac{\theta}{360}$ of the whole circle.

The area of a sector must be $\frac{\theta}{360}$ of the area of the whole circle.

$$\text{Area of sector} = \pi r^2 \times \frac{\theta}{360} \text{ or } \frac{\pi d^2}{4} \times \frac{\theta}{360}$$

$$= \frac{\pi r^2 \theta}{360} \quad \text{or} \quad \frac{\pi d^2 \theta}{1440}$$

To calculate the area of this sector

$$\text{Area} = \frac{\pi r^2 \theta}{360} \text{ with } r = 8, \text{ so } r^2 = 64 \text{ and } \theta = 72$$

$$= \frac{3 \cdot 14 \times 64 \times 72}{360} = \textbf{40} \cdot \textbf{192 cm}^2$$

The area of a segment

The area of a segment =
area of sector – area of triangle

$$\text{Area of triangle} = \tfrac{1}{2} r^2 \sin \theta \ (\tfrac{1}{2} ab \sin C)$$

$$\text{Area of segment} = \frac{\pi r^2 \theta}{360} - \tfrac{1}{2} r^2 \sin \theta$$

To calculate the area of this segment

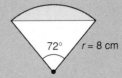

The area of the sector above was $40 \cdot 192$.

$$\text{The area of the triangle} = \tfrac{1}{2} \times 8^2 \times \sin 72$$

$$= \tfrac{1}{2} \times 64 \times \sin 72$$

$$= 30 \cdot 434 \text{ cm}^2$$

$$\text{Area of segment} = 40 \cdot 192 - 30 \cdot 434$$
$$= \textbf{9} \cdot \textbf{758 cm}^2$$

1

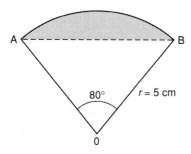

For this sector of a circle, calculate:
(a) the length of the arc AB
(b) the area of the sector OAB
(c) the area of the segment AB.

2

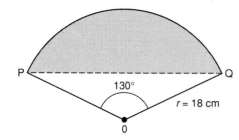

For this sector of a circle, calculate:
(a) the length of the arc PQ
(b) the area of the sector OPQ
(c) the area of the segment PQ.

3

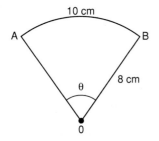

For this sector of a circle, calculate:
(a) the angle θ
(b) the area of the sector.

4

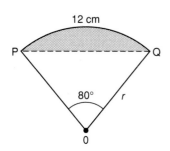

For this sector of a circle, calculate:
(a) the radius of the circle
(b) the area of the sector OPQ
(c) the area of the segment PQ.

5

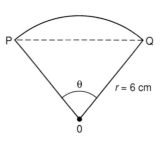

The area of the sector is 20 cm^2. Calculate:
(a) the angle θ at the centre of the circle
(b) the length of the arc PQ
(c) the area of the segment PQ.

6 Prove that when the length of a chord of a circle is equal to the radius of the circle the angle at the centre of the circle must be 60° (A chord is a line like PQ in question 5.)

7 Janine is having the glass in a window replaced.

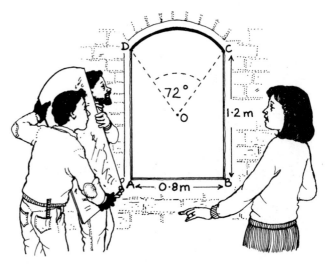

The window is in the shape of a rectangle ABCD with a segment of a circle. O is the rectangle's centre.

Calculate:
(a) the perimeter of the window
(b) the area of the window
(c) how much Janine will pay for the replacement glass at a cost of £26·45 per square metre.

Trigonometry 5

For an angle x, Sine, Cosine and Tangent are defined in terms of a unit circle by the distances shown.

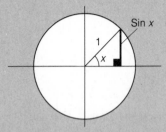 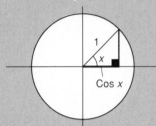 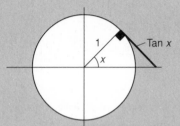

The first quadrant: 0° to 90°

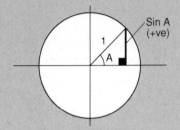 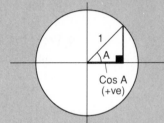 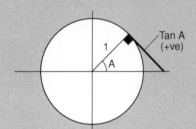

The second quadrant: 90° to 180°

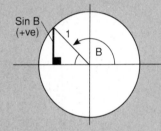 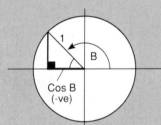 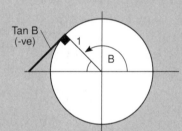

The third quadrant: 180° to 270°

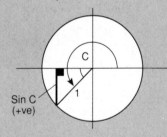 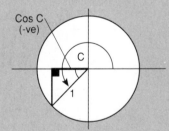 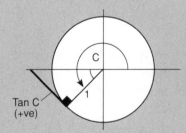

The fourth quadrant: 270° to 360°

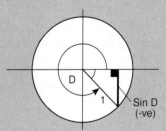 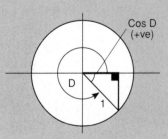 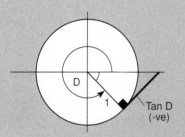

The graphs of Sine, Cosine and Tangent for angles from 0° to 360°

Sine *x*

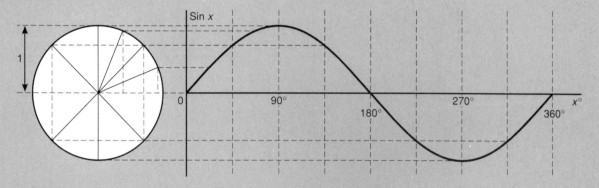

Cosine *x*

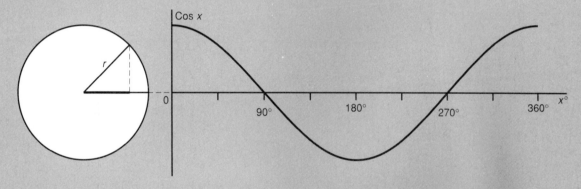

Tangent *x*

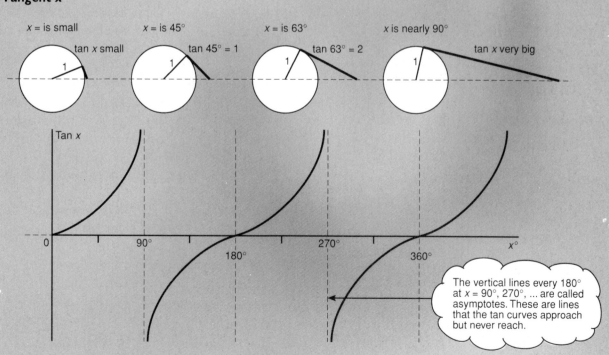

> The vertical lines every 180° at *x* = 90°, 270°, ... are called asymptotes. These are lines that the tan curves approach but never reach.

The graph of Sine 2x

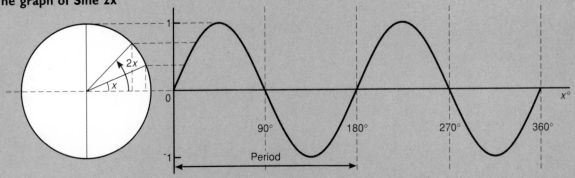

This graph can be constructed accurately using a calculator or computer.

x	2x	Sine 2x
0	0	0
15	30	0·5
20	40	0·64
30	60	0·87
45	90	1

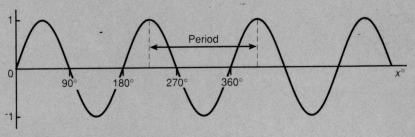

One full cycle of the curve is called its **period**. The period of Sine 2x is half the period of Sine x.

You need graph paper, and a calculator or computer.

1 **(a)** Sketch the graphs of:
Sine 6x, Sine 10x, Sine $\frac{1}{2}$x
(b) Comment on the periods of these three graphs in relation to the period of Sine x.

2 **(a)** Use a calculator to complete the table.

x	2x	Cos 2x
0	0	1
10	20	
20	40	
30	60	
.		
.		
.		
360		

(b) Draw the graph of Cos 2x for values of x from 0° to 360°
(c) Comment on the period of this graph.

3 **(a)** For the range 0° to 360° draw the graph of Tan 2x.
(b) Show that the graph has an asymptote at x = 45°
(c) State the positions of the other asymptotes for this graph.

4 Sketch the graphs of each of the following:
(a) Sin 2x **(b)** Cos 2x **(c)** Tan 3x
(d) Cos 4x **(e)** Cos $\frac{1}{2}$x **(f)** Tan 5x
(g) Tan $\frac{1}{2}$x **(h)** Sin 4x

5 With the aid of a calculator or computer, draw the graphs of:
(a) Sin (x + 30) **(b)** Cos (x − 30)
for values of x from 0° to 360°

6 Sketch the graphs of each of the following:
(a) Sin (x − 60) **(b)** Cos (x + 30)

The Cosine Rule is an extension of Pythagoras' theorem when the angle is not 90°

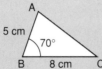

To work out the length of AC in the triangle ABC

- Draw AD, the perpendicular from A to BC. The unknown height is h.

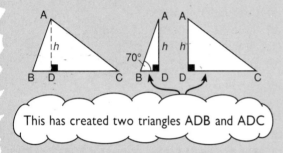

This has created two triangles ADB and ADC

- Find h by Pythagoras $AC^2 = AD^2 + DC^2$. (in triangle ADC)

But $\dfrac{AD}{AB} = Sin\ 70$ or $AD = AB \times Sin\ 70$
(in triangle ADB)

$AD = 5 \times Sin\ 70 = 5 \times 0.9397$
$= 4.6985 = h$

- Find DC
$DC = BC - BD$

and $\dfrac{BD}{AB} = Cos\ 70$ or $BD = AB \times Cos\ 70$

$BD = 5 \times 0.3420 = 1.7101$
$DC = BC - BD = 8 - 1.7101$
$= 6.2899$

- For the triangle ADC

Using Pythagoras again

$AC^2 = AD^2 + DC^2$

$AC^2 = 4.6985^2 + 6.2899^2$
$= 22.0759 + 39.5628$
$= 61.6387$

AC = 7.85 correct to 2 decimal places.

1 Calculate the length of the side marked x for each of these triangles.

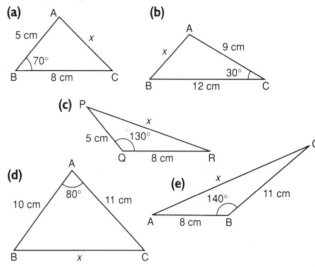

(a)

(b)

(c)

(d)

(e)

2 *The Maid of Skye* sets sail from a harbour, H, and travels 30 km due South to an island, I. At I it turns on a bearing of 060° and travels for a further 20 km to reach a lighthouse, L.

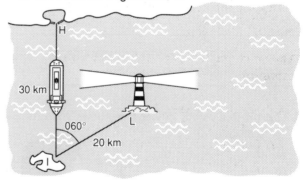

Calculate the distance from H to L.

3 Jenny runs 8 km due north and then turns on a bearing of 140°. She then runs for a further 10 km before stopping.

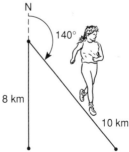

Calculate the straight line distance from her starting point to her finishing point.

Maybe, maybe not

A **combined event** in probability is when an event is repeated. When a coin is tossed three times, the outcome can be tabulated to help find the probability:

TTH   THT   HTT   TTT
HHT   HTH   THH   HHH

The probability of throwing two heads and a tail is

H   H   T

$\frac{1}{2} \times \frac{1}{2} \times \frac{1}{2} = \frac{1}{8}$

But there are three ways of getting two heads and a tail

$P(\text{two heads}) = \frac{1}{8} + \frac{1}{8} + \frac{1}{8} = \frac{3}{8}$

the probability of throwing **at least** two heads is

$P(\text{two heads}) \qquad + P(\text{three heads})$

$= 3 \times (\frac{1}{2} \times \frac{1}{2} \times \frac{1}{2}) + (\frac{1}{2} \times \frac{1}{2} \times \frac{1}{2})$

$= \qquad \frac{3}{8} + \frac{1}{8} = \frac{1}{2}$

Calculate the probabilities in each question, by tabulating all the possible outcomes.

---

1 Charmaine spins this spinner three times. What is the probability of spinning:

(a) three different letters
(b) three As
(c) at least two Bs
(d) at least two Cs?

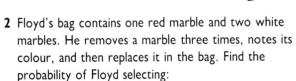

2 Floyd's bag contains one red marble and two white marbles. He removes a marble three times, notes its colour, and then replaces it in the bag. Find the probability of Floyd selecting:

(a) three red marbles (b) three white marbles
(c) two red marbles   (d) at least two red marbles.

3 In a bag Tom has three tins of peas, two tins of carrots, and one tin of potatoes. He selects a tin, notes its contents and replaces it in the bag. Tom does this three times altogether. Find the probability that Tom will pick:

(a) both tins of carrots (b) at least one tin of peas.

4 Janet makes three figure numbers using the digits 5, 2 and 7 (none are repeated). What is the probability of her selecting one of these numbers at random and getting:

(a) a number greater than 500
(b) a number less than 500
(c) an even number
(d) a multiple of 5?

5 Thomas spins this spinner three times. What is the probability of spinning:

(a) three different letters
(b) three Xs
(c) three Ys
(d) at least two Ys
(e) at least two Xs

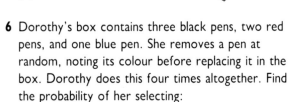

6 Dorothy's box contains three black pens, two red pens, and one blue pen. She removes a pen at random, noting its colour before replacing it in the box. Dorothy does this four times altogether. Find the probability of her selecting:

(a) four black pens
(b) four blue pens
(c) two black and two red pens
(d) at least three red pens.

7 Mumtaz places the four letters P, L, A, E in different arrangements, repeating none of them. If he picks one of these arrangements at random, what is the probability that:

(a) it is a real word
(b) it is in alphabetical order
(c) it does not begin with the letter P
(d) the letters A and E are adjacent?

8 Alison spins a five-sided spinner twice. She adds the scores together to give a final total. What is the probability that the total is:

(a) even
(b) odd
(c) a multiple of 3
(d) more than 6
(e) not 5, 6, or 7.

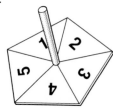

The Box Problem

This square sheet of cardboard has side length 100 cm.

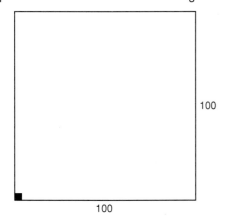

100

100

Squares of side x cm are cut from all four corners. The card is then folded along the dotted lines to make a box in the shape of a cuboid.

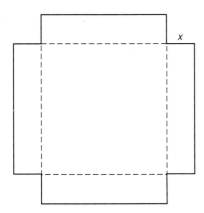

x

(a) Find, and simplify, a symbolic expression in terms of x for the volume of the box.

(b) Find a symbolic expression for the surface area of the box.

(c) Calculate the volume and surface area when $x = 5$ cm.

The Guttering Problem

This rectangular sheet of metal is folded along the centre line to create a guttering.

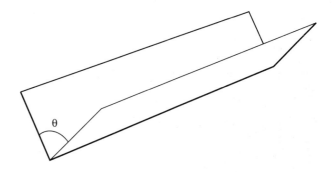

θ

■ Investigation

Investigate the relationship between the angle at the fold, shown as θ, and the volume of water it could hold if closed at each end. Find the angle for which the volume is greatest.

Branching out

An alternative to using tabulation is a tree diagram. These are also more flexible when considering different types of problem.

On average, Brian receives letters 2 days out of 3. Work out the probability of him receiving letters over a three day period.

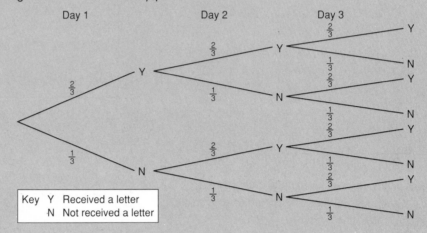

Key Y Received a letter
     N Not received a letter

By following the 'branches' of the tree diagram the probabilities for any of the eight possible events can be calculated:

(a) probability of post on all 3 days is $\frac{2}{3} \times \frac{2}{3} \times \frac{2}{3} = \frac{8}{27}$

(b) probability of post on at least two days is

$Y\,Y\,N = \frac{2}{3} \times \frac{2}{3} \times \frac{1}{3} = \frac{4}{27}$

$Y\,N\,Y = \frac{2}{3} \times \frac{1}{3} \times \frac{2}{3} = \frac{4}{27}$

$N\,Y\,Y = \frac{1}{3} \times \frac{2}{3} = \frac{2}{3} = \frac{4}{27}$

$Y\,Y\,Y = \frac{8}{27}$

Total $= \frac{20}{27}$

1 Gillian plays darts, and can hit the bulls-eye 1 in 5 times. Copy and complete the tree diagram.

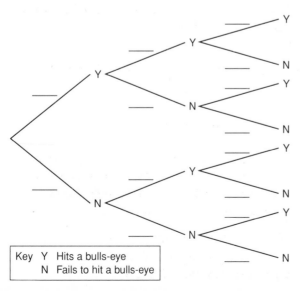

Key Y Hits a bulls-eye
     N Fails to hit a bulls-eye

2 Graham is throwing a dice. The probability of him throwing a 6 is $\frac{1}{6}$.

(a) Copy and complete the tree diagram.

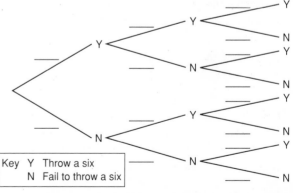

Key Y Throw a six
     N Fail to throw a six

(b) What is the probability of him throwing:

• three 6s

• no 6s

• 6 on one out of the three throws?

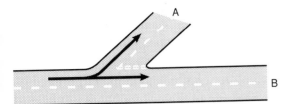

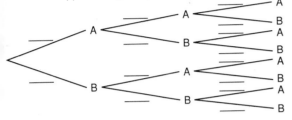

In a survey, Jameda found that that probability of a car turning left at a junction was $\frac{7}{10}$.

(a) Copy and complete her tree diagram for three cars approaching the junction.

(b) What is the probability that:

- the three cars will all turn left
- the three cars will not turn left
- two out of the three cars will turn left?

> Draw tree diagrams for each of the following questions, to help you find the answers to each problem.

4 Robert's box contains 4 red cards and 3 green cards. He chooses a card at random, three times, always replacing it.

Find the probability that:

(a) the three cards are red

(b) there are at least two red cards

(c) there are at least two green cards.

5

There are twelve tubs of yoghurt in Sharon's fridge. Five are strawberry flavoured, three raspberry flavoured, and four peach flavoured. She removes three cartons at random, and replaces them.

Find the probability that:

(a) all three are different flavours

(b) at least two are raspberry

(c) at least two are strawberry

(d) all three are peach.

6 Roger spins his spinner, and keeps a record of whether the score is even or odd. After three throws, find the probability that:

(a) all three scores are odd

(b) there are at least two even scores

(c) there is one odd score.

7 At High Lane School, students choose on average: chips for 7 out of 12 meals; mashed potato 3 times out of 12; and boiled potatoes 2 times out of 12. Three students are selected at random in the dinner queue.

Find the probability that:

(a) all three choose chips

(b) at least one chooses boiled potatoes

(c) two pick mashed potato

(d) no-one has chips.

8 $\frac{2}{3}$ of Easter eggs are milk chocolate. $\frac{1}{6}$ are dark chocolate and $\frac{1}{6}$ are made from white chocolate. Pauline chooses three Easter eggs at random.

What is the probability that:

(a) all three are dark chocolate

(b) at least two are milk chocolate

(c) none are white chocolate?

9 Miriam's box contains 50 cards. x are red and y are blue. She selects three cards at random, then replaces them.

Write an expression for the probability that:

(a) all three cards are red

(b) two cards are blue

(c) at least two cards are red.

10 In a market survey, Gerry found that x people favour Brand A tea, y people favour Brand B, whilst Brand C is favoured by z people. Gerry chose 3 people at random to sample the tea.

What is the probability that:

(a) all three people prefer Brand A

(b) at least two favour Brand B?

Histograms 1

When data is grouped the most suitable diagram is a **histogram**.

A **histogram** is similar to a **bar chart** except that the bars are joined together. The joining parts are the **common class boundaries**.

For frequency distributions that have **equal grouped** classes the height of each bar is equal to the *frequency* of **each class**.

Histogram for grouped frequency distribution based on **discrete data**.

Mark	Frequency
10–15	2
16–20	7
21–25	15
26–30	26
31–35	22
36–40	14
41–45	11
46–50	3

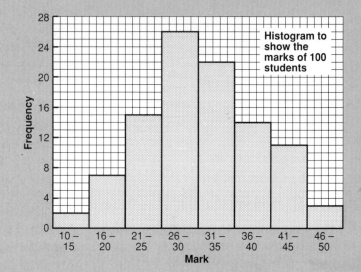

Histogram to show the marks of 100 students

Histogram for grouped frequency distribution based on **continous data**.

Weight	Frequency
10 to 15·9	1
16 to 21·9	6
22 to 27·9	20
28 to 33·9	31
34 to 39·9	13
40 to 45·9	7
46 to 51·9	2

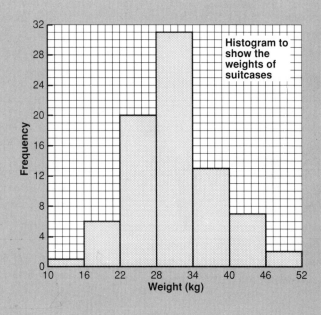

Histogram to show the weights of suitcases

Although this is continuous data, the bars are drawn at 16, 22, etc.

Draw histograms for the following frequency
distributions which have equal class widths.

(a)

Mark	Frequency
31–40	2
41–50	5
51–60	8
61–70	14
71–80	11
81–90	7
91–100	3

(b)

Height (cm)	Frequency
120–129	2
130–139	6
140–149	14
150–159	31
160–169	63
170–179	28
180–189	11
190–199	3

Note the class width is 119·5 to 129·5 = 10

(c)

Wage (£)	Frequency
1–50	1
51–100	6
101–150	55
151–200	29
201–250	7
251–300	2

Note the class width = 0·5 to 50·5 = 50

(d)

Weight (x)	Frequency
8< x <12	7
12< x <16	19
16< x <20	35
20< x <24	24
24< x <28	15

2 Draw a histogram for the following frequency
distribution about the yearly incomes of
450 teenagers.

Yearly income (£)	Frequency
500 up to 1500	80
1500 up to 2500	217
2500 up to 3500	96
3500 up to 4500	37
4500 up to 5500	12
5500 up to 6500	5
6500 up to 7500	3

Estimate the mean yearly income of this collection
of teenagers. Comment on your answer.

3 An enquiry was held into the weights of
160 students at art college. The results of this
enquiry are shown below.

Weight in kg (w)	Frequency
30 ≤ w < 35	3
35 ≤ w < 40	5
40 ≤ w < 45	17
45 ≤ w < 50	28
50 ≤ w < 55	56
55 ≤ w < 60	35
60 ≤ w < 65	9
65 ≤ w < 70	5
70 ≤ w < 75	2

(a) Draw a histogram for this distribution.
(b) Estimate the mean, median and modal group
weight of the students.
(c) Comment on your results.

Histograms may also be used to display grouped frequency distributions which have **unequal class intervals**.

In these histograms the **areas contained by the bars drawn are proportional to the frequencies**.

The height of each bar, called the **frequency density**, is calculated using the rule

$$\text{Frequency density} = \frac{\text{Frequency}}{\text{Width of class}}$$

Class Weight	Frequency	Width of class	Frequency density
0< x <4	12	4	3
4< x <8	16	4	4
8< x <13	34	5	6·8
13< x <18	30	5	6
18< x <28	41	10	4·1
28< x <38	24	10	2·4
38< x <48	8	10	·8
48< x <60	5	12	·42

To illustrate a distribution with a histogram:

- complete the width of class column
- calculate the frequency density
- draw the horizontal axis 0 to 60. Scale 1 cm represents 5
- draw the vertical axis 0 to 7. Scale 2 cm represents 1
- draw the bars
- label the axis and give the histogram a title.

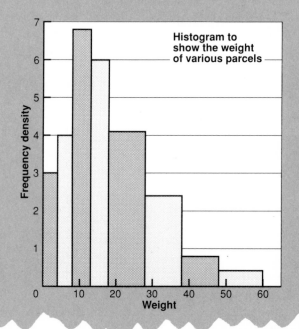

Histogram to show the weight of various parcels

1 Draw histograms for the following frequency distributions which have unequal class widths.

(a)

Height	Frequency
0< x <2	24
2< x <5	33
5< x <10	58
10< x <20	75
20< x <30	64
30< x <50	31
50< x <100	15

(b)

Age	Frequency
0< x <5	10
5< x <15	18
15< x <25	32
25< x <40	42
40< x <55	55
55< x <65	27
65< x <75	8

This graph shows the relationship

$$y = x^2 - 8x + 12$$

for values of x from $^-2$ to 10.

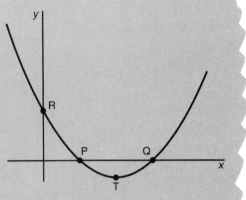

On the graph four points have been marked. These are:

P and Q   where the curve crosses the x-axis
R   where the curve crosses the y-axis
T   the turning point of the curve.

1 Plot each of the following graphs:

   (a) $y = x^2 - 7x + 12$ for values of x from $^-2$ to 10
   (b) $y = x^2 - 10x + 9$ for values of x from $^-1$ to 11
   (c) $y = x^2 + 10x + 7$ for values of x from $^-11$ to 1
   (d) $y = x^2 - 2x - 15$ for values of x from $^-5$ to 7
   (e) $y = 15 + 2x - x^2$ for values of x from $^-6$ to 8

On each graph mark and record the four salient points equivalent to P, Q, R and T shown in the illustration.

Comment on these points.

2 The general equation of a quadratic graph is

$$y = ax^2 + bx + c$$

where a, b and c are constants, called the parameters of the quadratic.

Investigate the general relationship between the parameters a, b and c and the coordinates of the four points where the curve:

   • crosses the x-axis   (two points)

   • crosses the y-axis

   • has a turning point.

You are advised to:

● **record your observations and comments**

● **make and test any conjectures**

● **form any generalisations, with appropriate explanations, justifications or proofs.**

You could use a computer or graphic calculator to explore quadratic equations. If you do, describe your equipment and how you used it.

Sampling 1

The most accurate way of obtaining facts or opinions from a large population of people is to survey them all.

To reduce the cost and effort involved, a **sample** is usually taken. This sample needs to be a **random** sample.

This method can be used to choose a random sample of 10% of a school population of 600 students.

You can use a normal die and 10 playing cards from ace to 10 in a box.

- Obtain a list of all the students and write the numbers 100 to 699 next to their names.
- Roll the normal die to obtain the first digit.
- Shake the box, select one card to give the second digit (10 to be read as 0).
- Put that card back in the box, shake it again and take out a card to give the third digit.
- Doing this 60 times will produce a 10% random sample. You can now contact those 60 and carry out your survey.

To be more accurate, and avoid the chance that opinions or facts may change with age, a 10% sample could be taken in each year group.

1 Describe a method of selecting a random sample of 20% of a population of 400 people. Explain how you would ensure that the sample is random.

Stratified sampling The whole collection being sampled is grouped into strata according to some characteristics such as age or gender. A random sample is taken **within** each strata.

2 You are asked to survey opinions throughout the school about the choice of dishes available at the midday break.

(a) Taking into account that opinions might vary with age and gender, describe how you would select a stratified random sample of the students. Describe clearly how you would overcome the difference in numbers of students in each age group.

(b) Would you include students who do not currently take a midday meal? Give reasons for your decision.

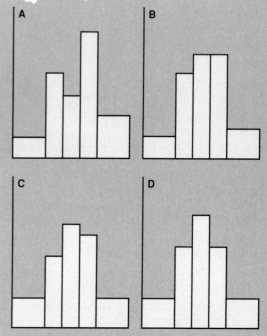

These histograms show how, as the sample increases, the data collected fits a normal distribution more closely.
Shape **A** might be given by a small sample.
Shapes **B** and **C** might be given by a bigger sample.
Shape **D** is the normal distribution.

3 (a) Carry out a survey on a 5% sample of the students in your school. The survey should aim to discover the distribution of the size of hand spans.

(b) Write a report and include in it:

- a description of how you selected your sample and why you did it that way
- a description of how you ensured the measurement from one person was taken in exactly the same way as from another
- a table of results
- a histogram illustrating your findings
- a comment upon the shape of your histogram and, by comparison with a histogram of normal distribution, a comment upon the quality of the distribution from your sample.

Some scientific calculators can generate random numbers, using a $\boxed{\text{RAN}}$ key. Find out how to do this.

To select a random sample of 40 students from a school population of under 1000, say 861 for example:

- press the 'RAN' key
- if the first 3 digits of the decimal are 000 or greater than 861 ignore it
- if the first 3 digits of the decimal are between 001 and 861 inclusive, record them
- if you have written down 40 numbers, stop; otherwise go back to the first step and repeat the process.

The 40 students can then be identified from a school list.

The method above is quite efficient because the population of 861 is close to 999 and you will not have to ignore many numbers. When a population is just over 1000 you would have to consider the first four decimal places and would find that the overwhelming majority of numbers have to be ignored. To overcome this problem:

- multiply each of the random numbers by the size of the population
- round off the answer to the nearest integer and use that as the number for each member of your sample.

For example, when the population is 1137:

Random number is 0·3247891, multiplied by 1137 gives 369·28521 to select member 369.
Random number is 0·9577835, multiplied by 1137 gives 1088·9998 to select member 1089.

1 (a) Use a calculator to generate a random sample of 50 numbers from a population of 1248.
(b) Explain how you will deal with a possible occurrence of 0.
(c) Group your numbers into appropriate intervals and draw a frequency diagram of their distribution.
(d) Comment on the shape of the graph in relation to expected spread.

You need a table of random numbers.
2 (a) Write a detailed report of how to use it to generate 100 random numbers.
(b) Group the numbers into appropriate intervals and draw a frequency diagram of their distribution.
(c) Comment upon the shape of your graph.
(d) How close is it to a rectangular shape?

When market research is carried out, **quota sampling** is used. Before the survey starts, the research company determines how many people in each category (for example, female and 25–34 years old) it needs to interview.

A survey to find the distribution of the size of hand spans of students in your school might show that the bigger the student the larger the hand span. A purely random sample might have too many small people and distort the result. To overcome this problem the sample must be drawn to include a spread of different heights. This might result in three people, short, tall and intermediate, being chosen from each class in order to match the whole population more closely.

3 A survey about the favourite subjects of the students in your school might suggest that opinions would be affected by how good students were at them.
(a) Describe how to select a sample of students to question.
(b) Can you include a quota sampling technique to take account of your suspicions?

4 (a) Carry out a survey of a physical characteristic of the students in your school using a quota sampling process.
(b) Illustrate your data using histograms.
(c) Calculate the mean and standard deviation of the results by year group and for the whole population.
(d) Comment upon trends in your results.

Pythagorean investigations

Pythagoras' theorem is well-known. This activity uses investigations to help you explore the work of Pythagoras in some interesting and unusual ways.

The activity is divided into five parts.

Part 1

These three triangles have squares drawn on each of their sides:

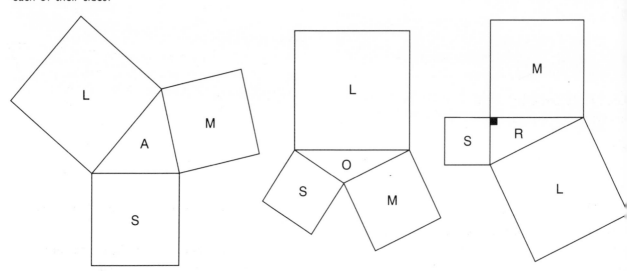

The areas of the squares have been marked as L, M and S, where:

L means the square of largest area
M means the square of middle-sized area
S means the square of smallest area.

The triangle marked A has all three angles acute.
The triangle marked O has an obtuse angle.
The triangle marked R has a right-angle.

You need square dot paper.

On the dotted paper draw at least 4 all-acute-angled triangles, at least 4 obtuse-angled triangles and at least 4 right-angled triangles.

Draw the squares on the sides of each triangle and find the areas of these squares.

Determine the conditions under which:

L < M + S
L > M + S
L = M + S

You are advised to record clearly and justify your results.

Part 2

Pythagoras' theorem states that when we draw squares on the three sides of a right-angled triangle the area of the square on the hypotenuse (the longest side) is equal to the sum of the areas of the other two squares.

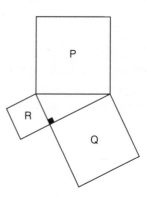

Area P = Area Q + Area R

Investigate whether the squares are essential to this theorem or whether the theorem would work with other shapes drawn on the three sides.

You are advised to justify clearly and attempt to generalise the results of your investigation.

Part 3

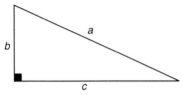

$$(3,4,5) \quad (5,12,13) \quad (7,24,25)$$

These are three of the best-known sets of Pythagorean triples, that is, three numbers satisfying the condition:

$a^2 = b^2 + c^2$

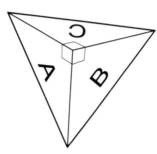

Look at the three well-known triples and comment on anything you notice.

Show that if you make

$a = m^2 + n^2$
$b = m^2 - n^2$
$c = 2mn$

then these will always produce sets of Pythagorean triples.

Obtain the values of m and n that give the three well-known triples.

Choose values of m and n to produce sets of Pythagorean triples.

You could use a computer or programmable calculator.

You are advised to:
- **record your observations and comments**
- **make and test any conjectures**
- **form any generalisations, with appropriate explanations, justifications or proofs.**

Part 4

Here is an obtuse-angled triangle with squares on each side.

The obtuse angle is 120°.

Extend Pythagoras' theorem beyond the right-angled case to cover the result when one of the angles is always 120°.

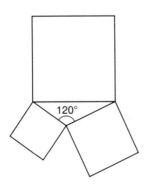

Part 5

Here is a cube with one of the corners sliced off.

The piece that has been sliced off is a tetrahedron.

The four faces of the tetrahedron have been labelled A, B, C and D.

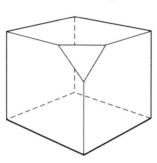

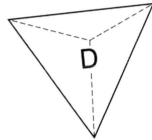

The three angles at the top of the tetrahedron are each 90°.

You need a collection of tetrahedra formed by slicing corners from a cube or cuboid.

Try to find the relationship which connects the four areas, A, B, C and D.

You are advised to explain, justify or prove the relationship in some way.

This is a Tringle Card.

Tringle cards can be used to record changes. For example, if you put the three letters A, B and C on the left and right of the card, this Tringle card means:

A changes with B
B changes with A
C remains unchanged

1 There is a maximum of 6 Tringle cards for the three letters A, B and C. These are three of them:

Find the remaining three.

T_1 T_2 T_3

2 What is the maximum number of Tringle cards for:

(a) 4 letters   (b) 5 letters   (c) n letters?

Explain, justify or prove your results.

The Tringle cards, T_1, T_2 and T_3 shown above are related.

You can see this by placing T_1 and T_2 together like this:

We write this as $T_1 * T_2$

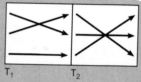

T_1 T_2

Following the arrows you will find:

A changes with B
B changes with C
C changes with A

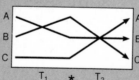

T_1 * T_2

This is equivalent to one Tringle card like this, called T_3:

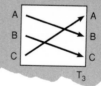

T_3

So $T_1 * T_2 = T_3$

3 Does $T_2 * T_1 = T_3$?

4 Investigate the geometry and algebra of the 6 Tringle cards for 3 letters.

You advised to look in particular for:

● **any relationships which are always true**
● **any relationships which are partly true or may be true for a limited selection of the cards**
● **how to solve equations such as $T_n * X = T_m$ where X is an unknown Tringle card**
● **how to work out T_n for any values of n and X.**

Carry your investigation beyond the 6 cards for 3 letters case.

This is the graph of

$y = x^2$

for values of x from 0 to 5.

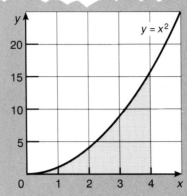

The area under the graph for $x = 0$ to $x = 4$ is shaded.

1 Show, in any way you can, that when $x = 4$ the area under the graph is greater than 20 square units and less than 25 square units.

This is a general graph of

$y = x^n$

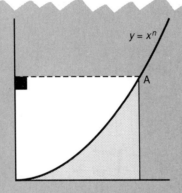

for positive values of x. Horizontal and vertical lines from point **A** make a rectangle with the two axes.

The area under the graph and **inside** the rectangle is shaded.

2 Investigate the relationship between the area under the graph and the area of the rectangle.

You are advised to:
● **vary the value of n**
● **vary the points on the graph**
● **make conjectures and ways of testing or justifying them**
● **make generalisations and try to justify them**
● **find any counter examples**
● **give any explanations or proofs.**

3 Investigate the relationship between the area under the graph and the area of the rectangle for:
   (a) $y = ax^n + bx^m$ where a and b are constants
   (b) any functions of your own choosing.

Straight line graphs obey the law $y = mx + c$ where m is the gradient and c is the amount of translation from $(0, 0)$ also known as the 'y intercept'.

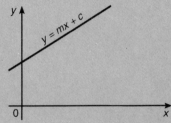

This law can be used to help draw and recognise straight line graphs.

If we sketch the graph of $y = \dfrac{3x}{5} + 2 \cdot 5$

the gradient is $\dfrac{3}{5}$

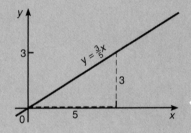

and the translation from $(0, 0)$ is $2 \cdot 5$

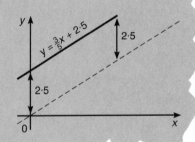

1 Use this method to sketch the graph of:

(a) $y = \dfrac{5x}{3} + 1$

(b) $y = \dfrac{4x}{7} - 2$

(c) $y = \dfrac{3x}{8} + 1 \cdot 5$

(d) $y = \dfrac{5x}{7} - 2 \cdot 5$

(e) $y = 3x + 2$

(f) $y = 2x - 1$

(g) $y = \dfrac{^{-}2x}{3} + 1$

(h) $y = \dfrac{4x}{^{-}3} - 1 \cdot 5$

2 Copy these diagrams and write the equations of the lines.

(a)

(b)

(c)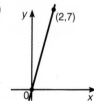

(d)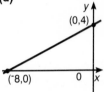

(e)

(f)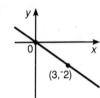

(g)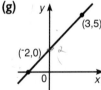

(h)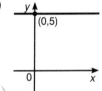

3 Write the equations of these lines.

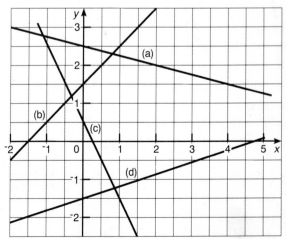

(a) Copy and complete this table for the equation $y = x^2$

x	$^-4$	$^-3$	$^-2$	$^-1$	0	1	2	3	4
y	16			1			4		

(b) On graph paper draw the line $y = x^2$

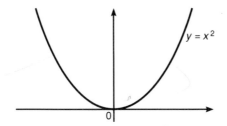

$y = x^2$

All quadratic graphs can be sketched by starting with $y = x^2$ and applying graphical transformations.

To sketch the graph $y = x^2 - 4$

The graph of $y = x^2 - 4$
is the graph of $y = x^2$
translated down 4 units or
$y = x^2$ moved down 4.

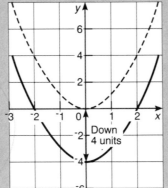

Down 4 units

2 Starting with $y = x^2$, sketch the following:

(a) $y = x^2 + 1$ **(b)** $y = x^2 - 2$
(c) $y = x^2 - 5$ **(d)** $y = x^2 + 10$

The graph of the equation $y = (x + 2)^2 - 3$ can be sketched using 2 transformations.

Start with $y = x^2$ | Translate 2 units left | Translate 3 units down

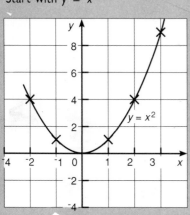

$y = x^2$

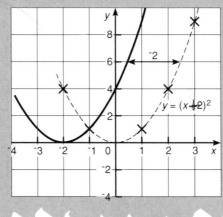

$y = (x+2)^2$

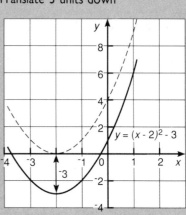

$y = (x - 2)^2 - 3$

Sketching graphs 2

3 Starting with $y = x^2$ sketch the graphs of:

(a) $y = (x + 2)^2$

(b) $y = (x - 3)^2$

(c) $y = (x + 4)^2$

(d) $y = (x + 4)^2 + 1$

(e) $y = (x - 2)^2 + 4$

(f) $y = (x + 5)^2 - 2$

(g) $y = (x - 5)^2 - 6$

(h) $y = (x + 6)^2 + 9$

Notice how the shape of the graph changes as the equation changes.

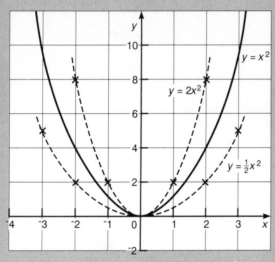
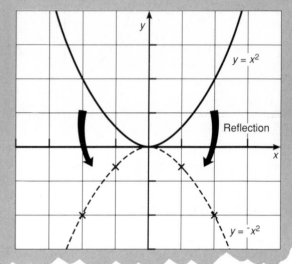

4 Starting with $y = x^2$ sketch the graphs of:

(a) $y = 3x^2$

(b) $y = {}^-2x^2$

(c) $y = 8x^2$

(d) $y = {}^-(x + 2)^2$

(e) $y = \frac{1}{2}x^2 + 2$

(f) $y = {}^-2x^2 + 1$

(g) $y = 2(x - 2)^2$

(h) $y = 2(x - 2)^2 - 4$

(i) $y = {}^-(x + 5)^2 - 2$

(j) $y = {}^-(x + 4)^2 + 5$

(k) $y = {}^-\frac{1}{2}(x - 4)^2 - 3$

(l) $y = 4(x - 2)^2 - 6$

This diagram shows the graphs of $y = \dfrac{1}{x}$

As x increases, the graphs get closer and closer to the x axis **but never touch it**.

As x decreases, the graphs get closer and closer to the y axis **but never touch it**.

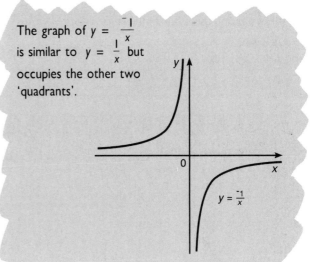

Note these types of graphs are in two parts and must **not** be joined together.

1 (a) Copy and complete this table for $y = \dfrac{6}{x}$

x	$^-6$	$^-4$	$^-3$	$^-2$	$^-1$	1	2	3	4	6
y	$^-1$		$^-2$						1·5	

(b) Draw the graph taking values of x from $^-12$ to 12.

The graph of $\dfrac{1}{x - 2}$ is the line $\dfrac{1}{x}$ translated two units to the right.

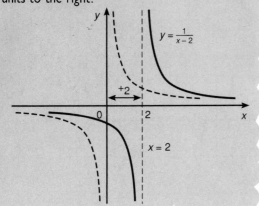

2 Sketch graphs of:

(a) $\dfrac{1}{x + 2}$ **(b)** $\dfrac{1}{x - 3}$

(c) $\dfrac{1}{x + 5}$ **(d)** $2\left(\dfrac{1}{x}\right)$

The graph of $y = \dfrac{^-1}{x}$ is similar to $y = \dfrac{1}{x}$ but occupies the other two 'quadrants'.

3 Sketch graphs of:

(a) $\dfrac{^-1}{x + 2}$ **(b)** $\dfrac{^-1}{x - 4}$

(c) $\dfrac{^-2}{x - 6}$ **(d)** $\dfrac{^-2}{x + 5}$

(e) $\dfrac{^-1}{(x + 3)}$ **(f)** $\dfrac{1}{3 - x}$

The graph of $\dfrac{1}{x} + 3$ is the line $\dfrac{1}{x}$ moved up 3 units.

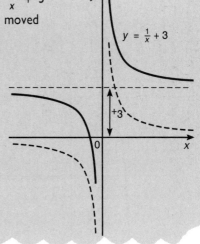

4 Sketch graphs of:

(a) $y = \dfrac{1}{x} - 2$ **(b)** $y = \dfrac{1}{x} + 4$

(c) $y = \dfrac{1}{x + 2} + 3$ **(d)** $y = \dfrac{1}{x - 2} - 5$

(e) $y = \dfrac{^-1}{x + 5} - 2$ **(f)** $y = \dfrac{^-1}{x - 3} + 4$

I (a) Copy and complete this table for values of $y = x^3$

x	-3	-2.5	-2	-1.5	-1	0	1	1.5	2	2.5	3
y	-27				-1				8		

(b) Using appropriate scales, draw the graph of $y = x^3$

2 Sketch the general shape of:

(a) $y = x^3 + 3$ **(b)** $y = x^3 - 3$

(c) $y = -x^3$

3 Write the equations of these lines.

(a)

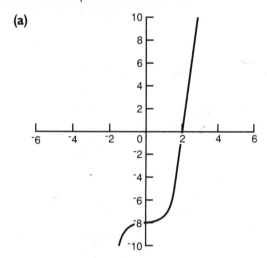

(b)

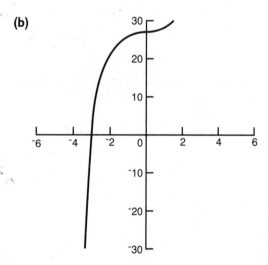

4 (a) On the same axes sketch graphs of $y = x^2$ and $y = x^3$

(b) Describe the differences between the general shapes of the two lines you have sketched. Try to give an explanation for any differences that you notice.

5 Without any calculations, sketch the general shape of the curves:

(a) $y = x^4$ **(b)** $y = x^5$ **(c)** $y = x^6$ **(d)** $y = x^7$

In parts (e) and (f) n is a positive integer:

(e) $y = x^{2n}$ **(f)** $y = x^{2n-1}$

6 The diagrams below are sketches of:

(a) $y = \dfrac{3x}{4} + 3$ **(b)** $y = \dfrac{-4x}{3} + 4$

(c) $y = \dfrac{3x}{4} - 3$ **(d)** $y = \dfrac{x^2}{2} - 2$

(e) $y = 2x^2$ **(f)** $y = x^2 + 1$

(g) $y = -x^2 + 2$ **(h)** $y = -(x^2 - 2)$

(i) $y = \dfrac{2}{x}$ **(j)** $y = \dfrac{-2}{x}$

(k) $y = \dfrac{-3x}{4} + 3$ **(l)** $y = -x^3 - 1$

Match the correct equation to each sketch.

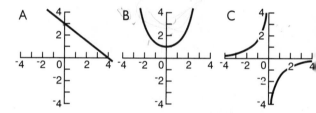

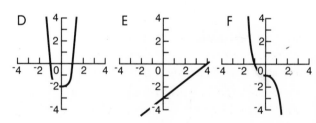

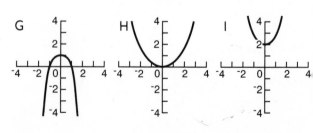

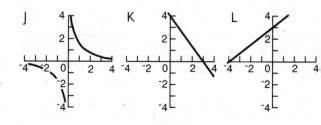

A car starts and reaches a velocity of 40 m/s after 5 seconds. It maintains this speed for 15 secs. The car then slows down, coming to a stop after a further 10 seconds.

The information is shown on this velocity-time graph.

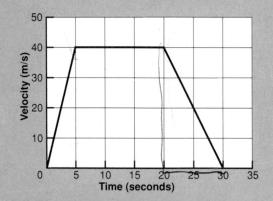

The gradient of the line = $\dfrac{\text{velocity}}{\text{time}}$ = acceleration

The acceleration of the car = $\dfrac{40}{5}$ = 8 m/s^2 during the speed-up stage.

1 What was the deceleration of the car during the slow-down stage?

2 A bus starting with zero velocity reaches a speed of 20 m/s after 10 seconds. It maintains this speed for 12 seconds before slowing down and coming to a rest after a further 8 seconds.

(a) Show this information on a velocity-time graph.
(b) What was the acceleration up to 10 seconds?
(c) What was the deceleration of the bus?

A cyclist, Peggy, starts at zero and reaches a speed of 6 m/s after 5 seconds.

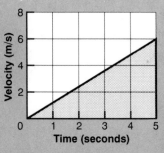

The area under the graph gives the distance she travels.

Area under the graph = $\dfrac{5 \times 6}{2}$ = 15

The distance Peggy travels is 15 metres.

3 For each of these velocity-time graphs calculate the distanced travelled.

(a)
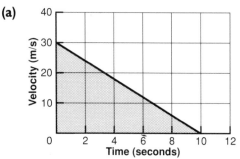

(b)
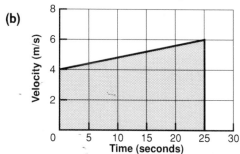

(c)
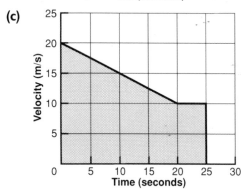

4 This diagram shows the velocity-time graph of a car with an initial velocity of 5 m/s.

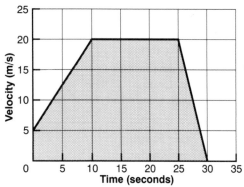

Find:

(a) the acceleration over the first 10 seconds
(b) the deceleration over the last 5 seconds
(c) the maximum speed reached
(d) the total distance travelled.

Work it out

1 This is a distance-time graph. Which of these descriptions best fits the graph:

(a) Mary walks to Jan's house, stays a while and then returns home

or

(b) Mary walks up a hill, along a flat path and then walks down a second hill?

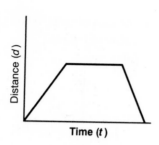

2 Match each explanation to the correct graph.

(a) Paul goes for a walk to the post-box, posts his letter and returns home. He walks at a constant speed in both directions.

(b) Ranjit runs to the post box, posts his letter and walks home. Halfway home he stops for a short rest.

(c) Mary walks half the way to the shop and runs the rest of the way. She completes her shopping and runs all the way back home.

(d) David walks to the shop and does some shopping. On the way home, being tired, David stops for a rest. He then walks very slowly the rest of the way home.

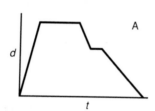

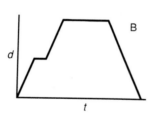

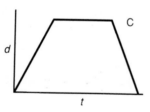

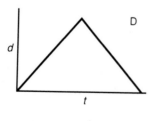

(e) Tony was going to have his lunch at a café. On the way he called for Oliver who went with him. After lunch Tony walked back home.

(f) Jean walked to Hayley's house and stayed for tea. After tea Hayley gave her a lift home in her car.

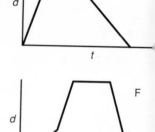

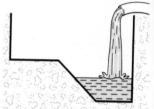

3 This fish pond is being filled from a hose pipe at a constant rate.

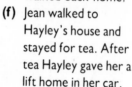

Copy and complete the graph.

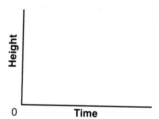

4 Water is leaking from this tank at a constant rate.

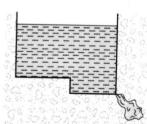

Copy and complete the graph.

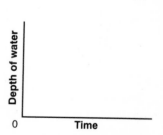

5 A train leaves St John's station and accelerates to a constant speed. It then slows down before coming to a stop at the next station. Draw a velocity-time graph to show this information.

6 Eliot, in a 100-metre race, accelerates all the way to the tape. He then slows down before coming to a stop. Draw a velocity-time graph to show this information.

7 This is a plan of a racing circuit. Eamonn Hill drives his racing car once round the track. Draw a velocity-time graph to show his possible progress.

8 This graph shows the progress of three atheletes, Angie, Bea and Clare, running a 400 m race.

(a) Describe separately the progress of each of the three athletes.

(b) Describe the race.

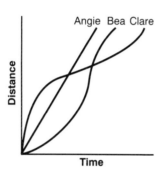

Angie Bea Clare

9 Suggest a possible sport which could produce graphs like these.

(a)

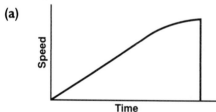

(b)

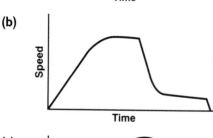

(c)

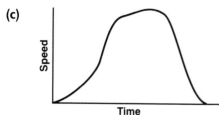

10 This graph shows the progress of the Barton family out for a picnic.

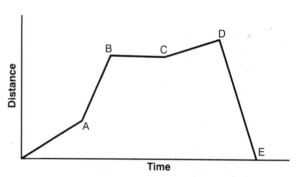

Which sections of the graph represent:

(a) the fastest part of their journey

(b) their picnic stop

(c) being slowed due to road repairs?

11 Jamie drives to his village post office and back.

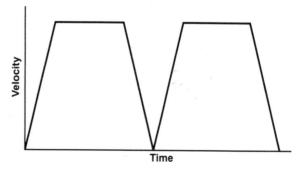

Draw a distance-time graph to match the velocity-time graph.

All straight line graphs obey the law $y = mx + c$ where m is the gradient and c is the amount of translation, the distance moved from $(0, 0)$.

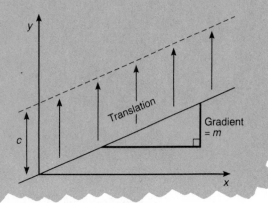

Carol was carrying out an experiment to find a relationship between the effort E and the load L lifted by a machine. She conducted an experiment and obtained these results:

L (kg)	2·0	5·0	6·0	8·0	11·0
E (kg)	2·8	3·4	3·6	4·0	4·6

Carol drew this graph.

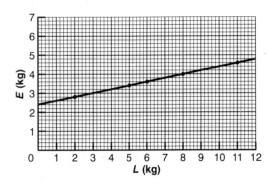

I **(a)** By choosing two suitable points on the line, work out its gradient.
(b) What is the amount of translation of the line from $(0, 0)$?
(c) Write the relationship in the form
$E = mL + c$
(d) Calculate the value of E when $L = 7·4$ kg

2 Tony is taking down a load-bearing wall in his house. He uses this table to help him decide the size of beam he needs to fit.

Thickness (t) of beam (cm)	10	30	70	100
Maximum load (L) in tonnes	120	270	570	795

(a) Make a copy of the following axes.

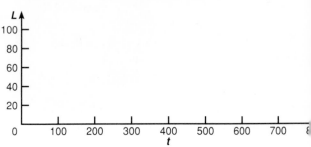

(b) Plot the points and join them together with a straight line.
(c) Find the gradient, showing the points you use on your graph.
(d) Find the translation of the line from $(0, 0)$.
(e) Write the equation of the line.

In practice, when you obtain information experimentally the points will not all fit exactly on a straight line. In these cases you draw the 'line of best fit'.

3 **(a)** Make a copy of this diagram and draw the line of best fit.

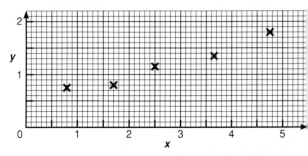

(b) What is the equation of your line?

4 The speedometer on Selina's car developed a fault. She took it to the garage to be checked. The mechanic took the car for a test drive and found these results.

Speedo reading (S mph)	10	20	25	45	60
True reading (T mph)	12	20	23	42	56

(a) Draw axes with S horizontal from 0 to 60 and T vertical from 0 to 60.

(b) Plot the points and draw the line of best fit.

(c) Find the equation of the line.

(d) When Selina's speedometer indicates 30 mph, what is her true speed?

(e) The legal maximum speed in the UK is 70 mph. What is the reading on the speedometer when the true speed is 70 mph?

5 An electrical test on Roger's television set gave these results.

Voltage (V volts)	65	72	90	100	115
Resistance (R ohms)	98	120	140	148	170

The engineer suspected that the relationship between the voltage and the resistance was of the form $R = mV + c$.

(a) Plot the points on graph paper and test the engineer's theory. Comment on your findings.

(b) By drawing the line of best fit, find the equation of the line.

(c) If a resistance reading of 85 ohms was indicated, what would the voltmeter be reading?

6 Peter decides to go on a diet to lose weight. However, his bathroom scales are not very accurate and he takes them to his local hardware shop to be tested. The shop finds these results:

Indicated weight (I kg)	5	15	30	45	55
True weight (T kg)	3	15	32	49	63

(a) Plot these values on graph paper.

(b) Find the equation of the line.

(c) Peter's true weight is 75 kg. He loses 10 kg. How much weight do his scales indicate that he has lost?

7 Toby had a remote-controlled model car. He carried out an experiment to see how far it could travel in a certain amount of time. These were his results:

Time taken (T seconds)	2	3	4	5	6
Distance (D metres)	28	40	55	75	98

Toby was trying to find a relationship between the distance travelled and the time taken.

(a) On graph paper draw these axes and a graph of D against T. Comment on your results.

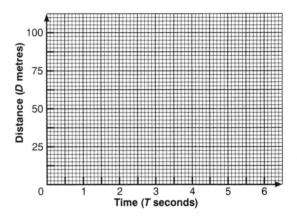

Toby thought that the relationship might be in the form $D = mT^2 + c$

(b) Copy and complete this table:

T^2	4	9			
D	28	40	55	75	98

(c) Test Toby's theory by drawing a graph of D against T^2. Comment on your findings.

(d) Express the relationship between distance and time in the form $D = mT^2 + c$.

(e) Work out how far Toby's car will travel in 3·6 seconds.

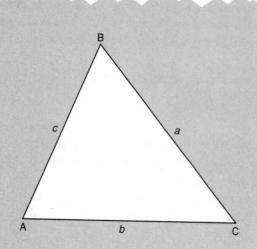

The Sine rule relates each angle to the side opposite to it.

The area of the triangle ABC is

$$\text{Area} = \frac{1}{2} bc \sin A$$

or

$$\text{Area} = \frac{1}{2} ac \sin B$$

So $\frac{1}{2} ac \sin B = \frac{1}{2} bc \sin A$

Dividing each side by $\frac{1}{2}$ and c gives

$$a \sin B = b \sin A$$

or, cross-dividing gives

$$\frac{a}{\sin A} = \frac{b}{\sin B}$$

This is known as **the Sine Rule**.

1 Show that $\dfrac{a}{\sin A} = \dfrac{c}{\sin C}$

and that the full sine rule is

$$\frac{a}{\sin A} = \frac{b}{\sin B} = \frac{c}{\sin C}$$

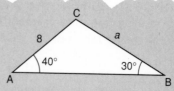

To calculate the length of BC

$$BC = a \qquad AC = b$$

By the Sine rule

$$\frac{a}{\sin A} = \frac{b}{\sin B}$$

so $\dfrac{a}{\sin 40} = \dfrac{8}{\sin 30}$

so $a = \dfrac{8 \times \sin 40}{\sin 30}$

$$a = \frac{8 \times 0 \cdot 6428}{0 \cdot 5}$$

$$a = 10 \cdot 28 \text{ units} = BC$$

2 For each triangle, calculate the length of the side marked x.

(a)   **(d)**

(b)   **(c)**

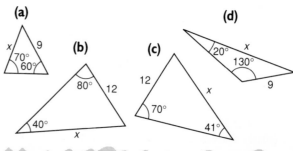

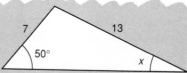

To calculate the angle marked x

$$\frac{7}{\sin x} = \frac{13}{\sin 50}$$

so $7 \sin 50 = 13 \sin x$

or $\sin x = \dfrac{7 \sin 50}{13}$

$$\sin x = \frac{7 \times 0 \cdot 7660}{13}$$

$$\sin x = \frac{5 \cdot 362}{13} = 0 \cdot 41246$$

$$x = 24 \cdot 36°$$

3 Calculate the angle marked *x* for each triangle.

(a)

(b)

15

70°

12

(c)

6 9

x

130°

4 For each triangle, calculate the side or angle marked with a letter.

(a)

52° 9·3

31°

x

(b)

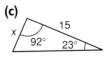

x 12

70°

10

(c)

x 15

92° 23°

(d)

20° 12

x

7

(e)

20°

x

65°

8

(f)

52° 10

a *b*

12

(g)

23 19

47° *x*

(i)

10 20

y 24°

(h)

14·3

x

72° 32°

5 Show that the use of the sine rule proves that the following triangle cannot be constructed.

7 cm 13 cm

50°

x

6 Construct a triangle PQR with angles at P, Q and R of 25°, 50° and 105° respectively. The side PR is 12 cm.

(a) Measure PQ and QR.

(b) Calculate PQ and QR using the sine rule.

(c) Compare the calculated and measured results.

7 XYZ is a triangular field.
Calculate:

(a) the angle at Z

(b) the angle at Y

(c) the length of XZ.

Y

300 m 500 m

55°

X Z

8 In a triangle ABC, AB = 8 cm, BC = 10 cm and the angle $A\hat{C}B$ is 40°

(a) Show that there are two possible values for the angle $B\hat{A}C$.

(b) Draw a sketch to illustrate the two possibilities.

9 A ship sets sail from a harbour H and travels *x* km due north to a point P. At P it turns to travel on a bearing of 070° and travels a further 23 km to reach a point Q.

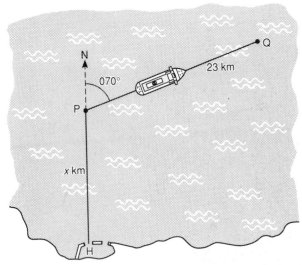

(a) When it is at Q the ship is 30 km from H. Calculate:

- the bearing of Q from H • the value of *x*.

(b) At Q the ship turns and sails back to H in a straight line.

Calculate the shortest distance between the ship and the point P on this return journey.

10 Write the full version of the sine rule for this triangle.

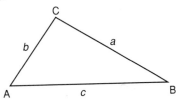

Show, fully, that where the angle at C is 90°, the sine rule reduces to the basic trigonometry formula for a right-angled triangle.

The Cosine rule relates the length c to the lengths a, b and the angle C.

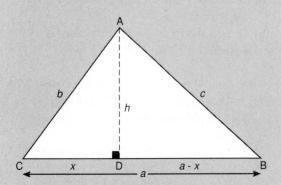

• Draw the perpendicular, h, from A to BC.

The distance from C to D, the foot of the perpendicular, is written as x.

Then DB is $a - x$

• By Pythagoras, in triangle ADB
$$c^2 = (a - x)^2 + h^2$$
$$c^2 = a^2 - 2ax + x^2 + h^2$$

• but by Pythagoras, in triangle ACD
$$x^2 + h^2 = b^2$$
so $c^2 = a^2 - 2ax + b^2$

• again considering the triangle ACD
$$\frac{x}{b} = \cos C \text{ or } x = b\cos C$$
so $c^2 = a^2 - 2ab\cos C + b^2$

This is usually written as
$$c^2 = a^2 + b^2 - 2ab\cos C$$
and this is **the Cosine Rule**.

The Cosine rule can be rearranged to give the angle C in terms of a, b and c as
$$c^2 = a^2 + b^2 - 2ab\cos C$$
so $2ab\cos C = a^2 + b^2 - c^2$
so $\cos C = \dfrac{a^2 + b^2 - c^2}{2ab}$

The Cosine rule could be written in any of these forms:

$$c^2 = a^2 + b^2 - 2ab\cos C$$
$$a^2 = b^2 + c^2 - 2bc\cos A$$
$$b^2 = a^2 + c^2 - 2ac\cos B$$

$$\cos C = \frac{a^2 + b^2 - c^2}{2ab}$$

$$\cos A = \frac{b^2 + c^2 - a^2}{2bc}$$

$$\cos B = \frac{a^2 + c^2 - b^2}{2ac}$$

To calculate the length of AB.

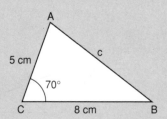

$$c^2 = 5^2 + 8^2 - 2 \times 5 \times 8\cos 70$$
$$= 25 + 64 - 80 \times 0.342$$
$$= 89 - 27.36 = 61.64$$
c = **7.85** correct to two decimal places.

To calculate the angle at A

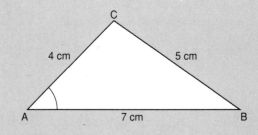

$$\cos A = \frac{b^2 + c^2 - a^2}{2bc}$$
$$= \frac{4^2 + 7^2 - 5^2}{2 \times 4 \times 7}$$
$$= \frac{16 + 49 - 25}{56}$$
$$= \frac{40}{56}$$
$$\cos A = 0.714285714$$
$$A = \mathbf{44.42°}$$

1 For each triangle calculate the length of each side marked *x*. The lengths of the sides are in centimetres.

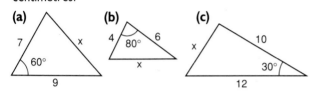

(a) 7, *x*, 60°, 9

(b) 4, 80°, 6, *x*

(c) *x*, 10, 30°, 12

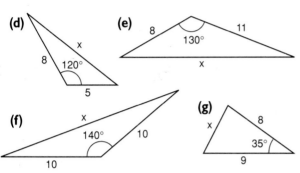

(d) *x*, 8, 120°, 5

(e) 8, 130°, 11, *x*

(f) *x*, 140°, 10, 10

(g) *x*, 8, 35°, 9

(h) 9, 42°, 6, *x*

(i) *x*, 7·3, 127°, 11·2

2 Calculate each angle marked *x*. In each of the triangles the lengths of the sides are given in centimetres.

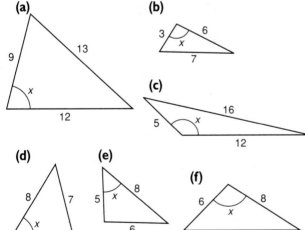

(a) 9, 13, *x*, 12

(b) 3, 6, *x*, 7

(c) 5, *x*, 16, 12

(d) 8, 7, *x*, 6

(e) 5, *x*, 8, 6

(f) 6, *x*, 8, 11

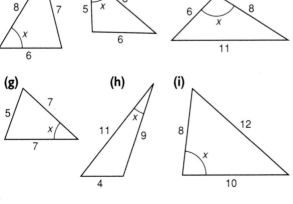

(g) 5, 7, *x*, 7

(h) 11, *x*, 9, 4

(i) 8, *x*, 12, 10

3 PQR is a triangular building plot. PQ = 17 m, QR = 123 m and the angle $P\hat{Q}R = 55°$. Calculate the length of PR, giving your answer correct to two decimal places.

4 A ship leaves a harbour, H, and travels 70 km due South to a lighthouse, L.
At L the ship turns on a bearing of 075° and travels for a further 30 km to reach a marker buoy, B.
Calculate the distance HB.

5 Jackie, sets out from her home, H, and travels 8 km due north to a post office, P.
At P she turns on a bearing of 70° and travels a further 6 km to reach a cafe, C.
At C she turns and walks back in a straight line to her home. Calculate the total distance of her walk.

6 James fences off a triangular sheep pen PQR using 40 m of fencing.
He makes PQ = 15 m and QR = 12 m.
Calculate the angle $P\hat{Q}R$.

7 ABCD is a parallelogram with
AB = CD = 10 cm and
AD = BC = 6 cm.
The angle $A\hat{B}C = 130°$. Calculate the lengths of the diagonals AC and BD.

8 Two ships, *Salamander* and *Firefly*, set out from the same point at the same time.
Salamander sets out on a bearing of 060° and travels at 30 km per hour.
Firefly sets out on a bearing of 170° and travels at 24 km per hour.
Calculate the distance between the two ships:
(a) one hour after they set out
(b) two hours after they set out.

9 Two runners, Anna and Belinda, set off at the same time from the same point.
Anna runs due east at a speed of 12 km per hour.
Belinda runs at 15 km per hour but on a bearing of X°.
One hour after setting off Anna and Belinda are exactly 8 km apart.
Calculate the possible values of X.

Introducing matrices

> ● **Remember**
>
> Reflections, rotations and enlargements are all transformations. In these transformations, triangle P is transformed to triangle Q. Q is known as **the image** of P.

> When the transformation is made, the whole plane moves and the triangle moves with the plane.

Reflections in the x and y axes

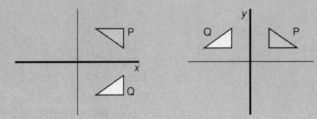

Reflections in the line y = x (or y − x = 0)

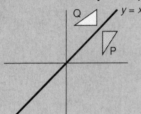

Reflections in the line y = ⁻x (or y + x = 0)

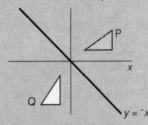

Rotations about the origin

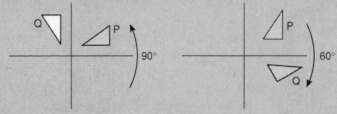

Enlargements, centred on the origin, but with various scale factors.

1 Draw the triangle ABC where A = (1, 1)
B = (3, 1) and C = (3, 4). Draw the images of
ABC when the whole plane is subject to each of
these transformations.

(a) a reflection in the y-axis

(b) a reflection in the x-axis

(c) a reflection in the line y = x

(d) a reflection in the line y = ⁻x

(e) a rotation about the origin through an angle of
90° in the anti-clockwise direction

(f) a rotation about the origin through 180°

(g) a reflection in the x-axis followed by a reflection
in the y-axis

(h) a reflection in the y-axis followed by a rotation
about the origin through 90° anti-clockwise

(i) a reflection in the x-axis followed by a reflection
in the line y = x

(j) two successive reflections in the y-axis

2 For each of the combined transformations in
question 1 **(g)** to **(j)** give the single transformation
to which they are equivalent.

A **matrix** (plural matrices) is a **coded or symbolic
means of representing a transformation.**
Matrices work only for transformations under
which **the origin remains fixed**.

**An enlargement, centred on the origin, scale
factor 3.**

Look first at the **base vectors**,
$\begin{pmatrix} 1 \\ 0 \end{pmatrix}$ and $\begin{pmatrix} 0 \\ 1 \end{pmatrix}$

Under the transformation all distances are
multiplied by 3.

$\begin{pmatrix} 1 \\ 0 \end{pmatrix}$ goes to $\begin{pmatrix} 3 \\ 0 \end{pmatrix}$

and

$\begin{pmatrix} 0 \\ 1 \end{pmatrix}$ goes to $\begin{pmatrix} 0 \\ 3 \end{pmatrix}$

The matrix representing the transformation is a
2 by 2 array

$\begin{pmatrix} 3 & 0 \\ 0 & 3 \end{pmatrix}$
The first column is where $\begin{pmatrix} 1 \\ 0 \end{pmatrix}$
goes to, the second column is
where $\begin{pmatrix} 0 \\ 1 \end{pmatrix}$ goes to.

3 Work out the matrices for these enlargements,
centred on the origin:

• scale factor 2 • scale factor ⁻2

• scale factor $\frac{1}{3}$ • scale factor ⁻$\frac{1}{3}$

4 Find the matrix representing an enlargement,
centred on the origin:

(a) of scale factor ⁻3 **(b)** of scale factor $\frac{1}{2}$

A reflection in the x-axis

Under this transformation

$\begin{pmatrix} 1 \\ 0 \end{pmatrix}$ remains fixed, or goes to $\begin{pmatrix} 1 \\ 0 \end{pmatrix}$

and

$\begin{pmatrix} 0 \\ 1 \end{pmatrix}$ goes to $\begin{pmatrix} 0 \\ -1 \end{pmatrix}$

The matrix representing a reflection in the x-axis is

$\begin{pmatrix} 1 & 0 \\ 0 & -1 \end{pmatrix}$

5 Find the matrix representing a reflection in:

(a) the y-axis **(b)** line y = ⁻x

**A clockwise rotation about the origin
through 90°**

Under this transformation

$\begin{pmatrix} 1 \\ 0 \end{pmatrix}$ goes to $\begin{pmatrix} 0 \\ -1 \end{pmatrix}$

and

$\begin{pmatrix} 0 \\ 1 \end{pmatrix}$ goes to $\begin{pmatrix} 1 \\ 0 \end{pmatrix}$

The matrix representing this rotation is

$\begin{pmatrix} 0 & 1 \\ -1 & 0 \end{pmatrix}$

Introducing matrices

6 Find the matrix representing each of these transformations:

(a) an anti-clockwise rotation about the origin through 90°

(b) an anti-clockwise rotation about the origin through 270°

(c) an anti-clockwise rotation about the origin through an angle Θ.

7 Find the transformation represented by each matrix:

(a) $\begin{pmatrix} 1 & 0 \\ 0 & ^-1 \end{pmatrix}$ (b) $\begin{pmatrix} 0 & 1 \\ 1 & 0 \end{pmatrix}$

(c) $\begin{pmatrix} 1 & 0 \\ 0 & 1 \end{pmatrix}$ (d) $\begin{pmatrix} ^-4 & 0 \\ 0 & ^-4 \end{pmatrix}$

(e) $\begin{pmatrix} 0 & ^-1 \\ 1 & 0 \end{pmatrix}$ (f) $\begin{pmatrix} 0.8 & ^-0.6 \\ 0.6 & 0.8 \end{pmatrix}$

> A matrix which undoes a transformation is its **inverse**.
>
> The inverse of a 90° anti-clockwise rotation about 0 is a 90° rotation clockwise about 0.
>
> So if A = $\begin{pmatrix} 0 & ^-1 \\ 1 & 0 \end{pmatrix}$
>
> Then the inverse, written as A^{-1}
>
> $\begin{pmatrix} 0 & 1 \\ ^-1 & 0 \end{pmatrix}$

> A^2 means 'do A twice'

8 A is the matrix $\begin{pmatrix} 0 & ^-1 \\ 1 & 0 \end{pmatrix}$

(a) Write the transformation represented by A.

(b) Write the transformation represented by A^2 and find the matrix A^2. Explain.

(c) Find the matrix A^3. Explain.

(d) Find the A inverse, the matrix A^{-1}

(e) What, if any, is the connection between A^3 and A^{-1}? Explain.

> BA means 'do A then do B'

9 A is the matrix $\begin{pmatrix} 3 & 0 \\ 0 & 3 \end{pmatrix}$ and B is the matrix $\begin{pmatrix} 2 & 0 \\ 0 & 2 \end{pmatrix}$

(a) What are the transformations represented by A and B?

(b) Find the matrix BA.

10 The transformation T is defined by the matrix A where

$A = \begin{pmatrix} ^-4 & 0 \\ 0 & ^-4 \end{pmatrix}$

(a) Write down the images of $\begin{pmatrix} 1 \\ 0 \end{pmatrix}$ and $\begin{pmatrix} 0 \\ 1 \end{pmatrix}$ under the transformation T.

(b) Describe fully, in words, the transformation T.

11 Write the transformations represented by each of the matrices:

(a) $\begin{pmatrix} ^-1 & 0 \\ 0 & ^-1 \end{pmatrix}$ (b) $\begin{pmatrix} 0 & ^-1 \\ 1 & 0 \end{pmatrix}$ (c) $\begin{pmatrix} 0 & 1 \\ ^-1 & 0 \end{pmatrix}$

Find the square and inverse of each matrix. Comment on your results.

12 The vertices of the triangle PQR are at the points P(1, 1) Q(4, 1) R(4, 3)

The triangle is subject to a transformation represented by the matrix A, where

$A = \begin{pmatrix} 0 & ^-1 \\ 1 & 0 \end{pmatrix}$

to create the image P′Q′R′

(a) Find the coordinates of P′, Q′ and R′ P′Q′R′ is transformed by the matrix B where

$B = \begin{pmatrix} 1 & 0 \\ 0 & ^-1 \end{pmatrix}$

to create the second image P″Q″R″

(b) Find the coordinates of P″, Q″ and R″.

(c) Find the single matrix equal to BA

(d) Write fully, in words, the single transformation represented by BA.

(e) Does BA = AB? Justify your answer.

13 (a) If Sin 30 = 0·5 and Cos 30 = 0·866, write the matrix which represents a rotation about the origin through an angle of 30°

(b) The matrix you have worked out in (a) is written as A.

Find: • the matrix A^2 • the matrix A^3

Dispersion is a measure of spread.

The **range** and **inter quartile range** are measures of spread.

Another measure of dispersion is the **standard deviation**. It measures the deviation from the mean.

The standard deviation, s, is calculated from the formula

$$s = \sqrt{\frac{\Sigma(x - \bar{x})^2}{n}}$$

To calculate the standard deviation for the set of data (2, 3, 4, 6, 10):

- work out the mean

The mean $\bar{x} = \dfrac{2 + 3 + 4 + 6 + 10}{5} = \dfrac{25}{5} = 5$

- use the table to help calculate s

x	$x - \bar{x}$	$(x - x)^2$
2	⁻3	9
3	⁻2	4
4	⁻1	1
6	1	1
10	5	25
Totals 25	0	40

$$s = \sqrt{\frac{\Sigma(x-\bar{x})^2}{n}} = \sqrt{\frac{40}{5}} = \sqrt{8} = 2.83 \text{ to 2D}$$

Note the $x - \bar{x}$ column total is **always zero**.

I Calculate the standard deviation for these sets of data:

(a) {2, 3, 7, 12}
(b) {4, 6, 9, 11, 15}
(c) {108, 108, 109, 109, 112, 112, 121}
(d) {1·1, 1·2, 1·4, 1·4, 1·5, 1·5, 1·5, 1·6, 1·8, 2·1}

It is sometimes easier to use a standard deviation formula in the form

$$s = \sqrt{\frac{\Sigma x^2}{n} - \bar{x}^2}$$

This is the case when n is large or the mean is not exact.

To calculate the standard deviation for the set of data {2, 3, 4, 6, 10}:

- calculate the mean

$$\bar{x} = \frac{\Sigma x}{n} = \frac{25}{5}$$

- use the table to help calculate s.

x	x^2
2	4
3	9
4	16
6	36
10	100

Totals $\Sigma x = 25$, $\Sigma x^2 = 165$

$$s = \sqrt{\frac{\Sigma x^2}{n} - \bar{x}^2}$$

$$s = \sqrt{\frac{165}{5} - 5^2} = \sqrt{33 - 25} = \sqrt{8}$$

$$= \quad 2.83 \text{ to 2 dp}$$

2 Calculate the standard deviation using the second formula for these sets of data:

(a) {2, 5, 7, 8, 11}
(b) {1·6, 1·8, 2·3, 2·4, 2·9, 3}
(c) {10, 9, 8, 9, 7, 4, 8, 6, 8, 5, 9, 7, 5}
(d) {9·31, 9·52, 9·59, 9·73, 9·89}
(e) {43·1, 44·2, 45·5, 46·3, 44·9, 47·8, 43·8}

Some electronic calculators may have statistical functions which may help simplify the calculations. However, these should only be used when it is clear that method and working need not be shown.

On one condition . . .

The probability that David is woken by his alarm is $\frac{4}{5}$. If he is **not** woken by the alarm, the probability that he misses breakfast is $\frac{3}{5}$. If he **is** woken by the alarm, the probability that he has breakfast is $\frac{4}{5}$. Find the probability that David has breakfast.

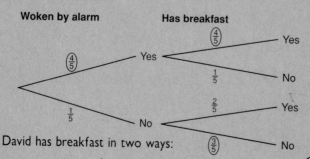

Woken by alarm   **Has breakfast**

This is the tree diagram for the problem. The probabilities which are circled are those given in the problem. The remaining probabilities have been added to complete the tree diagram.

David has breakfast in two ways:

branches Y Y = $\frac{4}{5} \times \frac{4}{5} = \frac{16}{25}$

branches N Y = $\frac{1}{5} \times \frac{2}{5} = \frac{2}{25}$

Total = $\frac{18}{25}$

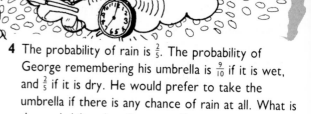

Draw a tree diagram for each of the following questions, to help you find the answers to each problem.

1 The probability that Lisa catches a bus to school is $\frac{3}{4}$. If she catches the bus, the probability of her being late is $\frac{1}{10}$, whilst if she misses the bus it is $\frac{3}{5}$. What is the probability of Lisa being late for school?

2 Barry cycles to school through two sets of traffic lights. The probability he will have to stop at the first set of lights is $\frac{3}{5}$. If he has to stop at the first set of lights, the probability he will have to stop at the second set is $\frac{5}{6}$, but only $\frac{3}{5}$ if he passes straight through the first set.
Find the probability that Barry:

(a) has to stop at both sets of lights
(b) has to stop for at least one set of lights.

3 The probability that Jane will apply for a particular type of job is $\frac{1}{10}$. If she applies, the probability of her being interviewed is $\frac{3}{5}$, and if she is interviewed the probability of her being offered the job is $\frac{7}{10}$ (she interviews well). Find the probability that:

(a) she gets the job
(b) she is not offered the job after being interviewed.

4 The probability of rain is $\frac{2}{5}$. The probability of George remembering his umbrella is $\frac{9}{10}$ if it is wet, and $\frac{2}{5}$ if it is dry. He would prefer to take the umbrella if there is any chance of rain at all. What is the probability that George will:

(a) remember the umbrella
(b) forget the umbrella and get wet?

5 Tim estimates the probability of his passing a test as $\frac{3}{5}$. He can retake the test, but feels the probability of passing the test on the second attempt would be $\frac{2}{5}$. Calculate the probability Tim will:

(a) pass on the second attempt
(b) fail both attempts.

6 An electrical component has two fuses. When tested to its maximum voltage the probability of the first fuse failing is $\frac{1}{20}$. The probability of the second fuse failing is also $\frac{1}{20}$, but is $\frac{1}{8}$ if the first fuse has already failed. Find the probability that:

(a) both fuses will fail
(b) at least one fuse will fail
(c) only one fuse will fail.

7 Shaheen travels to see her father either by bus or train. The probability she will go by bus is $\frac{3}{5}$. The probability she will be on time is $\frac{3}{4}$ by bus, and $\frac{2}{5}$ by train. Calculate the probability that:

(a) she is on time
(b) she is late by train.

1 What is the probability of throwing three 2s on a dice?

2 The probability of winning on a one-armed bandit is $\frac{2}{13}$. What is the probability of winning on two consecutive goes?

3 In a game there are 15 red, 8 black, 7 blue and 10 white counters left. What is the probability that the next counter picked is either a red or a blue counter?

4 Days can be fine or wet. If the chance of a fine day is $\frac{1}{5}$, find the probability of having:

(a) a wet day

(b) two fine days one after each other

(c) exactly one fine day out of two days.

5 One out of every four parcels is given priority delivery. If a parcel is given priority, the probability of it arriving on the first day is $\frac{3}{5}$, otherwise it will be delivered on the second day.

By normal delivery the probability of it arriving on the second day is $\frac{2}{5}$, otherwise it will arrive on the third day.

What is the probability that a parcel selected at random will arrive on the:

(a) 1st day   (b) 2nd day   (c) 3rd day?

6 A bag contains 5 white, 3 blue and 2 yellow balls. Two balls are each selected **and not replaced**. What is the probability that the two balls selected:

(a) are both white

(b) contain at least one blue

(c) include no yellow balls?

7 Liz spins a coin four times. Find the probability of her spinning:

(a) four heads   (b) at least two heads

(c) no heads.

8 Martin picks a pen at random from a box containing 4 blue pens and 7 black pens. He then selects a sheet of paper at random from a file containing 8 red sheets and 12 white sheets.

What is the probability that Martin then writes with a blue pen on a red sheet of paper?

9 Scott's packet of sweets contains five orange, four green and three yellow sweets. He takes two sweets out of the packet and eats them.

What is the probability that these two sweets will:

(a) both be orange

(b) be two different colours

(c) not be green?

10 Susan drives along a road which has two sets of traffic lights. The probability of the first set being on green is $\frac{3}{5}$, and of the second set being on green is $\frac{2}{5}$. What is the probability of:

(a) both sets being on green

(b) at least one set being on green?

11 A bag contains 8 blue and 6 red discs. Two discs are each removed at random and replaced.

What is the probability that the two discs are:

(a) both blue   (b) of different colours

(c) both red?

12 Mrs Herbert is very choosy about the films she watches. The probability she will begin watching a Western is $\frac{3}{4}$. If the film is a Western, the probability she will see it to the end is $\frac{7}{8}$, otherwise the probability is $\frac{2}{3}$ for any other film. Find the probability that Mrs Herbert will:

(a) not see the ending of the film

(b) see a Western all the way through to the end.

13 The probability of getting the first three questions of a test right are $\frac{3}{4}$, $\frac{3}{5}$, and $\frac{1}{3}$ respectively.

What is the probability of getting:

(a) all three answers right

(b) at least two answers right

(c) only one answer right?

14 A dice and a coin are tossed simultaneously. What is the probability of getting:

(a) a 'head' and a 'five'   (b) a 'head' or a 'five'?

Linear programming

The Mini-Trek club wants to hire a bus from the 'Maximus' minibus company for a trip to a National Park. The rules for the hire of the bus are:

* the total number of passengers must not exceed 14
* there must not be less than 10 passengers on each trip
* at least 3 of the passengers must pay full fare
* there must always be at least as many half-fare passengers as full-fare payers.

The full fare for the trip will be £10. What are the maximum and minimum amounts of money 'Maximus' will get for the trip following the rules?
f is the **number** of full fare payers and h is the **number** of half-fare payers.

$$f + h \leq 14$$
$$f + h \geq 10$$
$$f \geq 3$$
$$h \geq f$$

The unshaded area, ABCD, on the graph is the **feasible region**. Inside and on the boundaries of the feasible region, where the grid lines cross, are the points which represent all the feasible combinations of passengers using the rules.

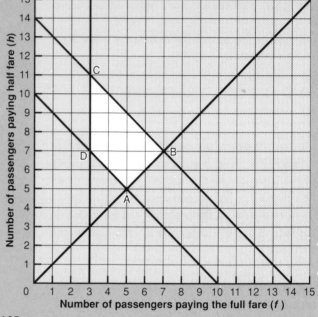

Point B gives the maximum of $7 \times £10 + 7 \times £5 = $ **£105**
and D gives the minimum of $3 \times £10 + 7 \times £5 = $ **£65**.

1 Mrs Arkwright runs a 'Choco-corner' franchise. When ordering products she must take at least 2 dozen of a normal item and at least half a dozen of a luxury item. A new line, 'Softees' is launched and costs the franchisees £2·50 for a normal sized box and £7·50 for the luxury size.

I'll order twice as many normal size boxes as luxury size boxes, because that's how they normally go. These Softees taste wonderful but I won't spend more than £180 in case they're not popular.

(a) Define your variables and draw the feasible region for this situation.
(b) The normal size of Softees sells for £4 and the luxury for £15. On the day her order arrived she sold all of the boxes, making the highest possible profit. Investigate inside the feasible region to find how many of each size Mrs Arkwright ordered and how much profit she made.

2 An open feasible region is defined by these boundaries.
(a) Using the same scales on both the x and y axis draw the feasible region.
(b) Using the same axes draw graphs of $x + 2y = n$ for $n = 24$ and 20 as well as 3 other values of your choice.
(c) Explain how it is possible to use lines parallel to $x + 2y = n$ to find the minimum feasible value of $x + 2y$. Where does it occur?

$$x \geq 0$$
$$y \geq 0$$
$$3x + y \geq 15$$
$$2x + 3y \geq 30$$
$$x + 4y \geq 20$$

This is an accurate drawing of the curve

$y = x^2$

for values of x from 0 to 5.

On the graph the tangent at the point P, with co-ordinates (4,16) has been drawn.

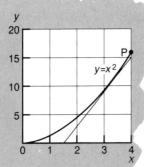

Show, by any means, that the gradient of the tangent at the point (4,16) on the curve $y = x^2$ is 8.

Draw tangents at other points on the curve $y = x^2$ and find the gradient of the tangent at each point.

In the seventeenth century mathematicians including the Englishmen Isaac Barrow and Isaac Newton, together with the German Gottfried Wilhelm Leibniz, created a method of calculating gradients of the tangents at points on various graphs.

Using $y = x^2$ as an example, this is a blown-up portion of the curve near the point (4,16). A point, Q, near to P is shown with co-ordinates (4·01, 16·0801).

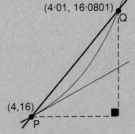

These mathematicians argued that the gradient of the tangent at P is nearly equal to the gradient of the chord PQ. They also argued that as Q gets closer and closer to P the gradient of the chord PQ gets closer and closer to the gradient of the tangent at P.

In the diagram the gradient of QP is

$$\frac{QA}{AP} = \frac{16\cdot0801 - 16}{4\cdot01 - 4} = \frac{0\cdot0601}{0\cdot01} = 8\cdot01$$

This value of 6·01 is very close to 6 which is the value of the gradient of the tangent at P.

If you make Q closer to P, perhaps letting the coordinates of Q be (4·001. 16·008001), you will find that the gradient of the chord PQ is even closer to 6.

3 Show that the gradient of the chord connecting the points (4·001, 16·008001) and (14,16) on the curve $y = x^2$ is 8·001.

4 Use the same method as Newton to obtain approximations for the gradients of the tangents at a range of points on the curve $y = x^2$. Make and record any comments or observations.

5 The gradient of the tangent to a point on a curve is related to the coordinates of the point. Examine this relationship for the curve with the equation:

$y = x^3$

The process which connects the general gradient of a tangent to the equation of the graph is known as **differentiation**.

6 Obtain the result of differentiating the following graphs and any other graphs of your own choosing.

(a) $y = 3x^2$ (b) $y = x^2 + x^3$ (c) $y = x^{\frac{1}{2}}$
(d) $y = x^{\frac{1}{3}}$ (e) $y = x^{\frac{1}{2}} + x^{\frac{1}{3}}$

The Sigma function

The factors of the number 6 are:

1, 2, 3 and 6

The sum of these factors is:

1 + 2 + 3 + 6 = 12

This fact is written as:

$\Sigma(6) = 12$

In a similar way
the sum of the factors of 8 is:

1 + 2 + 4 + 8 = 15, so $\Sigma(8) = 15$

and
the sum of the factors of 5 is:

1 + 5 = 6, so $\Sigma(5) = 6$

For any positive integer, $\Sigma(n)$ is called the Sigma function.

1 Show that:

$\Sigma(24) = 60$

and

$\Sigma(4 \times 6) = 60$ but $\Sigma(4) \times \Sigma(6) = 7 \times 12 = 84$

whilst

$\Sigma(3 \times 8) = 60 = \Sigma(3) \times \Sigma(8) = 4 \times 15 = 60$

2 Investigate the Sigma function of any number.

You are advised to look in particular at:
- Σp where p is any prime number
- $\Sigma(a \times b)$ in relation to $\Sigma(a)$ and $\Sigma(b)$
- $\Sigma(2^n)$ where n is an integer
- $\Sigma(p^n)$ where p is prime and n an integer
- $\Sigma(p_1^{n_1} p_2^{n_2} \ldots p_m^{n_m})$ where each p_1 is a prime number and each n_1 is an integer.

You are also advised to:
- **record your observations and comments**
- **make and test any conjectures**
- **form any generalisations, with appropriate explanations, justifications or proofs.**

3 Calculate:
  (a) $\Sigma(35)$ **(b)** $\Sigma(48)$ **(c)** $\Sigma(1024)$
  (d) $\Sigma(1001)$ **(e)** $\Sigma(5500)$

Explain or justify each answer in some way.

The whole number **divisors** of 6 are 1, 2, 3 and 6.
There are **four** of them.
This is written as T(**6**) = **4**

For any positive whole number n, its **Tor function** is defined as
the number of positive whole number divisors of n
and this is written as T(n).

The whole number divisors of 5 are 1 and 5.
There are **two** of them.
This is written as T(**5**) = **2**

The whole number divisors of 30 are 1, 2, 3, 5, 6, 10, 15 and 30.
There are **eight** of them.
This is written as T(**30**) = **8**

It is a fact that 5 × 6 = 30 and that T(30) = T(5) × T(6)

But is this always the case?

1 Write the Tor function values of at least six positive whole numbers of
your choice.

2 Investigate the Tor function for p, where p is a prime number.

3 Investigate the Tor function for various values of n. In particular, investigate
whether or not T($n \times m$) = T(n) × T(m)

4 If p is a prime number, investigate the Tor function of p^x where x is a
positive whole number. Illustrate your response by finding:
 (a) T(16)   **(b)** T(49)   **(c)** T(243)

In each case give a full explanation.

5 Given that p and q are both prime numbers, investigate

T($p^x q^y$)

where x and y are both positive whole numbers.
Illustrate your response by finding:
 (a) T(35)   **(b)** T(100)   **(c)** T(1001)   **(d)** T(19 600)

In each case give a full explanation.

You are advised to:
● **record your observations and comments**
● **make and test any conjectures**
● **form any generalisations, with appropriate explanations,
justifications or proofs.**

Simulating a tennis tie break

When a set in tennis reaches a score of six games all, the result of the set is often decided by a tie break.

The rules of the tie break are:

- the players play the best of 12 points or until someone has seven points with a two point lead

- if, after 12 points, the score is 6 points each, the players continue until someone has established a lead of two points.

At large competitions tie breaks can disrupt the scheduling of matches.

1 Explain why a tie break could last for a very long time.

Work in groups and pool your results.
You need some means of generating random numbers: a dice, playing cards, a random number table, a calculator or computer that can generate random numbers, or any other method of your own.

2 Assume that each player has a probability of 0·5 of winning a point.

Use your chosen method of producing random numbers to conduct a simulation of at least 25 tie breaks, and record your results.

From your results, obtain best estimates for:

(a) the most likely result of a tie break
(b) the number of points likely to be played to produce a winner of the set.

3 Repeat question 2 but vary the probabilities of each player winning a point.

In a real game one player serves first, then the opponent has two serves, after which they alternate the serve every two points. It is usual to assume that the server has the best chance of winning the point.

4 (a) Simulate this situation for at least five tie breaks.
(b) Comment on your results.

To gain maximum credit, try to relate the simulated results to theoretical models or real-life tennis matches. You may find it helpful to watch some tie breaks on television or videos.

A road running east-west is being repaired. Some temporary traffic lights have been set up to control one-way traffic. A 6-second time lag has been built into the system to let vehicles get through when the lights change. This is the lag between the halting of traffic in one direction (red light) and the release of traffic in the other direction (green light).

In the simulation assume this pattern for the traffic lights:

- the lights do not have a cautionary (amber) light
- lights in either direction are on green for 24 seconds
- both lights are simultaneously on red (the time lag) for 6 seconds
- except during the time lag, when one set of lights is on green the other is on red.

Also, assume this arrival pattern:

- during any 6 second interval either 0 or 1 vehicles travelling east can arrive at the lights, each event having a probability of $\frac{1}{2}$.
- during any 6 second interval either 2, 1 or 0 vehicles travelling west can arrive at the lights, these events having probabilities of $\frac{1}{6}$, $\frac{1}{2}$ and $\frac{1}{3}$ respectively.

Finally, assume that it takes a vehicle 3 seconds to pass through the one-way strip.

You need some means of producing random numbers to simulate these probabilities: a dice, playing cards, a random number table, a calculator or computer that can generate random numbers, or any other method of your own.

Investigate the growth of the traffic queues that will form at the traffic lights over a period of time up to ten minutes.

You are advised to:
- **look at any appropriate statistical measures**
- **record your observations and comments**
- **make and test any conjectures**
- **form any generalisations with appropriate explanations, justifications or proofs.**

For further credit you are advised to develop other patterns for the traffic lights and alter the probabilities for the arrival patterns. Try to form some conjectures which relate the arrival patterns to the traffic light patterns to minimise the queue lengths.

The number 17 can be made up from positive integer multiples of the numbers 3 and 5 as:

$17 = 12 + 5 = 4(3) + 1(5)$

Throughout this section the word **multiple** is taken to mean:

positive whole number multiples and zero unless otherwise stated.

The number 36 can be made up from multiples of 3 and 5 in different ways.

For example

$36 = 6 + 30 = 2(3) + 6(5)$

or

$36 = 12(3) + 0(5)$

or

$36 = 21 + 15 = 7(3) + 3(5)$

The number 4 cannot be made from whole number multiples of 3 and 5.

1 Try to make these numbers:
   (a) 17   **(b)** 26   **(c)** 32   **(d)** 101   **(e)** 13
   in as many ways as possible as multiples of:
   3 and 5,   4 and 7,   4 and 6,   5 and 7

   If you believe that a number cannot be made from multiples of the two numbers, say so and give your reasoning.

2 Investigate the largest number which cannot be made from multiples of two positive whole numbers n and m.

You are advised to try a selection of enquiries which *must* include:
- **variations on n and m, and**
- **the largest number which cannot be made and how this relates to the choice of n and m.**

You could also include some of the following:
- **the number of numbers which cannot be made and how this relates to n and m**
- **the number of ways a number can be made from multiples of n and m and how this relates to n and m**
- **changing the definition of the word 'multiple'**
- **and any ideas of your own choosing.**

Answers

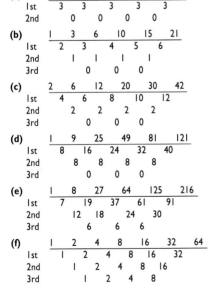

Page 1   It's all in the mind

(a) 5	(b) 3·4	(c) **20**	(d) 6·6
(e) 17·5	(f) 44·8	(g) 240	(h) 180
(i) 72	(j) 44	(k) 6	(l) 32
(m) 26	(n) 27		
(a) 200	(b) 1500	(c) 400	(d) 3000
(e) 400	(f) **300**	(g) 200	(h) 4000
(i) 40	(j) 12	(k) 40	(l) 400
(m) 80	(n) 4		
(a) 12	(b) 5	(c) 1·6	(d) 100
(e) 120	(f) 300	(g) 4	(h) 36
(i) 100	(j) 100	(k) 300	(l) 300
(m) 48	(n) 12		

Area	Length	Width
20	20	1
20	10	2
20	5	4
20	0·5	40
20	0·4	50
20	0·2	100
20	0·02	1000

Perimeter	Length	Width	Area
20	8	2	16
20	5	5	25
20	2	8	16
20	1	9	9
20	0·2	9·8	1·96
20	0·1	9·9	0·99

40 × 80 = 3200   40 ÷ 80 = 0·5
40 × 8 = 320   40 ÷ 8 = 5
40 × 0·8 = 32   40 ÷ 0·8 = 50
40 × 0·08 = 3·2   40 ÷ 0·08 = 500
40 × 0·008 = 0·32   40 ÷ 0·008 = 5000

Students' own answers

Page 2   Spot the difference

(a)

	5	8	11	14	17	20
1st	3	3	3	3	3	
2nd	0	0	0	0		

(b)

	1	3	6	10	15	21
1st	2	3	4	5	6	
2nd	1	1	1	1		
3rd	0	0	0			

(c)

	2	6	12	20	30	42
1st	4	6	8	10	12	
2nd	2	2	2	2		
3rd	0	0	0			

(d)

	1	9	25	49	81	121
1st	8	16	24	32	40	
2nd	8	8	8	8		
3rd	0	0	0			

(e)

	1	8	27	64	125	216
1st	7	19	37	61	91	
2nd	12	18	24	30		
3rd	6	6	6			

(f)

	1	2	4	8	16	32	64
1st	1	2	4	8	16	32	
2nd	1	2	4	8	16		
3rd	1	2	4	8			

2 (a)

	5	8	11	14	17	20
1st	3	3	3	3	3	
2nd	0	0	0	0		

(b)

	2	7	12	17	22	27
1st	5	5	5	5	5	
2nd	0	0	0	0		

(c)

	1	4	9	16	25	36
1st	3	5	7	9	11	
2nd	2	2	2	2		
3rd	0	0	0			

(d)

	4	10	18	28	40	54
1st	6	8	10	12	14	
2nd	2	2	2	2		
3rd	0	0	0			

(e)

	4	11	22	37	56	79
1st	7	11	15	19	23	
2nd	4	4	4	4		
3rd	0	0	0			

(f)

	3	10	29	66	127	218
1st	7	19	37	61	91	
2nd	12	18	24	30		
3rd	6	6	6			

(g)

	3	13	37	81	151	253
1st	10	24	44	70	102	
2nd	14	20	26	32		
3rd	6	6	6			

(h)

	2	4	8	16	32	64
1st	2	4	8	16	32	
2nd	2	4	8	16		
3rd	2	4	8			

(i)

	3	9	27	81	243	729
1st	6	18	54	162	486	
2nd	12	36	108	324		
3rd	24	72	216			

3

1	1	2	3	5	8	13	21	34	55	89
0	1	1	2	3	5	8	13	21	34	

4 (a) 88, 108
   (b) 4088, 6552
   (c) 58, 100
   (d) 76, 123

Pages 3 and 4   Whatever next?

1 (a) 62 mm   (b) 248 mm
2 10 gallons
3 (a) 23·6 miles   (b) 61·2 km
4 (a) 42·16 cm   (b) 581 sheets
5 (a) • 18·75 m • 4·578 m   (b) 6 bounces
6 (a) 87 066   (b) 4 527 432   (c) 2 572 404·5
7 (a) 464   (b) 680   (c) 4032 kg
8 (a) 28·575 mph   (b) 46 km/h
9 18 degrees (to 2 sig fig)
10 (a) 18·4 km per litre
11 (a) 20869·565 paces   (b) 248·4 minutes
12 (a) £2619·50   (b) £6629·35
   (c) 45·6 tonnes   (d) £322·40
13 (a) £60·55   (b) £63·50
   (c) £69·25, £80   (d) 195 miles
14 (a) £59·73   (b) £1493·25   (c) 16
15 (a) 454   (b) £54·54
16 (a) 2450   (b) £51·02   (c) £489·80
17 (a) £7·73   (b) £2·03   (c) 32·1 mins

Pages 5 and 6   Down memory lane

1 (a) 0·85   (b) 1·0535714   (c) 2·21666667   (d) 1·2366522
2 (a) 10·249 mm   (b) 5·68 mm   (c) 0·535 m

3 (a) 1·1 (b) £110 (c) £121 (d) £161·05
  (e) 8 years
4 (a) • £110 • £210 • £231 • £671·56 (b) End of 7th year
5 £319·78
6 (a) £10 395 (b) £8419·95 (c) £4304·34 (d) £2382
7 (a)

Cal	Number in	Number out
1st	2	3·5
2nd	3·5	2·8571429
3rd	2·8571429	3·05
4th	3·05	2·9836066
5th	2·9836066	3·0054945
6th	3·0054945	2·9981718
7th	2·9981718	3·0006098
8th	3·0006098	2·9997968

(b) 11

8 (a)

Cal	Number in	Number out
1st	0	-1·5
2nd	-1·5	0·8571428
3rd	-0·8571428	-1·05
4th	-1·05	-0·9836065
5th	-0·9836065	1·0054945
6th	-1·0054945	-0·9981718
7th	-0·9981718	-1·0006098
8th	-1·0006098	-0·9997967

(b) -1

9 (a)

Date	Balance
1st Jan·	£10000
1st Feb·	£952·57
1st March	£905·02
1st April	£857·34
1st May	£809·55
1st June	£761·63
1st July	£713·58
1st Aug·	£665·42
1st Sept·	£617·13
1st Oct·	£568·72
1st Nov·	£520·17
1st Dec·	£471·51

(b) £1422·72

Page 7 Prime time

1

Number	Product of primes	
2	2	2^1
3	3	3^1
4	2 × 2	2^2
5	5	5^1
6	2 × 3	$2^1 × 3^1$
7	7	7^1
8	2 × 2 × 2	2^3
9	3 × 3	3^2
10	2 × 5	$2^1 × 5^1$
11	11	11^1
12	2 × 2 × 3	$2^2 × 3$
13	13	13^1
14	2 × 7	$2^1 × 7^1$
15	3 × 5	$3^1 × 5^1$
16	2 × 2 × 2 × 2	2^4
17	17	17^1
18	2 × 3 × 3	$2 × 3^2$
19	19	19^1
20	2 × 2 × 5	$2^2 × 5$
21	3 × 7	$3^1 × 7^1$
22	2 × 11	$2^1 × 11^1$
23	23	23^1
24	2 × 2 × 2 × 3	$2^3 × 3^1$

2 (a) $2^4 × 3$ (b) $3^2 × 7$ (c) $2^2 × 3 × 7$
  (d) $2^2 × 3^3$ (e) 2^8 (f) $5 × 7 × 11$
  (g) $5^3 × 7$ (h) $2^4 × 7 × 11$ (i) $2^3 × 3^2 × 5 × 7$
3 (a) $1764 = 2^2 × 3^2 × 7^2$ (b) $1050 = 2 × 3 × 5^2 × 7$
  (c) 42 (d) Largest size tile = 42 × 42 = 1764 cm^2
  (e) 42 × 25 = 1050 tiles
4 (a) $168 = 2^3 × 3 × 7$ (b) $140 = 2^2 × 5 × 7$
  (c) 5 times and 6 times respectively
5 After 360 seconds (1cm. of 8, 9, 12 and 15)
6 (a) $140 = 2^2 × 5 × 7$ $168 = 2^3 × 3 × 7$
    $210 = 2 × 3 × 5 × 7$ $238 = 2 × 7 × 17$
  (b) • 14 cm • 54 pieces

Page 8 Adding 4S and 1

Students' own answers

Page 9 Compounding the problem 1

1 55·0 mph
2 42·8 mph
3 (a) 0·25 (b) 0·4 (c) 0·67
  (d) 0·7 (e) 0·58 (f) 0·13
4 1·4 hour or 1 hour 24 min
5 (a) 24 min (b) 5 h 36 min (c) 2 h 15 min
  (d) 6 h 10·8 min (e) 3 h 33·6 min (f) 9 h 25·2 min
6 (a) 50 m/min (b) 3 km/h
7 (a) 8 km/h (b) 133·3 m/min
8 40·1 km/h
9 5·2 km/h
10 (a) 270 km (b) 5 hours (c) 54 km/h
11 1·875 minutes or 1 min 52·5 sec

Page 10 Compounding the problem 2

1 10·7 km/litre
2 6·67 km/litre
3 (a) 1260 km (b) 2·38 litres (c) 45 min
4 (a) 0·125 litres/km (b) 7·5 litres/hour
5 (a) • 0·58 p, 0·536 p • 171·4 hrs, 186·6 hrs
  (b) Best buy super gold
6 (a) 0·63 dollars/mark (b) 1·57 mark/dollar
7 (a) Best buy 0·45 litres/£1·00
8 7·5 g/cm3
9 (a) 11250 cm^3 (b) 128 250 g
10 (a) 6 cm^3/sec (b) 0·36 litres/min
11 83 hours 20 min
12 (a) • 0·156 m^3/sec • 9360 litres/min
  (b) 6·4 sec (d) 4·86 sec

Page 11 To the nth degree

1

Term	Value	Difference
1st	4	
2nd	7	3
3rd	10	3
4th	13	3
5th	16	3

2 (a)

Number of triangles	Number of matchsticks	Difference column
1	3	
2	5	2
3	7	2
4	9	2
5	11	2

(b) 13, 15 (c) 21

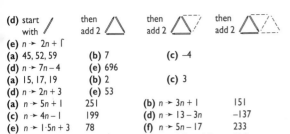

(d) start with / then add 2 △ then add 2 △/ then add 2 △▱

(e) $n \to 2n + 1$

(a) 45, 52, 59   **(b)** 7   **(c)** −4
(d) $n \to 7n - 4$ **(e)** 696
(a) 15, 17, 19   **(b)** 2   **(c)** 3
(d) $n \to 2n + 3$ **(e)** 53

(a) $n \to 5n + 1$ 251   **(b)** $n \to 3n + 1$ 151
(c) $n \to 4n - 1$ 199   **(d)** $n \to 13 - 3n$ −137
(e) $n \to 1\cdot5n + 3$ 78   **(f)** $n \to 5n - 17$ 233
(g) $n \to 1 - 3n$ −149   **(h)** $n \to 1\cdot2n + 1\cdot5$ 61·5
$n \to 4n - 3$

Page 12 To the nth degree 2

Term	Value	Difference
1st	3	
2nd	7	4
3rd	13	6
4th	21	8
5th	31	10
6th	43	12

(a)

Term	Value	Difference	Squared pattern
1st	6		$1^2 + 5$
2nd	11	5	$2^2 + 7$
3rd	18	7	$3^2 + 9$
4th	27	9	$4^2 + 11$
5th	38	11	$5^2 + 13$

(b) $10^2 + 20 + 3$ **(c)** $n^2 + 2n + 3$
(a) 28, 39
(b)

Term	Value	Difference	Pattern
1st	4		$1^2 + 3$
2nd	7	3	$2^2 + 3$
3rd	12	5	$3^2 + 3$
4th	19	7	$4^2 + 3$
5th	28	9	$5^2 + 3$
6th	39	11	$6^2 + 3$

(c) $n^2 + 3$ **(d)** 2503

(a)

Shape	Area	Difference	Pattern
1	2		$1^2 + 1$
2	6	4	$2^2 + 2$
3	12	6	$3^2 + 3$
4	20	8	$4^2 + 4$
5	30	10	$5^2 + 5$
6	42	12	$6^2 + 6$

(b) $n^2 + n$ **(c)** 10 100

(a) 20, 30 $n \to n^2 - n$ 2450
(b) 35, 48 $n \to n^2 + 2n$ 2600
(c) 16, 25 $n \to n^2 - 2n + 1$ 2401
(d) 32, 45 $n \to n^2 + 2n - 3$ 2597
(e) 44, 58 $n \to n^2 + 3n + 4$ 2654
(f) 27·5, 39 $n \to n^2 + 0\cdot5n$ 2525

(a) 2, 6, 12, 20, 30, 42, 56
(b) $n \to (n^2 + n)/2$ **(c)** 5050
(a) Position 1 should be 2 to give 2, 3, 6, 11, 18
(b)

Position	1	2	3	4	5
Number	2	3	6	11	18

(c) $n \to n^2 - 2n + 3$

---

8 (a) $n \to n^2 + 2n$ $n \to n^2 + 4n + 3$
(b)

Term	Value	Pattern
1st	3	$1^2 + 2$ or $(1+1)^2 - 1$
2nd	8	$2^2 + 4$ or $(2+1)^2 - 1$
3rd	15	$3^2 + 6$ or $(3+1)^2 - 1$
4th	24	$4^2 + 8$ or $(4+1)^2 - 1$
nth		$n^2 + 2n$ or $(n+1)^2 - 1$

Term	Value	Pattern
1st	8	$1^2 + 7$ or $(1+2)^2 - 1$
2nd	15	$2^2 + 11$ or $(2+2)^2 - 1$
3rd	24	$3^2 + 15$ or $(3+2)^2 - 1$
4th	35	$4^2 + 19$ or $(4+2)^2 - 1$
nth		$n^2 + 4n + 3$ or $(n+2)^2 - 1$

9 $n \to n^2 + n$ or $(n + 0\cdot5)^2 - 0\cdot25$

Page 13 Indices

1 729
2 (a) 16   **(b)** 256   **(c)** 1   **(d)** 390 625
   (e) 0·0625
3 (a) 216   **(b)** 243   **(c)** 20736   **(d)** 4096
   (e) 128   **(f)** 128   **(g)** 2187   **(h)** 2187
   (i) 2187
4 (a) y^{11} **(b)** a^{13} **(c)** y^{12} **(d)** b^{15}
   (e) y^9 **(f)** c^{15} **(g)** d^2 **(h)** h^3
5 (a) $8a^5$ **(b)** $20c^{11}$ **(c)** $6a^8b^7$ **(d)** $12c^{10}d^{11}$
   (e) $12b^9c^9$ **(f)** $4a^4b^4c^7$ **(g)** $16a^2b^2c^2$
   (h) $16a^4b^{10}$ **(i)** $10a^4b^7c^2$ **(j)** $14x^4y^{10}z^6$
6 (a) a^6 **(b)** b^8 **(c)** $25a^8b^6$ **(d)** $8a^9b^{15}$
   (e) $16a^{20}b^{16}$ **(f)** $81b^{28}c^4$
7 (a) b^3 **(b)** a^6 **(c)** $1/b$ **(d)** 1
   (e) b **(f)** c **(g)** $3c^2$ **(h)** $2d^2e^3$
   (i) $2bc$ **(j)** $2ab^2$ **(k)** $4km$ **(l)** 1
   (m) 1   **(n)** 6   **(o)** b^2c^3
   (p) $\dfrac{7ab^2}{9c}$ **(q)** $\dfrac{1}{2b^{10}c^9}$ **(r)** $\dfrac{16a^2}{27b^2c^{12}}$

Page 14 Play fair

1 (a) true   **(b)** false   **(c)** true   **(d)** false
   (e) true   **(f)** true
2 (a) ...⁻1 0 1 2 3 4 5 6 7 8...
(b) ...⁻1 0 1 2 3 4 5 6 7 8...
(c) ...⁻6 ⁻5 ⁻4 ⁻3 ⁻2 ⁻1 0 1 2...
(d) ...4 5 6 7 8 9 10 11 12...
(e) ...⁻6 ⁻5 ⁻4 ⁻3 ⁻2 ⁻1 0 1 2...
(f) ...⁻6 ⁻5 ⁻4 ⁻3 ⁻2 ⁻1 0 1 2...
3 (a) ...0 1 2 3 4 5 6 7 8 9...
(b) ...0 1 2 3 4 5 6 7 8...
(c) 4, 5
4 (a) 10, 11   **(b)** −1, 0, 1, 2, 3, 4, 5   **(c)** 0· 1, 2, 3, 4, 5   **(d)** none
   (e) −3, −2, −1, 0, 1, 2, 3   **(f)** 0, 1, 2, 3, 4, 5
5 (a) $n < 5$ **(b)** $n \geq 5$ **(c)** $n > 2$ **(d)** $n < 3$
   (e) $n < 4$ **(f)** $n > 2$ **(g)** $n \geq -2$ **(h)** $n > -3$
   (i) $n \leq -5$ **(j)** $n \geq 3$ **(k)** $n < -5$ **(l)** $n > -5$
   (m) $n \leq -5$ **(n)** $n > 4$
6 (a) $n \geq 2$ **(b)** $n < 8$ **(c)** $n < 2$ **(d)** $n > -8$
   (e) $n > 2$ **(f)** $n \geq -3$ **(g)** $n \leq -2$ **(h)** $n > 5$

7 (a) • $x \leqslant -3$ and • $x \leqslant 2$

(b) (c)

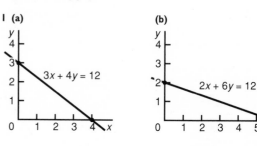

(number line labeled Solution, open circle at ⁻3, closed circle at 2, from ...⁻5 ⁻4 ⁻3 ⁻2 ⁻1 0 1 2 3 4 5 6)

(d) $-3 < x < 2$

8 $x < 5$ and $x < -1.5$ $-1.5 < x < 5$

Page 15 Tip it up

1 (a) 0·2   **(b)** 0·5   **(c)** 0·125   **(d)** 0·1
(e) 0·05   **(f)** 0·01   **(g)** $\frac{1}{a}$ **(h)** $\frac{1}{b}$

2 (a) 2   **(b)** 5   **(c)** 12   **(d)** a
(e) 2   **(f)** 4   **(g)** 10   **(h)** 20

3 (a) 1·5   **(b)** 2·5   **(c)** 2·25   **(d)** $\frac{2}{7}$
(e) $\frac{3}{8}$ **(f)** $\frac{a}{2}$ **(g)** $\frac{5}{b}$ **(h)** $\frac{b}{a}$

4 (a) 4·545454...   **(b)** 0·41666...   **(c)** 2·222...
(d) 0·27777...   **(e)** 19·230769   **(f)** 0·0190476

5 (a) 0·0625   **(b)** 0·05   **(c)** 0·25   **(d)** 0·031056
(e) 25   **(f)** 25   **(g)** $\frac{1}{a}$ **(h)** a

6 (a) 0·7   **(b)** 12·33...   **(c)** 1·566...

7 (a) 7   **(b)** $\frac{1}{7}$ **(d)** −12

8 (a)

x	1	2	4	5	10
y	1	0·5	0·25	0·2	0·1

(c) $0 \cdot 1\dot{6}...$ or $0.1\dot{6}$ • 1·25

9 (a) 6·13636...   **(b)** 0·1025   **(c)** −3·4375

(d) $f = \frac{uv}{u + v}$

Page 16 Frogs

Students' own answers

Pages 17, 18, 19 Graphs I

1 (a) steeper   **(b)** steeper   **(c)** less steep
(d) less steep   **(e)** steeper   **(f)** less steep

2 a 1, b $\frac{1}{4}$, c $\frac{4}{3}$, d 1$\frac{1}{2}$, e 3

3 (a) A(1, 1)   B(4, 3)   **(b)** $\frac{2}{3}$

4 (a) $\frac{3}{7}$ **(b)** $\frac{1}{2}$ **(c)** $\frac{1}{2}$ **(d)** $\frac{4}{3}$
(e) $\frac{2}{5}$ **(f)** 3

5 (a) gradient = 0   **(b)** $y = 0$

6 a $-\frac{3}{2}$, b −4, c 1, d 1$\frac{1}{4}$, e −3

7 (a) $-\frac{1}{2}$ **(b)** −3   **(c)** 2·5   **(d)** −1
(e) $-\frac{1}{7}$ **(f)** $\frac{2}{3}$ **(g)** $\frac{7}{3}$ **(h)** −2
(i) −1·5

8 (a) AB −3, BC $\frac{1}{3}$ **(b)** $-\frac{1}{2}$

9 (a) d and e, b and g **(b)** a and c, g and h

10 (a) $y = 2x + 2$ **(b)** $y = 2x - 3$

11 (a) $-\frac{2}{3}$ **(b)** $y = -\frac{2}{3}x + 2$ **(c)** $y = -\frac{2}{3}x - 1$

12 (a) (b)

(graph with solid line through origin sloping up, dashed line below labeled "down 3", axes from ⁻3 to 6 horizontal, ⁻3 to 3 vertical)

---

13 (a) gradient 4 translation 2
(b) gradient −5 translation −2
(c) gradient $\frac{3}{4}$ translation $-\frac{1}{2}$
(d) gradient 0·6 translation 0·8

14 $y = 5x + 9$

15 (a) $y = x + 4$ **(b)** $y = -\frac{3}{4}x + 6$ **(c)** $y = -4x - 6$ **(d)** $y = 0.583x - 3.83$

Page 20 Drawing graphs

1 (a)

(graph of $3x + 4y = 12$)

(b)

(graph of $2x + 6y = 12$)

(c)

(graph of $5x + 2y = 10$)

(d)

(graph of $3x - 2y = 6$)

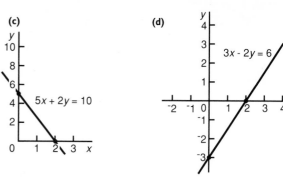

(e)

(graph of $4y - 2x = 8$)

(f)

(graph of $3x + 5y = 15$)

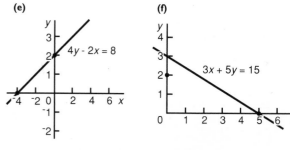

(g)

(graph of $3x + 4y = -12$)

(h)

(graph of $4x - 2y = -10$)

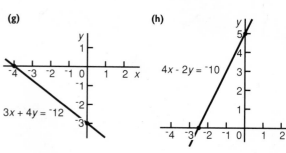

(i)

(graph of $2x + 2y = 7$)

(j)

(graph of $5y - 4x = 10$)

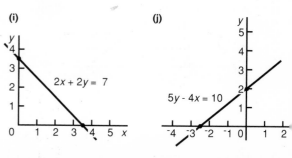

(b) $(^-1, 4)$

(a)

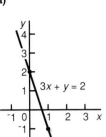

$3x + y = 2$

(b)

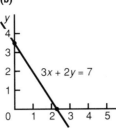

$3x + 2y = 7$

(c)

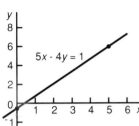

$5x - 4y = 1$

(d)

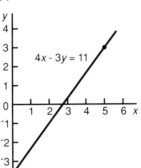

$4x - 3y = 11$

(e)

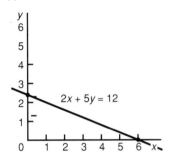

$2x + 5y = 12$

(a) When $x = 5, y = 1$
and when $y = 2, x = 6$
(b) The two points are too close to give an accurate graph
(c) Any values that separate the two points

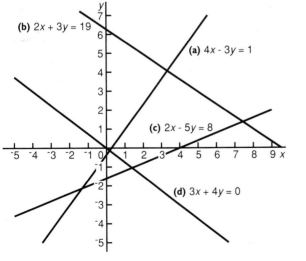

(b) $2x + 3y = 19$

(a) $4x - 3y = 1$

(c) $2x - 5y = 8$

(d) $3x + 4y = 0$

Page 21 Simultaneous equations

2 **(a)** $x = 3, y = ^-1$
(b) $x = 1, y = 0$
(c) $x = ^-1, y = ^-1$
(d) $x = 2 \cdot 5, y = 1 \cdot 5$
(e) $x = 0, y = 3$
(f) $x = 2, y = ^-3$
(g) $x = ^-2, y = 11$
(h) $x = ^-1, y = ^-2$

Page 21 Simultaneous equations

3 **(a)** Both lines are parallel
(b) No solution possible
4 **(a)** Both equations represent the same line
(b) Infinite number of solutions
5 **(a)** Infinite   **(b)** Infinite   **(c)** One solution
(d) No solution

Page 22 Positions in space

1 **(a)**

A (1, 0, 0)	E (0, 0, 1)
B (1, 1, 0)	F (1, 0, 1)
C (0, 1, 0)	G (1, 1, 1)
D (0, 1, 1)	O (0, 0, 0)

(b) $(\frac{1}{2}, \frac{1}{2}, \frac{1}{2})$

2   A (4, 0, 0)   E (0, 0, 2)
    B (4, 3, 0)   F (4, 0, 2)
    C (0, 3, 0)   G (4, 3, 2)
    D (0, 3, 2)   O (0, 0, 0)

3   A (4, 1, 2)   C (9, 4, 2)   E (4, 1, 4)   G (9, 4, 4)
    B (9, 1, 2)   D (4, 4, 2)   F (9, 1, 4)   H (4, 4, 4)
Other correct answers possible.

4 Many correct solutions depending upon the orientation of the cube. The most likely being
O (1, 2, 4)   A (4, 2, 4)   B (4, 4, 4)   C (1, 4, 4)
D (1, 4, 10)   E (1, 2, 10)   F (4, 2, 10)   G (4, 4, 10)
Accept other correct answers.

Pages 23 and 24 Flow diagrams

1 **(a)** • 39 • 140 • −5
(b) This flow diagram inputs two numbers. The output is the product of their sum and difference.
2 **(a)** 26   **(b)** 168   **(c)** −64
3 **(a)** • 36 • 49 • 64 •81   **(b)** Any two numbers whose sum is 60
4 **(a)** • 6 •12 • 8
(b) Any two numbers which when divided by each other have an answer of 70
5 **(a)**

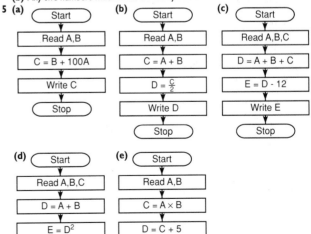

164

6 (a) Change decision box to

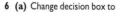

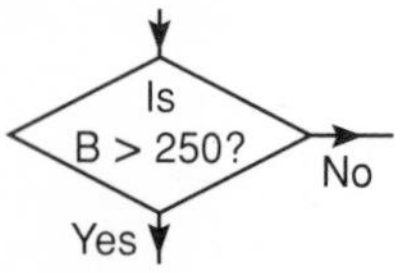
Is
B > 250?
No
Yes

(b) Change to

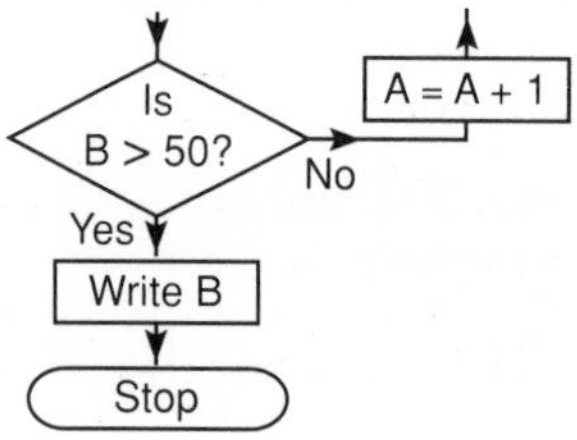
Is
B > 50?
A = A + 1
No
Yes
Write B
Stop

7 (a) 1, 8, 27, 64, 125
(b) Change decision box to

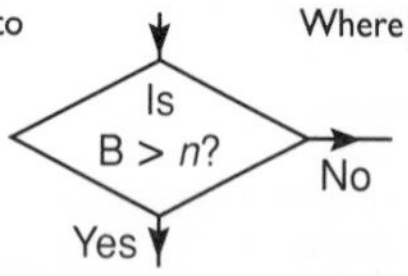
Is
B > n?
No
Yes

Where $27 < n < 64$

8 (a) 75, 52, 27, 0 **(b)** –20, –9, 0

9 (a)

Number of years	*Amount of money*
0	100
1	108
2	116·64
3	125·97
4	136·05
5	146·93

(b) Change decision box to

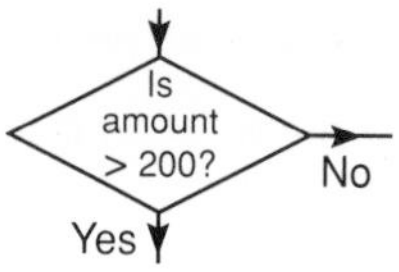
Is
amount
> 200?
No
Yes

10 •

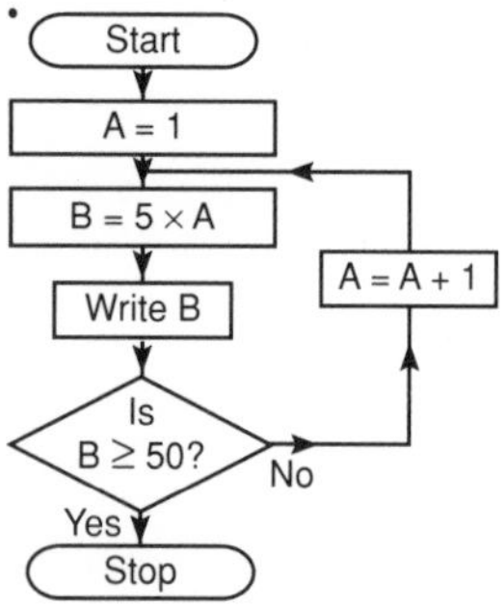
Start
A = 1
B = 5 × A
A = A + 1
Write B
Is
B ≥ 50?
No
Yes
Stop

•

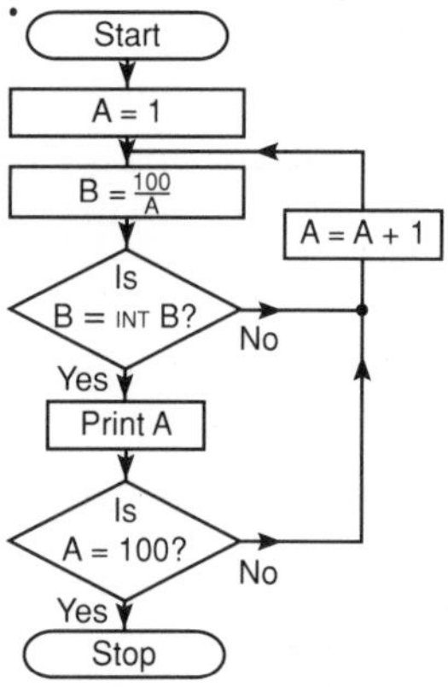
Start
A = 1
B = 100/A
A = A + 1
Is
B = INT B?
No
Yes
Print A
Is
A = 100?
No
Yes
Stop

•

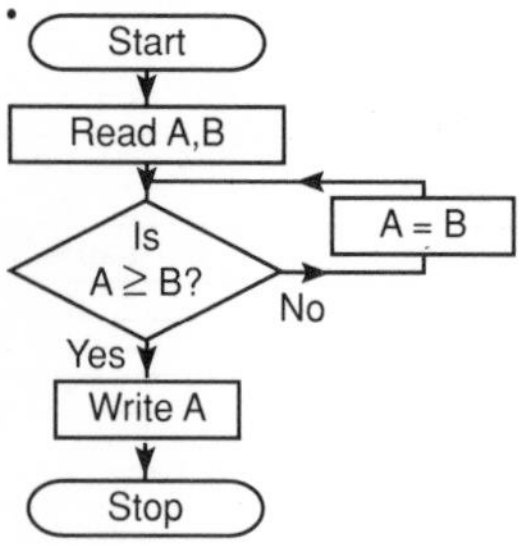
Start
Read A,B
A = B
Is
A ≥ B?
No
Yes
Write A
Stop

•

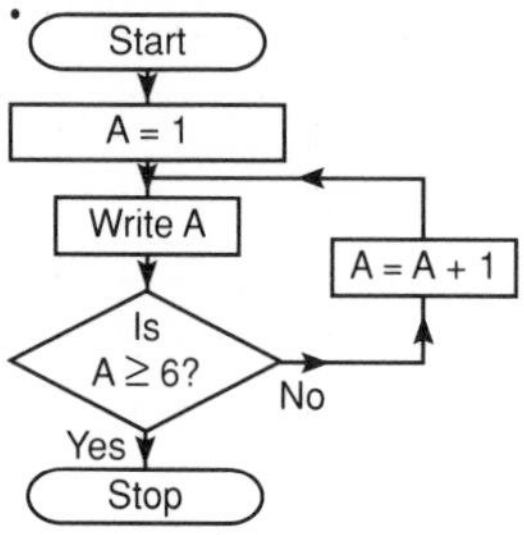
Start
A = 1
Write A
A = A + 1
Is
A ≥ 6?
No
Yes
Stop

•

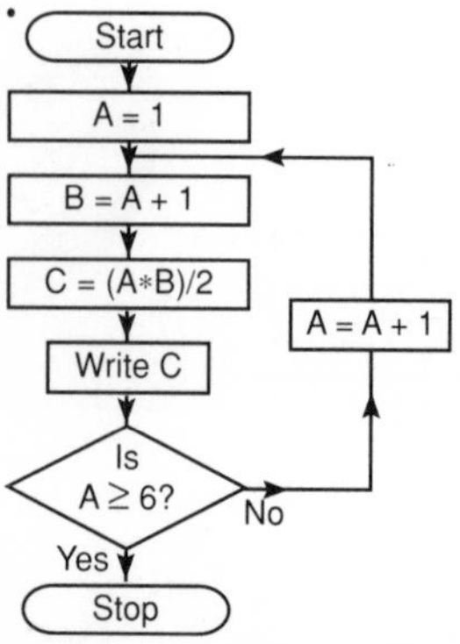
Start
A = 1
B = A + 1
C = (A*B)/2
A = A + 1
Write C
Is
A ≥ 6?
No
Yes
Stop

Pages 25 and 26 Pythagoras 1

1 (a) (b)
• 1, 1, 2 • 16, 1, 17 • 9, 4, 13 • 25, 64, 89 • 9, 16, 25
2 (a) 13 **(b)** 10 **(c)** 4 **(d)** 9 **(e)** 64
3 (a) 5 cm **(b)** 13 cm **(c)** 8 cm **(d)** 8·06 cm **(e)** 7 cm
4 13 cm
5 24 cm
6 11·66 km
7 9 cm
8 7·07 cm
9 1954·40 m
10 (a) $x = 5$ cm, $y = 13$ cm **(b)** $x = 6$ cm, $7 = 24$ cm
(c) $x = 9$cm, $y = 12·04$ cm **(d)** $x = 24$ cm, $y = 11$ cm, $z = 13·03$ cm
11 (a) 12·04 cm **(b)** 28·85 cm **(c)** 18·79 cm
12 (a) 26 **(b)** 5·20 **(c)** 9·11
(d) 9·27 **(e)** 10·82 **(f)** 11·045

Page 27 Pythagoras 2

1 (a) 4·12 **(b)** 3·61 **(c)** 4·24 **(d)** 7·21
2 (a) 5 **(b)** 13 **(e)** 10
(d) 8·94 **(e)** 7·07 **(f)** 10·2
3 $\sqrt{(x_1 - x_2)^2 + (y_1 - y_2)^2}$
4 (13,0) ; (0, 13) ; (–13, 0), (0 – 13)
(5, 12) ; (–5, 12) ; (12, –5), (–12, 5)
(–5, –12)
5 All the points are 5 units from (1, 2)
(a) centre of circle = (1, 2)
(b) (1, 7), (1, –3); (–4, 2), (4, –1) plus many others

Page 28 Crossing over/Crossing polygons

Students own answers

Pages 29 and 30 Pythagoras 3

Students own answers

Pages 31 and 32 Enlargements

1 (a) (b) Students' own answers
2 (a) (b) (c) Students' own answers
(d) A' (7, 1) B' (16, 1) C' (16, 7)
3 (a) (b) Students' own answers
(c) X' (–4, –4,) Y' (–16, –8) X' (–8, –16)
(d) Students' own answer
4 (a) (b) (c) Students' own answers
(d) A' (2, 1) B' (4, 1) C' (4, 2)
(e) A'' (–2, –1) B'' (–4, –1) C'' (–4, –2)
5 (a) See students diagrams
(b) P'(1·5, 1·5) Q'(3, 1·5) R'(1·5, 3)
6 (a) (17, 16) **(b)** Scale factor = $\frac{1}{2}$
7 (a)

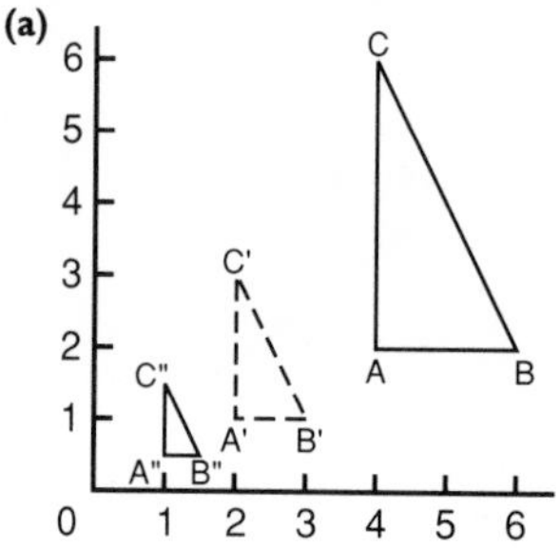
C
C'
C''
A
B
A'
B'
A''
B''
0
1
2
3
4
5
6

(b) 4 square units
(c) see diagram
(d) 1 square unit
(e) $\frac{1}{4}$ or $(\frac{1}{2})^2$
(f) see diagram
(g) $\frac{1}{4}$ square unit
(h) $\frac{1}{16}$ or $(\frac{1}{4})^2$

(a)

See students answers

(b) 4·5 square unit

(c) see diagram

(d) area = $\frac{1}{2}$ square unit which is $\frac{1}{9}$ or $(\frac{1}{3})^2$ of the area of PQR

ages 33, 34, 35 Lengths, areas and volumes

1 **(a)** $6x + 8$ **(b)** 5   **(c)** $(2x + 1)(x + 3)$ or $2x^2 + 7x + 3$
2 **(a)** 4 cm   **(b)** 5·66 cm
3 worksheet 1
4 **(a)** $4x + 1$ **(b)** 7·5
5 **(a)** 4 cm   **(b)** • 6 cm^2 • 12 cm   **(c)** • 54 cm^2 • 36 cm
6 worksheet 2
7 **(a)** 72 cm^2 **(b)** 105 cm^2
8 worksheet 3
9 60·2 cm^2
0 **(a)** $h = 12$ **(b)** 150 cm^2
1 Students' own answer
2 worksheet 4
3 78·54 cm^2
4 **(a)** 5·64 cm   **(b)** 35·42 cm
5 **(a)** 2 cm   **(b)** 12·56 cm
6 worksheet 5
7 21·95 cm^3
8 4·31 cm
9 **(a)** 4 cm   **(b)** 96 cm^2 **(c)** 6·93 cm
20 3·28 × 10^{-11} cm^3
21 $1 \times 1 \times 72$ $1 \times 2 \times 36$ $2 \times 1 \times 36$ $1 \times 3 \times 24 \dots$
    giving surface area of
    290, 240, 240, ... cm^2
    with smallest surface area of 108 cm^2 when cuboid is 3 cm by 4 cm by 6 cm
22 **(a)** $x^2h = 4 \cdot 8 => x = \sqrt{\frac{48}{h}}$ **(b)** 4·90 cm   **(c)** 3 cm
23 6 cm
24 **(a)** Students own answer
    (b) No +ve x solution to equation
25 worksheet 5
26 **(a)** 324 cm^2 **(b)** 360 cm^3
27 worksheet 6
28 **(a)** 600 cm^3 **(b)** 660 cm^2
29 worksheet 7
30 160 cm^3
31 **(a)** 10 cm   **(b)** 120 cm^3
32 **(a)** 534·07 cm^2 **(b)** 942·48 cm^3
33 201·06 cm^3
34 **(a)** 314·16 cm^3 **(b)** 523·6 cm^3

Page 36 Bell ringing

Students' own answers

Page 37 How probable

Students' own answers

Page 38 Probably I.T.

Students' own answers

Page 39 Ask me another

Student's own answers

Page 40 Testing a hypothesis

1 **(a)**

Marks	0 – 9	10 – 19	20 – 29	30 – 39	40 – 49
Frequency	3	11	22	9	5

(b) Hypothesis untrue·

2

Size (cm)	12	13	14	15	16	17	18	19	20	21	22	23	24	25	26
Frequency	1	0	0	1	2	4	10	17	5	6	3	0	0	0	0

Size (cm)	27	28	29
Frequency	0	0	1

3 Students' own answers

Page 41 Around the middle

1 **(a)**

Mean	Median	Mode	**(b)**
• 6·71	6	–	mean or median, not mode – no mode available
• 27·24	27·5	–	mean or median, not mode – no mode available
• 59	58	57, 58 or 60	mean or median, not mode. The sequencer is bi-modal
• 6·49	5·55	5·4	median or mode, not mean. The 15·2 will distort the mean

2 mean = 78·29 kg , median = 76 kg
3 **(a)** • mean = 21·9°C   • median = 21·5°C   • mode = 22°C
    (b) mean
4 **(a)** mean = 169·3 cm   **(b)** median = 169 cm

Page 42 Frequently so

1 **(a)**

x	f	fx
0	10	0
1	17	17
2	9	18
3	3	9
4	1	4
total		48

(b) • mean = 1·2
    • median = 1
    • mode = 1
(c) Bar chart or pie chart, see students' response

2 **(a)**

x	f	fx
165	1	165
166	2	332
167	3	501
168	5	840
169	9	1521
170	13	2210
171	8	1368
172	6	1032
173	3	519
174	4	696

(b) • mean = 170·07
    • median = 170
    • mode = 170
    Note a length recorded above as 170 means from 169·5 to 170·5 etc.
(c) Histogram
3 **(a)** Mean = 14·54   • median = 14   • mode = 14
    (b) Bar chart or histogram

Pages 43 and 44 Class marks

1 (a)

Half way x	f	fx
25	2	50
35	5	175
45	16	720
55	25	1375
65	13	845
75	6	450
85	3	255

(b) mean = 55·2

Students can choose other halfway values, such as 24·5 by taking 20 to 30 to mean 19·5 to 29·5 etc, or even 24·995 by taking 20 to 30 to mean 20 to 29·99. These choices will give slight variations to the estimate of the mean.

2

Half way x	f	fx
15·5	3	46·5
25·5	5	127·5
35·5	8	284·0
45·5	14	637·0
55·5	23	1276·5
65·5	28	1834·0
75·5	11	830·5
85·5	6	513·0
95·5	2	191·0

(b) mean = 57·4

3 (a)

Half way x	f	fx
100	1	100
300	4	1200
500	7	3500
700	10	7000
900	14	12600
1100	33	36300
1300	20	26000
1500	6	9000
1700	5	8500

(b) mean = 1042

4 (a)

Half way x	f	fx
85	1	85
95	4	380
105	9	945
115	28	3220
125	37	4625
135	11	1485
145	7	1015
155	3	465

(b) mean = 122·2

5 (a)

Half way x	f	fx
4·5	20	90
14·5	64	928
24·5	52	1274
34·5	21	724·5
44·5	2	89
54·5	1	54·5
	160	3160

(b) mean = 19·75 years

Pages 45 and 46 Frequency polygons

1

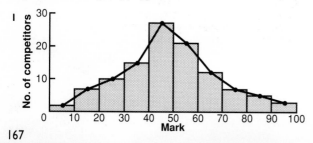

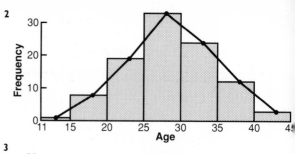

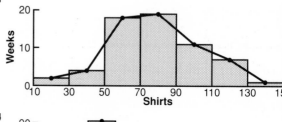

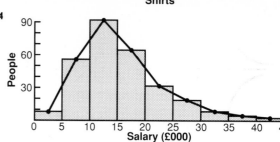

Pages 47 and 48 Scattered about

1 −ve correlation. Mean around 5 words
2 +ve correlation. Mean around 14 g
3 −ve correlation. Mean around 17° or 18° celsius
Note: Acceptable answers could vary according to the accuracy of graph and choice of line of best fit

Page 49 The flow of things 1

Students' own answers

Page 50 The flow of things 2

Students' own answers

Pages 51 and 52 Moving points: loci

1 (a)

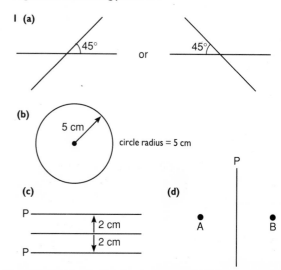

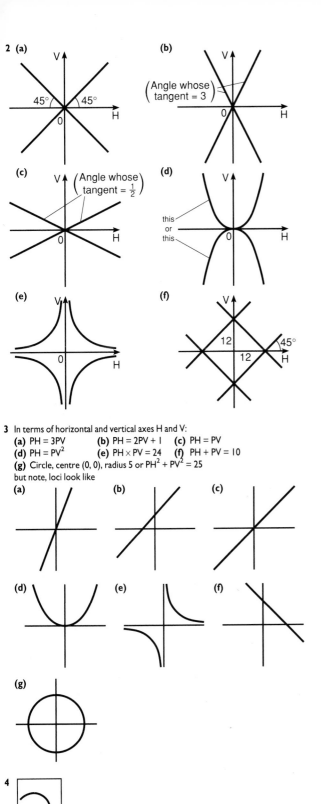

2 (a)

45° 45°
V, H, O

(b)

(Angle whose tangent = 3)
V, H, O

(c)

(Angle whose tangent = ½)
V, H, O

(d)

this or this
V, H, O

(e)

V, H, O

(f)

12 12 45°
V, H

3 In terms of horizontal and vertical axes H and V:
(a) PH = 3PV **(b)** PH = 2PV + 1 **(c)** PH = PV
(d) PH = PV² **(e)** PH × PV = 24 **(f)** PH + PV = 10
(g) Circle, centre (0, 0), radius 5 or PH² + PV² = 25
but note, loci look like

(a) **(b)** **(c)**
(d) **(e)** **(f)**
(g)

4

5 (a) A, B **(b)**
(c) A, B **(d)**

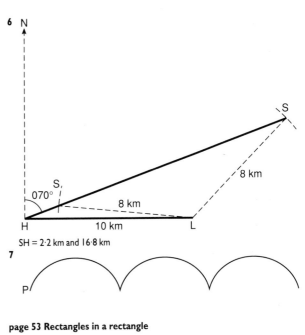

6

N
S
070° S₁
8 km
8 km
H 10 km L
P

SH = 2·2 km and 16·8 km

7

P

page 53 Rectangles in a rectangle

1 Students' own answers
2 (a) 18 **(b)** 90 **(c)** 150
3 Students' investigation

Page 54 Manhattan loci

Students' own answers

Pages 55 and 56 Bracketed together 1

1 (a) 51	**(b)** 3·22	**(c)** 5	**(d)** 10·83
(e) 0·15	**(f)** 1·1367		
2 (a) 30	**(b)** 373	**(c)** 14·1	
3 (a) 15·71	**(b)** 116·8	**(c)** 506·72	
4 (a) 50	**(b)** 30	**(c)** 100	**(d)** 0
(e) 23·8	**(f)** −26·6	**(g)** 232·2	**(h)** −31·6
(i) 537·7			

5 16·2
6 (a) 5·04 m², 6·16 m², 7·28 m², 8·4 m² **(b)** 26·88 m²
7 (a) 91·29 **(b)** −32·524
8 (a) £5916 **(b)** £15·60
9 (a) 544 **(b)** £6505·15 **(c)** £11·96

Children under 5 .... £5·75
Children 5 to 12 .... £8·39
Children 13 to 16 .... £11·90
Students 17 to 18 .... £12·24
Adults (over 18) .... £22·52

10 (a) 0·2948

(b)

n	Value
1·3	4·3442623
1·34	4·2604502
1·345	4·2502005
1·35	4·24
1·4	4·140625
1·5	3·9552239

11 (a) 1 **(b)** 1
12 (a) 0·2698618 **(b)** 0·3319171
13 (a) 3·333... **(b)** • 3·846 • 4·1522
(c) See students' work. They should try 1·75
14 2·933

Page 57 You've got the part

1 (a) $\frac{3}{5}$ (b) £7·29

2 (a) $\frac{3}{4}$ (b) 5

3 (a) 21 (b) $18\frac{2}{3}$ (c) 63

4 (a) 26 (b) 66 (c) 142 (d) 0·76

5 (a) $\frac{5}{6}$ (b) $\frac{13}{15}$ (c) $\frac{17}{20}$ (d) $\frac{19}{20}$

(e) $\frac{7}{12}$ (f) $\frac{23}{60}$

6 combinations $r + u$, $s + t$, $s + u$, $s + 2u$, $t + u$, $t + 2u$

6 (a)

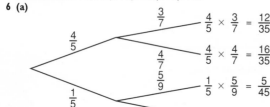

$\frac{4}{5} \times \frac{3}{7} = \frac{12}{35}$

$\frac{4}{5} \times \frac{4}{7} = \frac{16}{35}$

$\frac{1}{5} \times \frac{5}{9} = \frac{5}{45}$

$\frac{1}{5} \times \frac{4}{9} = \frac{4}{45}$

(b) $\frac{179}{315}$

7 (a) 1 student (b) £415

8 (a) $\frac{1}{3}$ (b) 78·54 cm^2 (c) 26·18 cm^2 (d) 20·47cm

Page 58 More than a guess 1

1 (a) 8·4 (b) 39·125 (c) 4·5549 (d) 136·0005
(e) 83·232 (f) 3·625 (g) 5·180232
(h) 8·745098 (i) 8·569428 (j) 383·54839

2 (a) 4·48 (b) 20·36

3 (a) 15·81 cm (b) 158·1 cm (c) 50 cm

4 (a) 2·491 (b) 0·009

5 (a) 12 (b) 4 (c) 45 (d) 20
(e) 20 (f) $\frac{1}{4}$ (g) 5 (h) 7·5
(i) 5 (j) 7 (k) 15 (l) 60

6 24 cm^2

7 8 cartons

8 30 litres

Page 59 More than a guess 2

1 (a) 10 (b) 300 (c) 10 (d) 30
(e) 5 (f) 2 (g) 2 (h) 25
(i) 225 (j) 6

2 (a) £2800 (b) £2681·25 (c) £118·75

3 (a) 20 (b) 20·25 (c) 0·25

4 (a) • 30 • 42 • 56 (b) • 30·25 • 42·25 • 56·25
(c) Take the whole number below and multiply it by the number above and add 0·25
(d) See students' statement (e) 132·25

5 5 units

6 (a) 8 cm (b) 48 cm^2

7 (a) 300 m/min (b) 18 km/h

8 60 revolutions

9 (a) 10 (b) 10·32

Page 60 Subject of a formula

1 (a) $d = a - bc$ (b) 12·4

2 (a) $c = \frac{a}{5}$ (b) $c = \frac{a}{b}$ (c) $c = a - b$ (d) $c = a - 3b$

(e) $b = a + c$ (f) $c = b - a$ (g) $t = us$ (h) $u = \frac{t}{s}$

(i) $a = p(r + q)$ (j) $p = \frac{a}{r - m}$ (k) $h = \frac{2A}{b}$ (l) $2 = \frac{bh}{A}$

3 (a) $h = \frac{3v}{\pi r^2}$ (b) 9·026

4 (a) $ab + ac$ (b) $b = \frac{x - ac}{a}$ (c) 0·225

5 (a) $c = \frac{y - ba}{3}$ (b) $a = y(b - 2c)$ (c) $c = \frac{xb - a}{5b}$

(d) $v = \frac{w + rx}{y}$ (e) $r = \frac{a - bc}{b}$ (f) $t = \frac{wr - y}{w}$

(g) $z = \frac{2ka - b}{8k}$ (h) $t = \frac{y - krw}{kr}$

6 (a) $t = \sqrt{\frac{s - b}{a}}$ (b) $r = \sqrt{A}$ (c) $g = \frac{s - ut}{t^2}$

(d) $r = \sqrt[3]{\frac{3A}{4}}$ (e) $R = \sqrt{\frac{A}{\pi} + r^2}$ (f) $n = \left(\frac{y - c}{a}\right)^2$

(g) $v = \frac{b}{c}$ (h) $f = \frac{uv}{u + v}$ (i) $u = \frac{2s}{t} + v$

(j) $g = \frac{n(2k)^2}{T^2}$

7 (a) 44·73 (b) $a = \frac{2A - hb}{h}$ (c) 4·066...

8 $k = \frac{u}{4y(r + t)}$

Page 61 Keep it in proportion 1

1 (b) 20·8 m (b) 4·3 sec

2 Graph (a) only

3 (b) 7·5 m (c) 12·8 m

4 (a) 4 m (b) $s = \frac{8h}{5}$ (c) 29·6

5 (b) $h = \frac{2s}{3}$ (c) 8·4 m (d) 24·75 m

6 (a) $h = \frac{v}{3}$ (b) 97·2 cm^3 (c) 21·6 cm (d) 0·388 cm

Page 62 Keep it proportion 2

1 (a)

w	6	9
h	8·4	12·6

(b)

h	12·0	16·8
s	24·5	34·3

(c)

p	7·8	20·19
s	6·8	17·6

(d)

y	14·4	10·2
x	33·74	23·9

2 (a) $w = 1·4w$ (b) $s = 2h$ (c) $s = 0·9p$ (d) $y = 2·3x$

3 (a)

Distance (cm)	1·4	
Diameter (cm)	4·2	21·6

(b) 7·2 m (c) dia = 3 × dist

4 (a) length = 56 mm, width = 39·05 mm (b) 70 mm (d) 48·82 mm

5 (a) 8·64 volts 4·8 amps (b) 3·77... amps (c) 3·8 volts

6 (b) 3·2, 3·9 (c) $i = 0·26v$ (d) 18·08 amps (e) 2·2568 v

Page 63 Bracketed together 2

1 (a) 12 red and 9 blue (b) 12 red and 10 blue (c) 20 r and 15 b
(d) 6 r, 9 b and 12 y (e) 20 r and 24 b (f) 14 r, 35 b and 21 y
(g) 10 r, 40 b, 35 y and 10 g

2 (a) $2p + 2q$ (b) $3a + 6$ (c) $12b + 16$ (d) $3r + br$
(e) $2yr + 3gr$ (f) $a^2 + 3a$ (g) $x^2 + xy$ (h) $xy + y^2$
(i) $2m^2 - 3m$ (j) $4x^2 - 2xy$ (k) $-2r - 2y$ (l) $12y - 8r$
(m) $3y - x$ (n) $x^2y - x^2$

3 (a) $4x - 12$ (b) $3x + 21$ (c) $2x + 6y$

4 (a) $3r + 6b = 3(r + 2b)$ (b) $2r + 8b = 2(r + 2b)$
(c) $4r + 10y = 2(2r + 5y)$ (d) $5g + 10r = 5(g + 2r)$
(e) $9r + 12y = 3(3r + 4y)$ (f) $4r + 8g = 4(r + 2g)$
(g) $6r + 9b = 3(2r + 3b)$ (h) $12y + 10b = 2(6y + 5b)$
(i) $18g + 12b = 6(3g + 2b)$ (j) $24r + 32g = 8(3r + 4g)$

5 (a) $c(a + b)$ (b) $p(t + 3)$ (c) $r(2 + g)$ (d) $r(b - 2g)$
(e) $a(3b - 2c)$ (f) $6(2x - 3y)$ (g) $x(x + 3)$ (h) $a(ab - 2)$
(i) $r(2b + 3w - 4b)$ (j) $x(a^2 + b)$ (k) $x(x - 6y)$ (l) $2y(2y - 3)$
(m) $ay(y + 1)$ (n) $rb(r + b)$ (o) $8rb(3r + 2b)$
(p) $2y(6y^2 - 3y + 4)$

Page 64 Seeing double

1 (a) 24   (b) 14   (c) 30   (d) 700

2

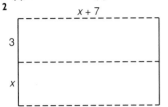

x + 7   3   *x*

3 **(a) (b)** for rectangle of length ($x + 4$) and width ($x + 1$):
$A = x(x + 1) + 4(x + 1)$
$= x^2 + x + 4x + 4$
$= x^2 + 5x + 4$

For rectangle of length ($x + 1$) and width ($x + 4$):
$A = x(x + 4) + 1(x + 4)$
$= x^2 + 4x + x + 4$
$= x^2 + 5x + 4$

For rectangle of length ($x + 4$) and width ($x + 6$):
$A = x(x + 6) + 4(x + 6)$
$= x^2 + 6x + 4x + 24$
$= x^2 + 10x + 24$

4 **(a)** • $x - 2$ • $x^2 + 3x$ • $2x + 6$ **(b)** $(x^2 + 3x) - (2x + 6) = x^2 + x - 6$

5 **(a)** $x^2 + 12x + 32$ **(b)** $p^2 + 9p + 14$ **(c)** $y^2 + 2y - 8$
(d) $w^2 - 6w - 27$ **(e)** $x^2 - 11x + 30$

6 **(a)** $x^2 + 9x + 20$ **(b)** $a^2 + 2a - 8$ **(c)** $x^2 + 3x - 18$
(d) $p^2 - 11p + 28$ **(e)** $y^2 + 8y + 16$ **(f)** $2x^2 + 11x + 5$
(g) $3x^2 + 13x - 10$ **(h)** $6r^2 + r - 2$ **(i)** $acx^2 + adx + bcx + bd$
(j) $abr^2 + 2ar - 2br - 4$ **(k)** $a^2x^2 + 2ax - 35$
(l) $y^3 + 5xy^2 - 5x^2 - yx$

7 **(a)**

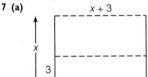

$x + 3$ x 3

$A = (x^2 + 3x) - (3x + 9)$
$= x^2 - 9$

(b)

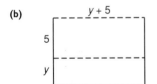

$y + 5$ 5 y

$A = (y^2 + 5y) + (5y + 25)$
$= y^2 + 10y + 25$

(c)

$y + 6$ y

$A = y^2 + 6y$

(d)

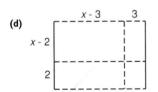

$x - 3$ 3 $x - 2$ 2

$A = x^2 - (2x - 6) - (3x - 6) - 6$
$= x^2 + 2x + 6 - 3x + 6 - 6$
$= x^2 - 5x + 6$

Page 65 Simultaneous equations 2

1 $x = 2, y = 3$

2 **(a)** $x = -3$ $y = 6$ **(b)** $x = 1$ $y = 2$
(c) $x = 1$ $y = 2$ **(d)** $x = 2.5$ $y = 1.5$

3 **(a)** $x = 2$ $y = 2$ **(b)** $x = 1$ $y = 3$
(c) $x = 2$ $y = 1$ **(d)** $x = -8$ $y = -2$

4 **(a)** $x = 2$ $y = 3$ **(b)** $x = 2$ $y = 1$
(c) $x = 0$ $y = 3$ **(d)** $x = 2$ $y = -1$
(e) $x = 3$ $y = -4$ **(f)** $x = 2$ $y = 1$

5 $x = 3, \ y = 2 \ (3, 2)$

6 $(8, 5)$

7 **(a)** From the information given $y = 5$ when $x = 1$. Therefore $5 = 1m + c$
(b) $11 = 3m + c$ **(c)** $m = 3, c = 2, y = 3x + 2$

Page 66 Simultaneous equations 3

1 **(a)** $7x + y = 38$ **(b)** $x - 5y = -10$ **(c)** $-x + 5y = 10$

2    $12x - 6y = 42$
     $6x + 6y = 48$
  add $18x \quad = 90$

3 **(a)** $x = 2, y = 1$ **(b)** $x = 2, y = 4$ **(c)** $x = 0, y = -2$
(d) $x = 0, y = 3$ **(e)** $x = -2, y = 3$ **(f)** $x = -2, y = 3$

4 **(a)** $x = 2, y = -2$ **(b)** $x = 1, y = 2$ **(c)** $x = 1, y = 2$
(d) $x = -2, y = 3$ **(e)** $x = -1, y = -2$ **(f)** $x = 7, y = 3$
(g) $x = 1.5, y = 2$ **(h)** $x = -2, y = 1$ **(i)** $x = 3, y = 4$
(j) $x = -2, y = 2$ **(k)** $h = 2.5, k = -3.25$ **(l)** $h = -3.5, k = 3$

5 $(30, 6)$

6 **(a)** $x = -2, y = 2$ hence $2 = -2m + c$ **(b)** $4 = 0m + c$
(c) $m = 1, c = 4$ **(d)** $y = x + c$

7 **(a)** rectangle $a + 2b = 16$, triangle $5a - b = 25$
(b) $a = 6, b = 5$ **(c)** $5, 8, 12$

Pages 67 and 68 Travel graphs 1

1 **(a)** 4 hours   **(b)** 62·5 km/h   **(c)** 195 km
(d) 350 km   **(e)** 40 km/h   **(f)** 6 hours 15 min

2 **(a)** 60 km/h   **(b)** resting/traffic jam   **(c)** 60 km/h
(d)

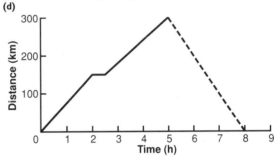

3 **(a)** 2 km/min   **(b)** 1·6 km/min   **(c)** 160 km/hour

4 **(a)**

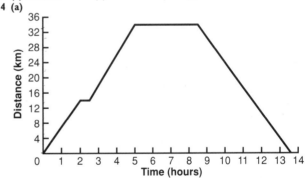

(b) • 7 km/h • 8 km/h • 6·8 km/h

5 **(a)** 14 km   **(b)** $3\frac{1}{2}$ hours   **(c)** 10 km
(d) 15 min   **(e)** • 2·6 km/hr, 6 km/hr, 5·3 km/hr • 4 km/hr

6 **(a)**

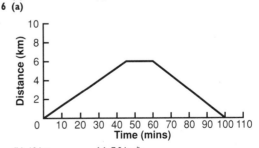

(b) 12 km   **(c)** 7·2 km/h·

7 (a)

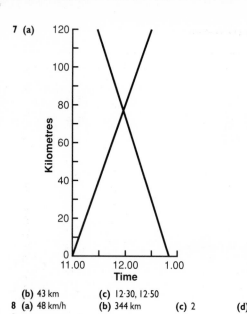

(b) 43 km **(c)** 12·30, 12·50

8 (a) 48 km/h **(b)** 344 km **(c)** 2 **(d)** 45·87 km/h

9

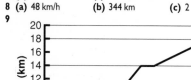
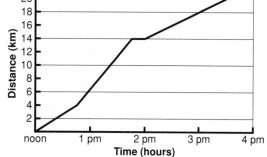

(a) 8·4 km/h **(b)** 20 min **(c)** see graph **(d)** 5·71 km/h

10 (a)

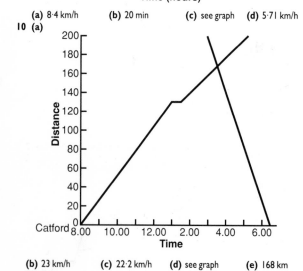

(b) 23 km/h **(c)** 22·2 km/h **(d)** see graph **(e)** 168 km
(f) 3·30 pm

Page 69 Trial and improvement

1 Answers around
  (a) 6·3 **(b)** 7·7 **(c)** 9·5 **(d)** 2·6
  (e) 2·3 **(f)** 5·8

2 $4^2 + 8 = 24$, $5^2 + 20 = 35$, 4·57

3 5·53

4 (a) $3^2 + \frac{3}{3} = 10$, $4^2 + \frac{4}{3} = 17·33$ **(b)** Around 3·5 or below
  (c) 3·33

5 (a)
(b)

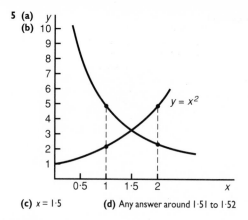

(c) $x = 1·5$ **(d)** Any answer around 1·51 to 1·52

Page 70 True story of trigonometry

Students' own answers

Pages 71 and 72 Trigonometry 1

1

Angle	Sine	Cosine	Tangent
36	0·5878	0·8090	0·7265
50	0·7660	0·6428	1·1918
60	0·8660	0·5000	1·7321
88	0·9994	0·0349	28·6363
100	0·9848	−0·1736	−5·6713
120	0·8660	−0·5000	−1·7321
175	0·0872	−0·9962	−0·0875
200	−0·3420	−0·9397	0·3639
250	−0·9397	−0·3420	2·7475
300	−0·8660	0·5000	−1·7321

2 (a) 60° **(b)** 30° **(c)** 45° **(d)** 26·57°
  (e) 70° **(f)** 26·31° **(g)** 83·43° **(h)** 75°
  (i) 80·50° **(j)** 20·5°

3 (a)

Angle	Sine	Cosine	Tangent
0	0	1	0
10	0·1736	0·9848	0·1763
20	0·3420	0·9397	0·3640
30	0·5	0·8660	0·5773
40	0·6428	0·7660	0·8391
50	0·7660	0·6428	1·1918
60	0·8660	0·5	1·7320
70	0·9397	0·3420	2·7475
80	0·9848	0·1736	5·6713
90	1	0	∞

(b) Sine x Cosine x

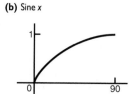
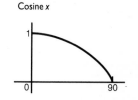

Tangent x

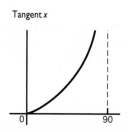

4 Students' own answers

5 $OB_1 = 2\cos x$ $A_1T_1 = 2\tan x$

6 (a) $OA = 1$ $OB = 0.766$ $AT = 0.839$
  (b) $OP = 4$ $OQ = 3.064$ $PR = 3.356$

7 (a) 10, 6·248, 11·918   **(b)** 8, 2·736, 21·98

  (c) $\frac{1}{2}$, 0·25, 0·866

8 (a) 45°   **(b)** 45°

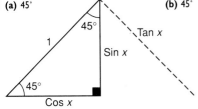

Pages 73, 74 and 75 Trigonometry 2

1 (a) 5   **(b)** 5·14   **(c)** 11·3
  (d) 2·62   **(e)** 36·87°   **(f)** 53·13°
  (g) 4·77   **(h)** 38·68°   **(i)** 38·68°

2 (a) 9·4   **(b)** 41·41°   **(c)** 3·18
  (d) 11·59   **(e)** 66·42°   **(f)** 9·27
  (g) 16·58   **(h)** 5·77   **(i)** 33·53°

3 (a) 36·87°   **(b)** 2·89   **(c)** 57·99°
  (d) 21·80°   **(e)** 56·31°   **(f)** 13·86
  (g) 15·94°   **(h)** 1·82   **(i)** 33·54°

4 (a) 23·58°   **(b)** 66·42°   **(c)** 23·20°
  (d) 53·13°   **(e)** 17·46°   **(f)** 67·98°
  (g) 23·58°   **(h)** 31·00°   **(i)** 23·96°

5 (a) 6·43 cm   **(b)** 2·89 cm   **(c)** 11·49 cm
  (d) 1·87 cm   **(e)** 9·58 cm   **(f)** 7·41 cm
  (g) 7·56 cm   **(h)** 1·22 cm   **(i)** 17·44 cm

6 38·66°

7 25·5 m

8 5·74°

9 (a) 23·58°   **(b)** 91·65m   **(c)** 109·9 m   **(d)** 311·55m
  (e) 116·95 m   **(f)** 11·21°   **(g)** 10·31°   **(h)** 223·51 m

10 22·62°

11 3·82°

12 10·73 m

13 11·69 cm

14 (a) 2·83 m   **(b)** 3·98 m   **(c)** 45·31°

15 (a) 10·39 cm   **(b)** 62·34 cm^2

Page 76 Trigonometry 3

1 (a) 15·32   **(b)** 21·08   **(c)** 43·3
  (d) 24·48   **(e)** 56·38   **(f)** 55·16
  (g) 41·94   **(h)** 46·28   **(i)** 62·00

2 882·39 m^2

3 44·32 cm^2

4 62·98 cm^2

5 35·29° (or 144·71°)

6 8·98 cm

Pages 77 and 78 Similar figures

1 (a) $x = 7$, $y = 15$ **(b)** $x = 2.4$ **(c)** $x = 3.43$, $y = 5.71$
  (d) $x = 3.27$, $y = 13.75$ **(e)** $x = 2.06$, $y = 6.3$

2 $x = 5.29$ cm

3 $x = 0.6$

4 worksheets 8 and 9

5 (a) $x = 4$, $y = 14$ **(b)** $x = 5\frac{5}{16}$ (or 5·83), $y = 6\frac{2}{3}$ (or 6·67)
  (c) $x = 6.67$, $y = 3.6$ **(d)** $x = 14.12$, $y = 12.75$

6 worksheet 10

7 (a) 2·4   **(b)** 1·143   **(c)** 6

  (d) 13·86   **(e)** $3\frac{3}{4}$ (or 3·75)

8 BM = 4·8 cm

9 worksheet 11

Pages 79 and 80 Vectors

1

	Length	Angle
(a)	5	53·15°
(b)	10	36·87°
(c)	13	22·62°
(d)	4·24	45°
(e)	5	53·13°
(f)	2·24	26·56°
(g)	5·39	21·8°
(h)	7·21	56·31°
(i)	13	67·38°
(j)	25	16·26°
(k)	7·07	45°
(l)	6	0° 180° or 0°
(m)	3	90°
(n)	4	90°
(o)	5	180° 180° or 0°

2 (a) $\begin{pmatrix} 3 \\ 0 \end{pmatrix}$ **(b)** $\begin{pmatrix} -3 \\ 0 \end{pmatrix}$ **(c)** $\begin{pmatrix} 3 \\ 2 \end{pmatrix}$ **(d)** $\begin{pmatrix} -3 \\ -2 \end{pmatrix}$ **(e)** $\begin{pmatrix} 1\frac{1}{2} \\ 1 \end{pmatrix}$

3 (b) $\begin{pmatrix} 4 \\ 2 \end{pmatrix}$ $\begin{pmatrix} 1 \\ 3 \end{pmatrix}$ $\begin{pmatrix} 1 \\ 3 \end{pmatrix}$ $\begin{pmatrix} 1 \\ 3 \end{pmatrix}$ **(c)**   **(d)**

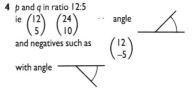

4 p and q in ratio 12:5

  ie $\begin{pmatrix} 12 \\ 5 \end{pmatrix}$ $\begin{pmatrix} 24 \\ 10 \end{pmatrix}$ ∴ angle

  and negatives such as $\begin{pmatrix} 12 \\ -5 \end{pmatrix}$

  with angle

  or $\begin{pmatrix} 12 \\ -5 \end{pmatrix}$ or $\begin{pmatrix} -12 \\ -5 \end{pmatrix}$

5 (a) $\begin{pmatrix} 10 \\ 8 \end{pmatrix}$ **(b)** $\begin{pmatrix} 2 \\ 10 \end{pmatrix}$

  (c) length $\sqrt{10^2 + 8^2} = \sqrt{164} = 12.81$ angle = 38·66°

  (d) length $\sqrt{2^2 + 10^2} = \sqrt{104} = 10.2$ angle = 78·69°

6 (a) $\begin{pmatrix} p+r \\ q+s \end{pmatrix}$ **(b)** $\begin{pmatrix} r-p \\ s-q \end{pmatrix}$ **(c)** $\begin{pmatrix} 3p \\ 3q \end{pmatrix}$ **(d)** $\begin{pmatrix} 5r \\ 5s \end{pmatrix}$

  (e) $\begin{pmatrix} 3p+5r \\ 3q+5s \end{pmatrix}$ **(f)** $\sqrt{p^2+q^2}$ **(g)** tan of angle = $\frac{q-s}{p-r}$

7 (a) a makes angle 53·13°

  b makes angle 36·87
  hence angle between a and b is 90°

  (b) $\begin{pmatrix} 1 \\ 7 \end{pmatrix}$

  (c) 50 sq units

172

8

(a) $\overline{OB} = a + b$
(b) $\overline{OC} = b$
(c) $\overline{AC} = b - a$

Pages 81 and 82 Take a chance

1 **(a)** $\frac{1}{2}$ **(b)** $\frac{1}{2}$ **(c)** $\frac{1}{4}$ **(d)** $\frac{3}{8}$

2 **(a)** $\frac{3}{4}$ **(b)** $\frac{5}{8}$ **(c)** $\frac{5}{8}$

3 **(a)** $\frac{1}{10}$ **(b)** $\frac{1}{2}$ **(c)** $\frac{3}{5}$

4 **(a)** $\frac{12}{25}$ **(b)** $\frac{21}{25}$ **(c)** $\frac{17}{25}$

5 **(a)** $\frac{1}{3}$ **(b)** $\frac{4}{9}$ **(c)** $\frac{5}{9}$ **(d)** $\frac{4}{9}$

6 **(a)** $\frac{13}{32}$ **(b)** $\frac{9}{32}$ **(c)** $\frac{5}{16}$ **(d)** $\frac{3}{8}$ **(e)** $\frac{1}{2}$
   (f) $\frac{1}{2}$

7 **(a)** $\frac{1}{2}$ **(b)** $\frac{5}{12}$ **(c)** $\frac{1}{3}$ **(d)** $\frac{11}{12}$ **(e)** $\frac{7}{12}$

8 **(a)** $\frac{1}{10}$ **(b)** $\frac{7}{30}$ **(c)** $\frac{2}{15}$ **(d)** $\frac{1}{6}$ **(e)** $\frac{1}{15}$
   (f) $\frac{1}{10}$ **(g)** $\frac{1}{6}$

9 **(a)** $\frac{2}{13}$ **(b)** $\frac{9}{13}$ **(c)** $\frac{4}{13}$ **(d)** $\frac{8}{13}$

10 **(a)** $\frac{4}{5}$ **(b)** $\frac{3}{10}$ **(c)** $\frac{7}{10}$ **(d)** $\frac{9}{10}$

11 **(a)** $2x$ **(b)** $y + z$ **(c)** $y + z$ **(d)** $x + 2y$
   (e) $2x + 3y$ or $1 - z$ **(f)** $x + 3y + z$ or $1 - x$

12 **(a)** $3w + 3x$ **(b)** $2y + 4z$ **(c)** $3w$ **(d)** $4z$ **(e)** $(1 - 3w)$

Page 83 Guess what?

1 **(a)** Not subjective – experimental   **(e)** Subjective
  (b) Not subjective – calculable   **(f)** Subjective
  (c) Subjective   **(g)** Not subjective – experimental
  (d) Not subjective – experimental   **(h)** Not subjective – calculable
2 **(a)** See students answer   **(b)** See students answer

Page 84 Cumulative frequency

1

Shoe size	Cumulative frequency
4	4
5	9
6	25
7	55
8	100
9	126
10	140
11	148
12	150

2

Examination mark	Cumulative frequency
5	3
10	11
15	26
20	54
25	91
30	136
35	159
40	175
45	179
50	180

3

Weight (kg)	Cumulative frequency
110	2
120	23
130	62
140	122
150	175
160	209
170	225
180	228
190	230

Pages 85 and 86 Cumulative frequency curves 1

1 **(a)**

Marks	Frequency	Cumulative frequency
10	2	2
11	9	11
12	21	32
13	45	77
14	81	158
15	53	211
16	34	245
17	15	260
18	7	267
19	3	270

(b) Plot marks (x-axis) against cumulative frequency (y-axis)

2 **(a)**

Weight	Frequency	Cumulative frequency
20 – 29	8	8
30 – 39	13	21
40 – 49	41	62
50 – 59	20	82
60 – 69	14	96
70 – 79	3	99
80 – 89	1	100

(b) See students' diagram

3 **(a)**

Height	Frequency	Cumulative frequency
130 – 135	2	2
136 – 140	5	7
141 – 145	13	20
146 – 150	22	42
151 – 155	36	78
156 – 160	57	135
161 – 165	87	222
165 – 170	37	259
171 – 175	21	280
176 – 180	7	287
181 – 185	1	288

(b) See students' diagram

Pages 87, 88, 89 Cumulative frequency curves 2

1

Length	Cumulative frequency
5	5
10	46
15	123
20	181
25	220
30	237
35	240

(b) • median = about 15   • l.q. = about 12   • u.q. = about 18
   • i.q.r. = about 6

2 **(a)**

Age	Cumulative frequency
10	5
20	24
30	71
40	150
50	182
60	197
70	199
80	200

• median = around 33   • l.q. = around 26   • u.q. = around 40
• i.q.r. = about 14

3 (a)

Weight	Cumulative frequency
39	3
49	14
59	38
69	94
79	217
89	287
99	300

(c) • median around 74 • l.q. = around 66 • u.q. = around 80

• i.q.r. = about 14

(d) just over 10% (e) about 55%

4

Age	Cumulative frequency
8	71
16	181
24	367
32	498
40	586
48	638
56	663
64	670

(c) • median = around 23 • l.q. = around 15 • u.q. = around 33

• i.q.r. = about 18

(d) approx 4·8% (e) approx 55% (f) approx 63·7%

Page 90 Dimension Theory

1 (a) 2 (b) 1 (c) 2 (d) 3 (e) 2
2 See students' answers
3 (a) Dimension 1 (b) Dimension 3 (c) Dimension 1
   (d) Dimension 2 (e) Dimension 2 (f) Dimension 2
   (g) Dimension 3

Pages 91, 92 Question time 1

Students' own answers

Page 93 Question time 2

Students' own answers

Page 94 The line of counters

Students' own answers

Page 95 Hopping about

Students' own answers

Page 96 Spin around

1, 2, 3 Students' own answers

Page 97 The cowboy's dilemma

Students' own answers

Page 98 Hexonmoes

Students' own answers

Pages 99 and 100 Some special numbers

Students' own answers

Page 101 Not exactly!

1 12 250 to 12 350, 8150 to 8250, 14 650 to 14 750, 9750 to 9850
2 (a) 58 150 (b) 58 650 (c) 500
3 (a) 58 385 (b) 58 435 (c) 50
4 (a) smallest 9·9 cm longest 10·1 cm
   (b) smallest 49·5 cm longest 50·5 cm
5 (a) min 11·9 cm max 12·1 cm
   (b) max 1·9 cm min 2·1 cm
6 (a) mn 19 km max 21 km
   (b) min difference 3 km max difference 5 km
7 slowest 7·37 m/sec fastest 8·04 m/sec

Page 102 On your marks!

1 The most realistic answer is Leroy 2·0 m
2 (a) 4995 to 5005 (b) 4950 to 5050
   (c) It depends upon why you want the figures
3 (a) 341 500 to 342 500 (b) 797 000 to 799 000
   (c) min 113 000 max 115 000
4

Basic	Equivalent	Interval
1 inch	2·52 cm	2·535 to 2·545
1 yard	91·4 cm	91·35 to 91·45
1 litre	1·76 pints	1·755 to 1·765
1 ton	1·016 tonnes	1·0155 to 1·0165
1 km	0·621 miles	0·6205 to 0·6215
1 mile	1609 metres	1608·5 to 1609·5

5 (a) 5·55 to 5·65 and 4·75 to 4·85
   (b) min 20·6 cm, max 21 cm
   (c) min 26·3625, max 27·4025
6 (a) 4·8 m/sec (b) 119·5 metres to 120·5 metres
   (c) 24·5 sec to 25·5 sec (d) 4·918 m/sec (e) 4·686 m/sec

Page 103 Tolerating the difference

1 (a) 5·57 cm (b) 5·63 cm
2 (a) 5·55, 5·65 (b) 5·58, 5·62 (c) 5·575, 5·625
   (d) 5·59, 5·61
3 (a) min 12·625, max 12·775 (b) min 2·225, max 2·375
4 (a) The drill may be manufactured to a tighter tolerance than the bolts he
       makes.
   (b) Use a slightly larger drill or manufacture the bolts he makes to a tighter
       tolerance.
5 (a) • precision engineering 2·2 0·025
       • general engineering 2·2 0·05
       • home and domestic 2·2 0·02
       • car manufacturing 2·2 0·01
   (b) The tighter the tolerance the more expensive the bearing are to produce.
       Either by more expensive machines or selection process.
6 (a) min 11·98, max 12·02 (b) min 143·52, max 144·48
   (c) 48·0 ± 0·8
7 56·0 ± 0·025

Page 104 Factorising

1 (a) $x^2 + 12x + 20$ (b) $x^2 + 10x + 9$ (c) $x^2 + 10x + 25$
   (d) $x^2 - 5x + 6$ (e) $x^2 + 4x - 21$ (f) $x^2 + x - 42$
2 (a) $x(x + 4)$ (b) $5(x + 4)$ (c) $x(x + 3)$
   (d) $6(x + 3)$ (e) $x(x - 5)$ (f) $3(x - 5)$
3 (a) $x^2 + 6x + 2x + 12$ (b) $x^2 + 5x + 2x + 10$ (c) $x^2 + 8x + 3x + 24$
   (d) $x^2 + 4x + x + 4$ (e) $x^2 + 3x + 3x + 9$ (f) $x^2 + 5x + 4x + 20$
   (g) $x^2 + 6x + 3x + 18$ (h) $x^2 + 13x + 3x + 39$ (i) $x^2 + 10x + 10x + 100$
   (j) $x^2 + 9x + 6x + 54$

4 (a) $(x+6)$ and $(x+2)$ **(b)** $(x+5)$ and $(x+2)$ **(c)** $(x+8)$ and $(x+3)$
(d) $(x+4)$ and $(x+1)$ **(e)** $(x+3)$ and $(x+3)$ **(f)** $(x+5)$ and $(x+4)$
(g) $(x+6)$ and $(x+3)$ **(h)** $(x+13)$ and $(x+3)$
(i) $(x+10)$ and $(x+10)$ **(j)** $(x+9)$ and $(x+6)$
5 (a) $(x+5)(x+6)$ **(b)** $(y+9)(y+3)$ **(c)** $(r+8)(r+2)$
(d) $(f+6)(f+8)$ **(e)** $(x+12)(x+5)$ **(f)** $(y+7)(y+8)$
(g) $(h+11)(h+10)$ **(h)** $(x+13)(x+12)$
6 (a) $(x+4)(x-2)$ **(b)** $(x+9)(x-3)$ **(c)** $(y+8)(y-7)$
(d) $(p+7)(p-3)$ **(e)** $(p-3)(p-4)$ **(f)** $(x-8)(x-3)$
(g) $(w-9)(w-4)$ **(h)** $(x-5)(x+1)$ **(i)** $(y-7)(y-9)$
(j) $(r-10)(r+5)$ **(k)** $(m-10)(m+9)$ **(l)** $(m+6)(m-5)$
(m) $(x+15)(x-4)$ **(n)** $(x+12)(x+11)$ **(o)** $(y+3)(y-3)$
(p) $(x+4)(x-4)$ **(q)** $(x+8)(x-8)$ **(r)** $(x+10)(x-10)$
7 (a) $(x+2)$ **(b)** $(x-3)$ **(c)** $(x-6)$
(d) $(x+7)$
8 $(3x+5)$
9 (a) $(2x+1)(x+2)$ **(b)** $(3x+2)(x+4)$ **(c)** $(x+2)(4x+3)$
(d) $(2x+3)(2x+2)$ **(e)** $(2x+1)(x-3)$ **(f)** $(3x-2)(2x+4)$

Page 105 Keep it in proportion 3

1 (a) The time decreases **(b)** 2 hours **(c)** 8 hours

2

Time (t)	4	2·5	3·33
$\frac{1}{t}$	0·25	0·4	0·3
Speed	50	80	60

3

Time (t)	8·0	22·2...	0·323
$\frac{1}{t}$	0·125	0·045	3·1
Speed	0·5	14·4	12·4

4

Balloon	A	B
diameter	3 cm	2 cm
$\frac{1}{d}$	$\frac{1}{3}$	$\frac{1}{2}$
p	1000	1500

5 (b) Yes, confirmed by straight line through the origin
(c) 470 **(d)** $f = \frac{165}{w}$

6 (a) 1·4 kg/m **(b)** 5·6 m³ **(c)** $d = \frac{3.36}{v}$

Page 106 keep it in proportion 4

1 (a)

r	6	4	2·8
r^2	36	16	71·43
y	452	201	100

(b) 1256·6 mm²

2 (a) $h = 81.67$ m **(b)** $u = 44.09$ m/s
3 (a) 14·70 m **(b)** 86·80 m/s
4 928 millilitres
5 (a) 61·44 Joules **(b)** $E = 6T^2$
6 (a) 12 800 km **(b)** 0·1523 g
7 (a) 3·5625 ... ohms **(b)** 0·594 **(c)** $R = \frac{7.125}{d}$
8 (a) $a \propto t^2,\ a = 3t^2$ **(b)** $a \propto \frac{1}{t},\ a = \frac{4}{t}$
(c) $a \propto t,\ a = 6\sqrt{t}$ **(d)** $a \propto t,\ a = 2t + 6$
9 (a) 16·66...% decrease **(b)** 100% increase **(c)** 300% increase
10 (a) 33·1% increase **(b)** 57·8125% decrease **(c)** 14·47% increase

Pages 107, 108, 109 Put in the shade

1 (a) Example only $(1, 2)$ $(2 \times 1) + (2 \times 3) < 12$ **(b)** point lies on line
2 (a) 10 – below **(b)** 18 – above **(c)** 13 – above
(d) 12 – on the line **(e)** –5 – below **(f)** 12·9 – above
3 (a) $(5, 1)$ **(b)** 3 **(c)** • $x - 2y < 6$ • $x - 2y > 6$
4 (a) $x - y > 1$ Example test point $(3, 1)$
$3 - 1 > 1$ true
(b) $0 < x < 2$ Example test point $(1, 2)$
$1 < 2$

5 (a)

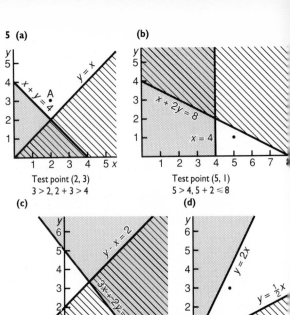

Test point $(2, 3)$
$3 > 2, 2 + 3 > 4$

(b)

Test point $(5, 1)$
$5 > 4, 5 + 2 \leqslant 8$

(c)

Test point $(0, 3)$
$3 - 0 \geqslant 2, 0 + 6 < 12$

(d)

Test point $(2, 3)$
$3 \leqslant 6, 3 > 1$

6 Region A $x + y > 3$ and $y > x - 2$
Region B $x + y > 3$ and $y < x - 2$
Region C $x + y < 3$ and $y < x - 2$
Region D $x + y < 3$ and $y > x - 2$

7 (a) $2x + y = 4, y = 2x$ and $y = 0$ **(b)** $2x + y < 4, y < 2x$ and $y > 0$
(c) Test point $(1, 1)$ $(2 \times 1) + 1 < 4$
$1 < (2 \times 1)$ and $1 > 0$

$2y + x = 4$ $y = \frac{2x}{3}$ and $x = 4$

$2y + x > 4$ $y < \frac{2x}{3}$ and $x > 4$

Test point $(3, 1)$ $(2 \times 1) + 3 > 4$
$1 < 2$ and $3 < 4$

8 (a)

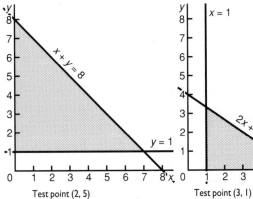

Test point $(2, 5)$
$2 \geqslant 0, 5 \geqslant 1, 2 + 5 \leqslant 8$

(b)

Test point $(3, 1)$
$3 \geqslant 1, 1 \geqslant 0, 6 + 2 < 12$

(c)

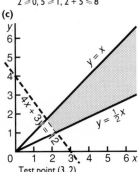

Test point $(3, 2)$
$2 \leqslant 3, 2 \geqslant 1.5, 1.2 + 6 > 12$

(d)

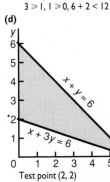

Test point $(2, 2)$
$2 > 0, 2 + 6 \geqslant 6, 2 + 2 \leqslant 6$

(e)

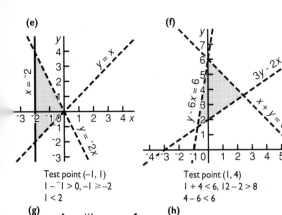

Test point $(-1, 1)$
$1 - {}^-1 > 0, -1 \geqslant -2$
$1 < 2$

(f)

Test point $(1, 4)$
$1 + 4 < 6, 12 - 2 > 8$
$4 - 6 < 6$

(g)

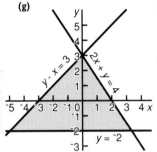

Test point $(0, 1)$
$1 - 0 < 3, 0 + 1 < 4$
$1 \geqslant -2$

(h)

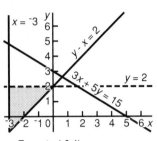

Test point $(-2, 1)$
$3 + {}^-10 < 15, 1 - {}^-2 \geqslant 2$
$1 < 2 - 2 > -3$

9 (a)

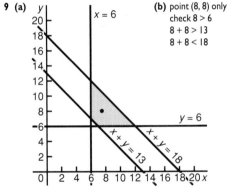

(b) point $(8, 8)$ only
check $8 > 6$
$8 + 8 > 13$
$8 + 8 < 18$

10 (c) $y < 2x + 3 \quad y > x^2 - 1$
Test point $(1, 1)$
$1 < 2 + 3 \quad 1 > 1 - 1$

11 (a) £2 × no of chocolates + £5 × no of bottles ⩽ £30

(b)

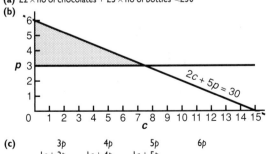

(c)

	3p	4p	5p	6p
	1c + 3p	1c + 4p	1c + 5p	
	2c + 3p	2c + 4p	2c + 5p	
	3c + 3p	3c + 4p		
	4c + 3p	4c + 4p		
	5c + 3p	5c + 4p		
	6c + 3p			
	7c + 3p			

(d) 18 presents **(e)** £30 buy 6 bottles of perfume or
4 bottles of perfume and 5 boxes of chocolates

12 (a) (2 × number of standard shades)m + 2·5 (no of deluxe shades)m ⩽ 20m,
(number of standard)hours + 2(no of deluxe)hours ⩽ 8 hours
(b) **(c)** £108

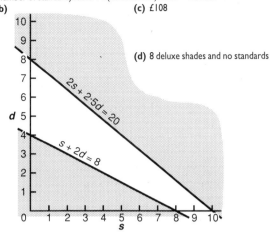

(d) 8 deluxe shades and no standards

Page 110 Cutting planes/consecutive powers

Students' own answers

Pages 111 and 112 Trigonometry 4

1 **(a)** 480 cm³ **(b)** PV = 9·43 cm QU = 13 cm QS = 14·42 cm
(c) 32° **(d)** 15·26 cm **(e)** 19·12°
2 **(a)** 15 m **(b)** UB = 12·65 mm UC = 15·52 m UD = 9·85 m
(c) 90°, 14·93° 66·04°

3 $\sqrt{x^2 + y^2}$ $\sqrt{x^2 + z^2}$ $\sqrt{y^2 + z^2}$ $\sqrt{x^2 + y^2 + z^2}$

4 **(a)** 22·62° **(b)** 13 units **(c)** 13 units **(d)** 12·1°
(e) 600 cubic units
5 **(a)** 17 cm **(b)** 13·23 cm **(c)** 15·46 cm **(d)** 28·07°
(e) 48·59°
6 **(a)** 14·14 cm **(b)** 18·71 cm **(c)** 28·96° **(d)** 19·36 cm
(e) 75·04°

Pages 113 and 114 Parts of circles

1 **(a)** 6·98 cm **(b)** 17·45 cm² **(c)** 5·14 cm²
2 **(a)** 40·84 cm **(b)** 367·57 cm² **(c)** 243·47 cm²
3 **(a)** 71·62° **(b)** 40 cm²
4 **(a)** 8·59 cm **(b)** 51·57 cm² **(c)** 15·2 cm²
5 **(a)** 63·66° **(b)** 6·67 cm **(c)** 3·87 cm²
6 equilateral triangle: 0 = 60°

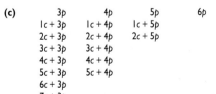

7 **(a)** 4·104 m **(b)** 1·046 m² **(c)** £27·67

Pages 115, 116 and 117 Trigonometry 5

1 **(a)** Sine 6x

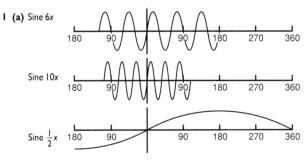

(b) Periods: $\frac{1}{6}$ that of Sine x, $\frac{1}{10}$ that of Sine x, twice that of Sine x

2 (a)

x	$2x$	$Cos\ 2x$
0	0	1
10	20	0·9397
20	40	0·7660
30	60	0·5
40	80	0·1736
50	100	−0·1736
60	120	−0·5
70	140	−0·7660
80	160	−0·9397
90	180	−1
100	200	−0·9397
110	220	−0·7660
120	240	−0·5
130	260	−0·1736
140	280	0·1736
150	300	0·5
160	320	0·7660
170	340	0·9397
180	360	1
190	380	0·9397
200	400	0·7660
210	420	0·5
220	440	0·1736
230	460	−0·1736
240	480	−0·5
250	500	−0·7660
260	520	−0·9397
270	540	−1
280	560	−0·9397
290	580	−0·7660
300	600	−0·5
310	620	−0·1736
320	640	0·1736
330	660	0·5
340	680	0·7660
350	700	0·9397
360	720	1

(b)

(c) Period of $Cos\ 2x = \frac{1}{2}$ period of $Cos\ x$

3 (a) (b) (c) Tan $2x$

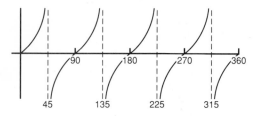

4 (a) Sin $2x$

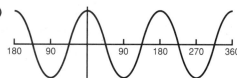

(b) Cos $2x$

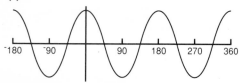

(c) Tan $3x$

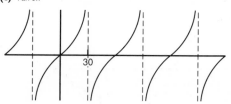

(d) Cos $4x$

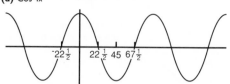

(e) Cos $\frac{1}{2}x$

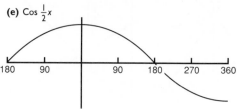

(f) Tan $5x$

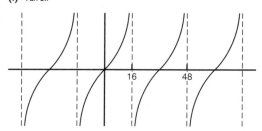

(g) Tan $\frac{1}{2}x$

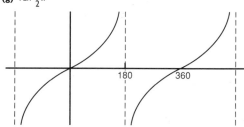

(h) Sin $4x$

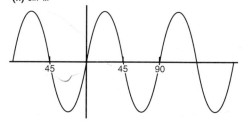

(a) Sin $(x + 30)$

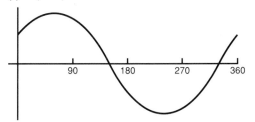

(b) Cos $(x - 30)$

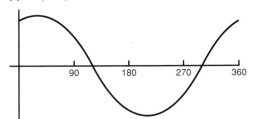

(a) Sin $(x - 60)$

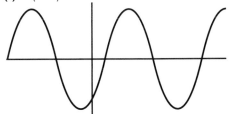

(b) Cos $(x + 30)$

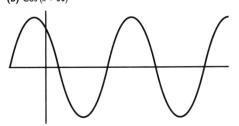

Page 118 Trigonometry 6

I (a) 7·85 cm   (b) 6·16 cm   (c) 11·85 cm
   (d) 13·52 cm   (e) 17·88 cm

2 26·46 km

3 6·44 km

Page 119 Maybe, maybe not

I (a) $\frac{2}{9}$ (b) $\frac{1}{27}$ (c) $\frac{7}{27}$ (d) $\frac{7}{27}$

2 (a) $\frac{1}{27}$ (b) $\frac{8}{27}$ (c) $\frac{2}{9}$ (d) $\frac{7}{27}$

3 (a) $\frac{2}{9}$ (b) $\frac{17}{18}$

4 (a) $\frac{2}{3}$ (b) $\frac{1}{3}$ (c) $\frac{1}{3}$ (d) $\frac{1}{3}$

5 (a) $\frac{3}{16}$ (b) $\frac{1}{8}$ (c) $\frac{1}{64}$ (d) $\frac{5}{32}$
   (e) $\frac{1}{2}$

6 (a) $\frac{1}{16}$ (b) $\frac{1}{1296}$ (c) $\frac{1}{6}$ (d) 0

7 (a) $\frac{1}{8}$ (b) $\frac{1}{24}$ (c) $\frac{3}{4}$ (d) $\frac{1}{2}$

8 (a) $\frac{13}{25}$ (b) $\frac{12}{25}$ (c) $\frac{9}{25}$ (d) $\frac{2}{5}$
   (e) $\frac{12}{25}$

Page 120 Volume control

Students' own answers

Pages 121 and 122 Branching out

1

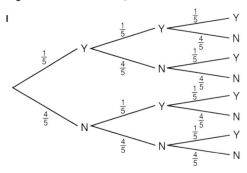

2 (a)

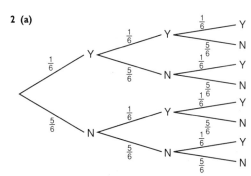

(b) · $\frac{1}{216}$ · $\frac{125}{216}$ · $\frac{75}{216}$

3 (a)

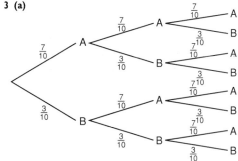

(b) · $\frac{343}{1000}$ · $\frac{27}{1000}$ · $\frac{441}{1000}$

4 (a) $\frac{64}{343}$ (b) $\frac{208}{343}$ (c) $\frac{135}{343}$

5 (a) $\frac{5}{24}$ (b) $3\left(\frac{1}{4}\right)^2\left(\frac{1}{3}\right) + 3\left(\frac{1}{4}\right)^2\left(\frac{5}{12}\right) + \left(\frac{1}{4}\right)^3 = \frac{5}{32}$
   (c) $\frac{650}{1728} = \frac{325}{864}$ (d) $\frac{1}{27}$

6 (a) $\frac{27}{125}$ (b) $\frac{44}{125}$ (c) $\frac{36}{125}$

7 (a) $\frac{343}{1728}$ (b) $\frac{728}{1728}$ (c) $\frac{243}{1728}$ (d) $\frac{125}{1728}$

8 (a) $\frac{1}{216}$ (b) $\frac{20}{27}$ (c) $\frac{125}{216}$

9 (a) $\frac{x^3}{50^3}$ (b) $3\left(\frac{y}{50}\right)^2\left(\frac{x}{50}\right)$ (c) $\frac{x^3 + 3x^2 y}{50^3}$

10 (a) $\left(\frac{x}{x+y+z}\right)^3$ (b) $\frac{3y^2(x+z) + y^3}{(x+y+z)^3}$

Pages 123 and 124 continued

1 (a)
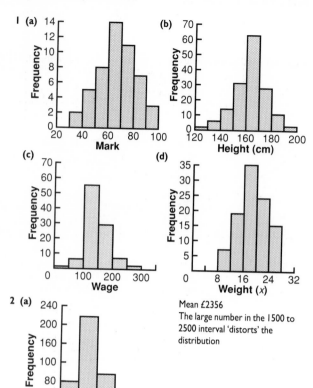

(b)

(c)

(d)
Mean £2356
The large number in the 1500 to 2500 interval 'distorts' the distribution

2 (a)
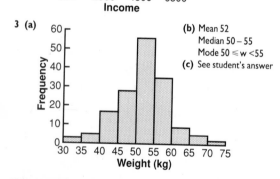

3 (a)
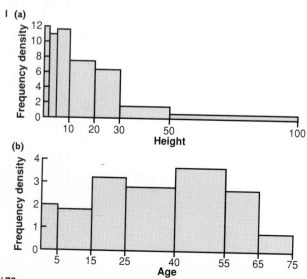

(b) Mean 52
Median 50 – 55
Mode $50 \leq w < 55$
(c) See student's answer

Page 125 Histograms 2

1 (a)

(b)

179

Page 126 Quadratic graphs

Students' own answers

Page 127 Sampling 1

Students' own answers

Page 128 Sampling 2

Students' own answers

Pages 129 and 130 Pythagorean investigations

Students' own answers

Page 131 Triangles

1
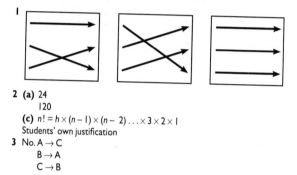

2 (a) 24
120
(c) $n! = h \times (n-1) \times (n-2) \dots \times 3 \times 2 \times 1$
Students' own justification
3 No. A → C
B → A
C → B

Page 132 Areas under graphs

Students' own answers

Page 133 Sketching graphs 1

1 (a)
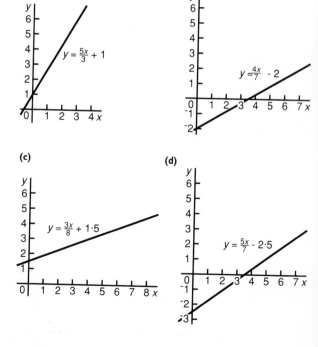

(b)
$y = \frac{5x}{3} + 1$

$y = \frac{4x}{7} - 2$

(c)
$y = \frac{3x}{8} + 1.5$

(d)
$y = \frac{5x}{7} - 2.5$

(e)

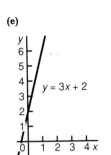

$y = 3x + 2$

(f)

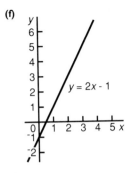

$y = 2x - 1$

(g)

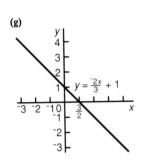

$y = \frac{-2x}{3} + 1$

(h)

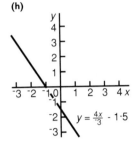

$y = \frac{4x}{3} - 1.5$

2 (a) $y = 5x$ **(b)** $y = x + 3$ **(c)** $y = \frac{7}{2}x$

(d) $y = \frac{1}{2}x + 4$ **(e)** $y = -x + 3$ **(f)** $y = -\frac{2}{3}x$

(g) $y = x + 2$ **(h)** $y = 5$

3 (a) $y = -\frac{1}{4}x + 2.5$ **(b)** $y = x + 1.5$ **(c)** $y = -2x + 1$

(d) $y = \frac{x}{3} - 1.5$

Pages 134 and 135 Sketching graphs 2

1 (a)

x	-4	-3	-2	-1	0	1	2	3	4
y	16	9	4	1	0	1	4	9	16

2 (a)

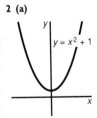

$y = x^2 + 1$

(b)

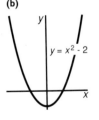

$y = x^2 - 2$

(c)

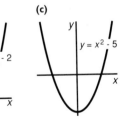

$y = x^2 - 5$

(d)

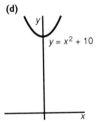

$y = x^2 + 10$

3 (a)

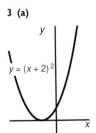

$y = (x + 2)^2$

(b)

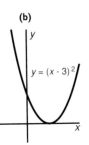

$y = (x - 3)^2$

(c)

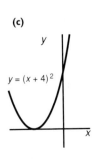

$y = (x + 4)^2$

(d)

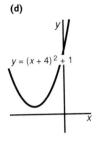

$y = (x + 4)^2 + 1$

(e)

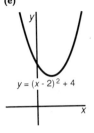

$y = (x - 2)^2 + 4$

(f)

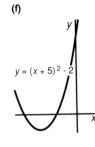

$y = (x + 5)^2 - 2$

(g)

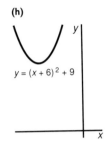

$y = (x - 5)^2 - 6$

(h)

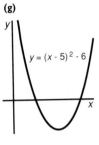

$y = (x + 6)^2 + 9$

4 (a)

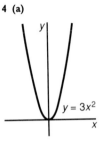

$y = 3x^2$

(b)

$y = -2x^2$

(c)

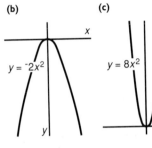

$y = 8x^2$

(d)

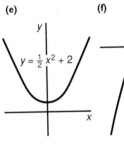

$y = -(x + 2)^2$

(e)

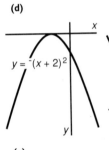

$y = \frac{1}{2}x^2 + 2$

(f)

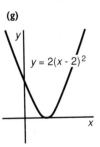

$y = -2x^2 + 1$

(g)

$y = 2(x - 2)^2$

(h)

$y = 2(x - 2)^2 - 4$

(i)

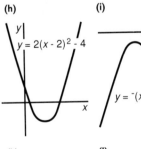

$y = -(x + 5)^2 - 2$

(j)

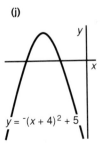

$y = -(x + 4)^2 + 5$

(k)

$y = -\frac{1}{2}(x - 4)^2 - 3$

(l)

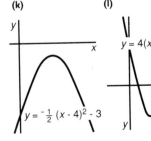

$y = 4(x - 2)^2 - 6$

1 (a)

x	−6	−4	−3	−2	−1	1	2	3	4	6
y	−1	−1·5	−2	−3	−6	6	3	2	1·5	1

2 (a)

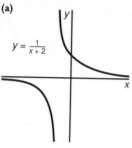

$y = \frac{1}{x+2}$

(b)

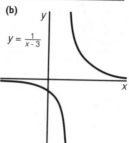

$y = \frac{1}{x-3}$

(c)

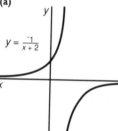

$y = \frac{1}{x+5}$

(d)

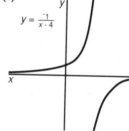

$y = \frac{2}{x}$

3 (a)

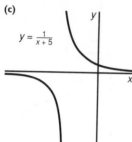

$y = \frac{-1}{x+2}$

(b)

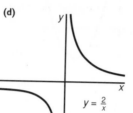

$y = \frac{-1}{x-4}$

(c)

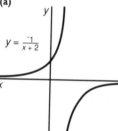

$y = \frac{-2}{x-6}$

(d)

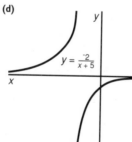

$y = \frac{-2}{x+5}$

(e)

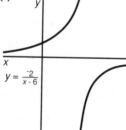

$\frac{-1}{x+3}$

(f)

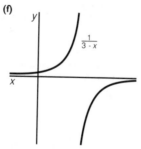

$\frac{1}{3-x}$

4 (a)

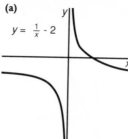

$y = \frac{1}{x} - 2$

(b)

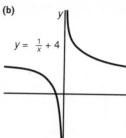

$y = \frac{1}{x} + 4$

(c)

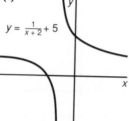

$y = \frac{1}{x+2} + 5$

(d)

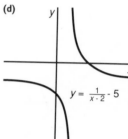

$y = \frac{1}{x-2} - 5$

(e)

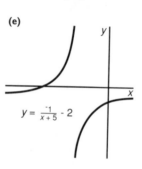

$y = \frac{-1}{x+5} - 2$

(f)

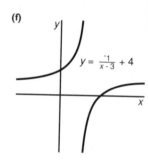

$y = \frac{-1}{x-3} + 4$

1 (a)

x	−3	−2·5	−2	−1·5	−1	0	1	1·5	2	2·5	3
y	−27	−15·6	−8	−3·4	−1	0	1	3·4	8	15·6	27

2 (a)

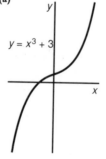

$y = x^3 + 3$

(b)

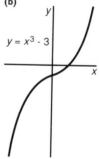

$y = x^3 - 3$

(c)

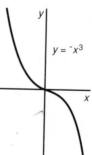

$y = {}^-x^3$

3 (a) $y = x^3 - 8$ **(b)** $y = x^3 + 27$

4 (a)

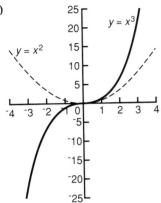

(b) Curves intersect at (1, 1) with x^2 above x^3 from 0 to 1.

5 (a)

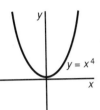

(b)

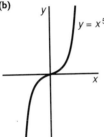

$y = x^5$

(c)

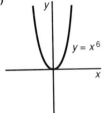

$y = x^6$

(d)

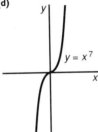

$y = x^7$

(e)

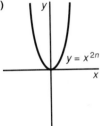

$y = x^{2n}$

$y = x^{2n-1}$

6 (a) $y = \frac{3x}{4} + 3$ graph L   **(b)** $y = \frac{-4x}{3} + 4$ graph K

(c) $y = \frac{3x}{4} - 3$ graph E   **(d)** $y = \frac{x^2}{2} - 2$ graph D

(e) $y = 2x^2$ graph H   **(f)** $y = x^2 + 1$ graph B

(g) $y = -x^2 + 2$ graph I   **(h)** $y = -(x^2 - 2)$ graph G

(i) $y = \frac{2}{x}$ graph J   **(j)** $y = \frac{-2}{x}$ graph C

(k) $y = \frac{-3x}{4} + 3$ graph A   **(l)** $y = -x^3 - 1$ graph F

Page 138 Travel graphs 2

1 2 m/s^2

2 (a)

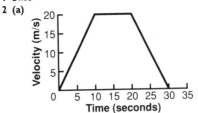

(b) 2 m/s^2 **(c)** $2 \cdot 5 \text{ m/s}^2$

3 (a) 150 m   **(b)** 125 m   **(c)** 350 m

4 (a) $1 \cdot 5 \text{ m/s}^2$ **(b)** 4 m/s^2 **(c)** 20 m/s   **(d)** 475 m

Pages 139 and 140 Work it out

1 Explanation **(a)**

2 (a) graph – D   **(b)** graph – E   **(c)** graph – F
    (d) graph – A   **(e)** graph – B   **(f)** graph – C

3   **4**

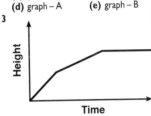

5

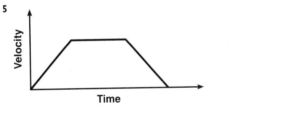

6   **7**

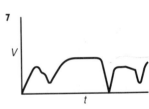

8 (a) Angie maintains the same speed for the total distance
Bea starts slowly, accelerates during the middle of the race, slows slightly at the lake
Clare accelerates rapidly at the beginning but slows during the middle part. She accelerates again towards the end

(b) Clare goes into the lead followed by Angie. Clare starts to tire and is passed by Angie. Bea starts to accelerate, passes Clare but fails to catch Angie. Result Angie 1st, Bea 2nd, Clare 3rd

9 Possible answers:
(a) Short sprint race   **(b)** Long jump/High jump
(c) 400 m sprint or fast bowler

10 (a) D to E   **(b)** B to C   **(c)** C to D

11

I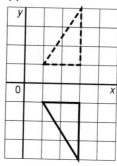

(a)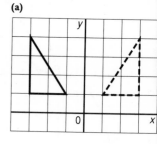

Pages 141 and 142 Lining them up

1 **(a)** 0·2   **(b)** 2·4   **(c)** $E = 0·2L + 2·4$
  (d) 3·88
2 **(a) (b)** Students' own answer and graph
  (c) 7·5   **(d)** 45   **(e)** $L = 7·5t + 45$
3 **(a)** See students' graph
  (b) $y = \frac{x}{4} + 0·5$
4 **(a) (b)** Students' graph
  (c) $T = 0·9S + 2$ **(d)** 29 mph   **(e)** 75 mph
5 **(b)** $R = 1·2V + 32$ **(c)** 44
6 **(b)** $T = 1·05I + 125$ **(c)** 9·5 kg
7 **(a)** See students' graph. The points lie on a curve
  (b)

T^2	4	9	16	25	36
D	28	40	55	75	98

  (c) The graph of D against T^2 gives a straight line
  (d) $D = 2·2T^2 + 20$ **(e)** 48 m

(b) 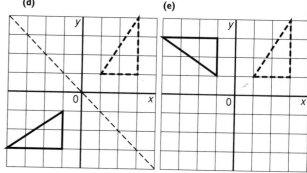 **(c)**

Pages 143 and 144 Trigonometry

2 **(a)** 8·29   **(b)** 18·39   **(c)** 17·19   **(d)** 20·16
3 **(a)** 26·74°   **(b)** 48·74°   **(c)** 30·71
4 **(a)** 14·23   **(b)** 51·54°   **(c)** 6·47   **(d)** 144·1°
  (e) 21·2   **(f)** $a = 41·05°$ $b = 86·95°$ **(g)** 62·29°
  (h) 7·97   **(i)** 54·44
5   $\frac{\sin x}{13} = \frac{\sin 50}{7}$

  $\sin x = \frac{13 \times \sin 50}{7} = 1·42$ impossible $\sin x \leqslant 1$

6 **(a)** Students' measurement
  (b) PQ = 15·13 cm QR = 6·62
  (c) Students' own answer
7 **(a)** $\hat{Z} = 29·44°$ **(b)** $\hat{Y} = 95·56°$ **(c)** XZ = 607·52m
8 **(a)** $\frac{\sin A}{10} = \frac{\sin 40}{8}$ $\sin A = \frac{10 \times \sin 40}{8} = 0·8035$
    $\widehat{BAC} = 53·46°$ or 126·54°
  (b) Students' own drawing
9 **(a)** • 046·09°   • 12·94 km   **(b)** 9·32 km
10   $\frac{a}{\sin A} = \frac{b}{\sin B}$
  $A = 90° \Rightarrow \sin A = 1$
  $\frac{a}{1} = \frac{b}{\sin B}$ $\sin B = \frac{b}{a}$

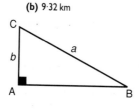

(d) 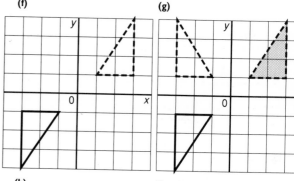 **(e)**

Pages 145 and 146 Trigonometry 8

1 **(a)** 8·19 cm   **(b)** 6·61 cm   **(c)** 6·01 cm
  (d) 11·36 cm   **(e)** 17·27 cm   **(f)** 18·79 cm
  (g) 5·20 cm   **(h)** 6·06 cm   **(i)** 16·65 cm
2 **(a)** 74·97°   **(b)** 96·38°   **(c)** 136·47°
  (d) 57·91°   **(e)** 48·51   **(f)** 102·63°
  (g) 41·85°   **(h)** 20·05   **(i)** 82·82°
3 114·10 m
4 68·65 m
5 25·53 km
6 56·25°
7 14·60 and 7·67 cm
8 44·37 km and 88·74 km
9 057·91° or 122·09°

(f) **(g)**

(h) 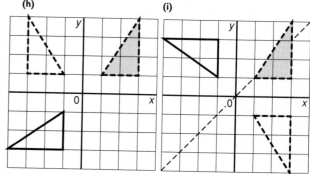 **(i)**

(j)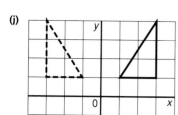

2 (g) → rotation 180° about origin
(h) → reflection in $y = -x$
(i) → rotation, 90° anti-clockwise about origin
(j) → does nothing – the identical transformation

3 • $\begin{pmatrix} 2 & 0 \\ 0 & 2 \end{pmatrix}$

• $\begin{pmatrix} -2 & 0 \\ 0 & -2 \end{pmatrix}$

• $\begin{pmatrix} \frac{1}{3} & 0 \\ 0 & \frac{1}{3} \end{pmatrix}$

• $\begin{pmatrix} -\frac{1}{3} & 0 \\ 0 & -\frac{1}{3} \end{pmatrix}$

4 (a) $\begin{pmatrix} -3 & 0 \\ 0 & -3 \end{pmatrix}$ **(b)** $\begin{pmatrix} \frac{1}{2} & 0 \\ 0 & \frac{1}{2} \end{pmatrix}$

5 (a) $\begin{pmatrix} -1 & 0 \\ 0 & 1 \end{pmatrix}$ **(b)** $\begin{pmatrix} 0 & -1 \\ -1 & 0 \end{pmatrix}$

6 (a) $\begin{pmatrix} 0 & -1 \\ 1 & 0 \end{pmatrix}$ **(b)** $\begin{pmatrix} 0 & 1 \\ -1 & 0 \end{pmatrix}$

(c) $\begin{pmatrix} \cos\theta & -\sin\theta \\ \sin\theta & \cos\theta \end{pmatrix}$

7 (a) reflection in x-axis
(b) reflection in line $y = x$
(c) identical – does nothing
(d) enlargement, centre origin, scale factor -4
(e) rotation, 90° anti-clockwise about origin
(f) rotation, about origin through angle whose $\cos\theta = 0.8$

8 (a) rotation, 90° about origin, anti-clockwise
(b) rotation, 180° about origin → $\begin{pmatrix} -1 & 0 \\ 0 & -1 \end{pmatrix}$
(c) rotation, 270° about origin, anti-clockwise → $\begin{pmatrix} 0 & 1 \\ -1 & 0 \end{pmatrix}$

(d) $\begin{pmatrix} 0 & 1 \\ -1 & 0 \end{pmatrix}$

(e) $A^3 = A^{-1}$

9 (a) A, B are enlargements, centre origin, scale factor 3 and 2 respectively
(b) BA is enlargement, centre origin, scale factor 6
10 (a) $\begin{pmatrix} 1 \\ 0 \end{pmatrix} \rightarrow \begin{pmatrix} -4 \\ 0 \end{pmatrix}$ $\begin{pmatrix} 0 \\ 1 \end{pmatrix} \rightarrow \begin{pmatrix} 0 \\ -4 \end{pmatrix}$

(b) Enlargement, centre origin, scale factor -4
11 (a) rotation 180° about origin
(b) rotation 90° about origin, anti-clockwise
(c) rotation 90° about origin, clockwise
(a) square is $\begin{pmatrix} 1 & 0 \\ 0 & 1 \end{pmatrix}$ inverse $\begin{pmatrix} -1 & 0 \\ 0 & -1 \end{pmatrix}$

(b) square is $\begin{pmatrix} -1 & 0 \\ 0 & -1 \end{pmatrix}$ inverse $\begin{pmatrix} 0 & 1 \\ -1 & 0 \end{pmatrix}$

(c) square is $\begin{pmatrix} -1 & 0 \\ 0 & -1 \end{pmatrix}$ inverse $\begin{pmatrix} 0 & -1 \\ 1 & 0 \end{pmatrix}$

12 (a)

	P'	Q'	R'
	$(-1, 1)$	$(-1, 4)$	$(-3, 4)$

(b)

	P''	Q''	R''
	$(-1, -1)$	$(-1, -4)$	$(-3, -4)$

(c) $\begin{pmatrix} 0 & -1 \\ -1 & 0 \end{pmatrix}$

(d) BA is a reflection in the line $y = -x$
(e) No, AB represents a reflection in $y = x$

13 (a) A = $\begin{pmatrix} 0.866 & -0.5 \\ 0.5 & 0.866 \end{pmatrix}$ = $\begin{pmatrix} \sin 30 & -\cos 30 \\ \cos 30 & \sin 30 \end{pmatrix}$

(b) • A^2 = $\begin{pmatrix} \sin 60 & -\cos 60 \\ \cos 60 & \sin 30 \end{pmatrix}$ = $\begin{pmatrix} 0.5 & -0.866 \\ 0.866 & 0.5 \end{pmatrix}$

• A^3 = $\begin{pmatrix} \sin 90 & -\cos 90 \\ \cos 90 & \sin 90 \end{pmatrix}$ = $\begin{pmatrix} 0 & -1 \\ 1 & 0 \end{pmatrix}$

Page 150 Spreading out

1 (a) 3·94 **(b)** 3·85 **(c)** 4·27 **(d)** 0·27
2 (a) 3·01 **(b)** 0·52 **(c)** 1·77 **(d)** 0·196
(e) 1·485

Page 151 On one condition

1 $\frac{9}{40}$

2 (a) $\frac{1}{2}$ **(b)** $\frac{21}{25}$

3 (a) $\frac{21}{500}$ **(b)** $\frac{9}{500}$

4 (a) $\frac{3}{5}$ **(b)** $\frac{1}{25}$

5 (a) $\frac{4}{25}$ **(b)** $\frac{6}{25}$

6 (a) $\frac{1}{160}$ **(b)** $\frac{39}{400}$ **(c)** $\frac{73}{800}$

7 (a) $\frac{61}{100}$ **(b)** $\frac{6}{25}$

Page 152 Probability puzzlers

1 $\frac{1}{216}$ **2** $\frac{4}{169}$ **3** $\frac{11}{20}$

4 (a) $\frac{4}{5}$ **(b)** $\frac{1}{25}$ **(c)** $\frac{8}{25}$

5 (a) $\frac{3}{20}$ **(b)** $\frac{2}{5}$ **(c)** $\frac{9}{20}$

6 (a) $\frac{2}{9}$ **(b)** $\frac{8}{15}$ **(c)** $\frac{28}{45}$

7 (a) $\frac{1}{16}$ **(b)** $\frac{11}{16}$ **(c)** $\frac{1}{16}$

8 $\frac{8}{55}$

9 (a) $\frac{5}{33}$ **(b)** $\frac{47}{60}$ **(c)** $\frac{14}{33}$

10 (a) $\frac{6}{25}$ **(b)** $\frac{19}{25}$

11 (a) $\frac{16}{49}$ **(b)** $\frac{24}{49}$ **(c)** $\frac{9}{49}$

12 (a) $\frac{17}{96}$ **(b)** $\frac{21}{32}$

13 (a) $\frac{3}{20}$ **(b)** $\frac{3}{5}$ **(c)** $\frac{1}{3}$

14 (a) $\frac{1}{12}$ **(b)** $\frac{7}{12}$

Page 153 Linear programming

1 (a) Choosing x to represent normal
y to represent luxury gives
$x \geqslant 24$ $y \geqslant 6$
$x \geqslant 2y$
$2.5x + 7.5y \leqslant 180$
and profit 'line' of
$p = 1.5x + 7.5y$
(b) Profit 'line' of $p = 1.5x + 7.5y$ giving maximum profit £148·50.
$x = 29, y = 14$

2 (a)

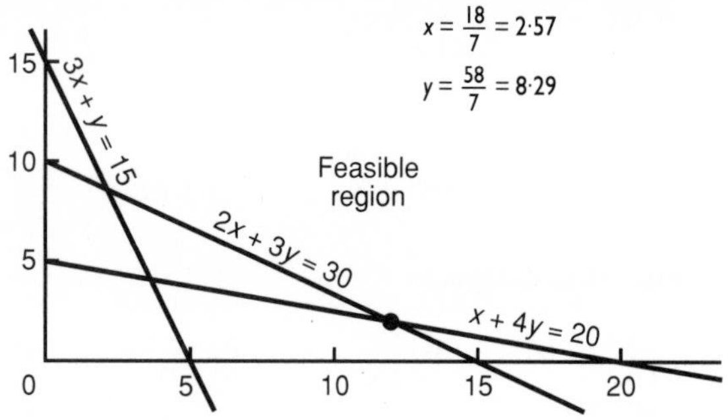

$$x = \frac{18}{7} = 2{\cdot}57$$

$$y = \frac{58}{7} = 8{\cdot}29$$

Graph labels: $3x + y = 15$, $2x + 3y = 30$, $x + 4y = 20$, Feasible region

(b) See students' graph
(c) See students' answer

Page 154 Gradients

Students' own answers

Page 154 Gradients

Students' own answers

Page 155 The Sigma function

Students' own answers

Page 156 The Tor function T(n)

Students' own answers

Page 157 Simulating a tennis tie break

Students' own answers

Page 158 Simulating traffic lights

Students' own answers

Page 159 Multiples

Students' own answers

Heinemann Educational Publishers
Halley Court, Jordan Hill, Oxford OX2 8EJ
a division of Reed Educational & Professional Publishing Ltd

MELBOURNE   AUCKLAND   FLORENCE
PRAGUE   MADRID   ATHENS   SINGAPORE
TOKYO   SÃO PAULO   CHICAGO   PORTSMOUTH (NH)
MEXICO   IBADAN   GABORONE
JOHANNESBURG   KAMPALA   NAIROBI

First published 1994

96   97   98   10   9   8   7   6   5   4   3

ISBN 0 435 52986 2

Designed and typeset by VAP Group Ltd., Kidlington, Oxon

Illustrated by Jane Bottomley and Trevor Mason

Printed in Great Britain by The Bath Press, Somerset

The authors and publishers would like to thank the following for permission to use photographs.

Cover photo: Oxford Scientific Films
p. 36 Bell ringer/Sally and Richard Greenhill; p. 157 Tennis players/Pictor International

Acknowledgements:

We would also like to thank the following for permission to reproduce extracts from 'Badger on the Barge' by Janni Howker and 'Deadly drifters' by Susannah Ward on page 48.
Every effort has been made to contact copyright holders of material reproduced in this book. Any omissions will be rectified in subsequent printings if notice is given to the publisher.